Francis Bacon

Francis Bacon
From Magic to Science

by

Paolo Rossi

translated by
Sacha Rabinovitch

THE UNIVERSITY OF CHICAGO PRESS

Library of Congress Catalog Card Number: 68–13113

The University of Chicago Press, Chicago 60637
Routledge & Kegan Paul Limited, London, E.C.4

English translation © 1968
by Routledge & Kegan Paul Ltd

Translated from the Italian
FRANCESCO BACONE: DALLA MAGIA ALLA SCIENZA
(Bari: Editori Laterza, 1957)

to the memory of my father

Contents

Introduction   *page*   ix

Introduction to the English edition   xvi

I The Mechanical Arts, Magic, and Science   1

II The Refutation of Philosophies   36

III The Classical Fable   73

IV Logic, Rhetoric, and Method   135

V Language and Communication   152

VI Rhetorical Tradition and the Method of Science   186

List of Abbreviations used in the Notes   224

Notes   227

Index   273

Introduction

Among the asserters of free reason's claim
Our nation's not the least in worth or fame
The world to Bacon does not only owe
Its present knowledge, but its future too.

JOHN DRYDEN

On y voit que Locke est successeur de Bacon, ce qui est incon-
testable; on y voit que Locke, à son tour, engendre Helvetius;
et que tous ces ennemis du genre humain réunis . . . descendent
de Bacon.

J. DE MAISTRE

Francis Bacon lived between 1561 and 1626 in an age of conflicting political and cultural ideas. In those years the seeds of
England's political and industrial power were sown, the foundations of the Empire were laid; England was drawn into international politics by her support of the Dutch rebels and the
French Protestants; Raleigh's establishment in Virginia opened
the doors to colonisation; England defeated the Spanish
Armada and sacked Cadiz; Scotland, Ireland, and England
were united to form a political whole; the struggle of Parliament against monopolies foreshadowed the increasing inter-
vention of both Houses in financial and commercial legislation
and religious matters. This was the age of Elizabeth, Marlowe,
and Shakespeare; an age of vitality and exuberance where new
urges rubbed shoulders with century-old traditions; a decisive
age both for English and European history.

Many aspects of this civilisation were not new but derived

from medieval English and European culture. For instance, the typical seventeenth-century intellectual probings are a direct legacy of Occamist empiricism, the Occamist concept of knowledge as experience, and of nominalism—of all those doctrines, in fact, which questioned the Thomist compromise and the translation of Christianity into Aristotelian terms on which Scholastic learning was based. A new science of nature and a new form of religious belief were inspired by Occam's notion of experience. Further, a revival of the classics, the anti-clerical revolt, and the birth of a new philosophy of nature widened the gap that separated English culture from systematic theology and Aristotelianism. The English humanists' distaste for 'barbarous' forms of theological erudition and their partiality to a religious revival that would reveal the practical aspects of the Gospels and oppose theological definitions, implied a radical change of attitude towards the *corpus* of metaphysical doctrines. Thus the urge to reinstate the Gospels in their integrity that we find in John Colet and Thomas More was merged with an Erasmian rebellion against Scholasticism. Yet scholars have discovered links between this period of history and earlier traditions, even where these had previously been denied.

However the fact remains that around 1600 the English intellectual was more than half medieval and around 1660 he was more than half modern.[1] Such a transformation, involving the whole economic and social structure of a country, besides its intellectual manifestations, is too far-reaching to be dealt with here in detail. But it is only against the background of this upheaval that the peculiar mentality of an age which opened with Bacon's programme and closed with Newton's laws can be fully appreciated.

After the great reforms of King Henry VIII a new class of landed gentry came to occupy the political foreground, replacing the clergy and that feudal aristocracy which had perished in the Wars of the Roses. Macaulay, in his famous essay on Bacon, paints a brilliant portrait of this first generation of 'new men' to which Bacon's father belonged. They were the first professional statesmen England had ever produced; though they had grown up in the midst of theological controversies and were in the vanguard of intellectual life because they were

Protestants, they showed little religious zeal or fanaticism, and their reform of the Church of England was accomplished by appealing to the anti-Catholicism of public opinion and banking on the success of the European Protestants. These men had none of the pomp and majesty of the next generation of courtiers and politicians, nor their daring adventurousness, but the future greatness of England was built on their skilful, cautious diplomacy. Queen Elizabeth's England, governed by this new class of men of law and country squires, knew a period of extraordinary prosperity; and from France and Holland, where religious dissensions were raging, came workmen and merchants bringing with them capital, technical ability, and initiative.

As more and more new industries sprang up England was changed from an agricultural into an industrial nation. Her first industrial revolution took place in the hundred years following Cromwell's abolition of the monasteries. Between 1575 and 1642 England became the leading European country in mining and heavy industries; the average annual production of pit coal rose from 210 tons in the decade 1551–60 to nearly two million in the decade 1681–90. Wool had always been sent to Flanders for the manufacture of cloth, but now there were cloth-weavers in every town and village; companies were chartering fleets for trade, voyages of discovery, and piracy, thus adding to England's wealth and power. The number of ships weighing over 100 tons rose from 35 in 1545, to 183 in 1558, to 350 in 1620. The port of London saw ships from Asia berthed beside ships from the New World, and expeditions launched against the galleons of Spain. In 1557, while the sixteen-year-old Bacon was rebelling against Aristotelianism, Drake, who had repeated Magellan's venture, was returning home laden with Spanish spoil. In 1584 Walter Raleigh founded the first English colony in America and the same year the Levant Company—later to become the East India Company—was established in London.

Technology, commerce, and banking are the principal activities of such a society, and Puritanism responded admirably to its needs; the idea of a God who could be reached by a diligent conquest of reality was, indeed, far more amenable to these practical men and women than the idea of contemplation. 'It is for action that God maintaineth us and our activities, work is the moral as well as the natural end of power.' This is a passage from a contemporary religious text and not, as one might suppose, from Bacon. Literature too reflects this attitude. The one desire of Marlowe's Faustus is to satisfy his thirst for knowledge and power. He wants to know and to possess all: he is willing to sell his soul to Mephistopheles in order to acquire all the gold of the Indies and the Oceans, to know every plant that grows on the earth and every star that shines in the heavens. Hell and the after-life are 'trifles and mere old-wives' tales' but 'oh might I see Hell and return again, how happy were I then!'

But the merry pagan aspect of Elizabethan England had its counterpart in the pessimistic, morbid vein that runs through English literature from Sackville to Spenser, from Shakespeare to Donne and Browne, reaching its climax in the reign of James I. In the same way Bacon's attitude was balanced by the survival of medieval Scholastic traditions in men such as Everard Digby, Richard Hooker, and John Case. Though we tend to forget it, the great Elizabethans, Shakespeare, Spenser, Marlowe, and Sidney drew their cosmology neither from Ramus nor from atomist physics, but from these medieval Scholastic and magico-Platonist traditions.

Besides showing the dangers of indiscriminate generalisations these reflections may throw some light on the complexity of the English intellectual scene in its transition from Renaissance to modern times. Many early seventeenth-century writers reveal an assortment of conflicting influences: classical culture and the demands of a new logic; scientific experimentalism and magico-alchemical enquiries; astrology and Copernican astronomy; atomistic theories of matter and the quest for the philosophers' stone; classical mythology and the evocation of demons; pagan and evangelical moralities; political agitation and contemplative ideals,[2] while others lived passionately through a tumultuous succession of contradictory experiences whose diversity—in true Renaissance style—they did not attempt to reconcile or justify.

Complexity and contradiction are certainly not absent from Bacon's own writings. Thus he has quite naturally been seen as the first modern philosopher, a typical product of Renaissance culture, the theorist and father of empiricism, a rationalist,

alist, the philosopher of industrial science, a man who was saturated in magic and alchemy, the demolisher of Scholastic tradition, a medieval philosopher haunted by a modern dream. Bacon was an active man who played a prominent part in the political and intellectual life of his time. But he was an isolated, disappointed philosopher who never attained his main objective—the realisation of his dream of co-operative science and scientific institutions. It was not until the second half of the century that this dream came true. There is not a single important scientific discovery that can be attributed to Bacon, neither the circulation of the blood, universal magnetism, logarithms nor telescopic observations, to mention only those made in England; but an awareness of the social importance of scientific research, an amelioration of the conditions of human existence, and organised scientific collaboration were all consequences of his teachings. After the middle of the century we notice the increasing importance given to that 'verulamian design' mentioned by one of Boyle's correspondents. Solomon's House in the *New Atlantis* was for Joseph Glanville a prophetic plan of the Royal Society, and Dr Wallis described in the following way the same Royal Society, of which he was one of the founders:

> About the year 1645, while I lived in London (at a time when, by our Civil Wars, academical studies were much interrupted in both universities) . . . I had opportunity of being acquaintanced with divers worthy persons, inquisitive into Natural Philosophy and other parts of human Learning. And particularly of what hath been called the New Philosophy or Experimental Philosophy. . . . Our business was (precluding matters of theology and state-affairs) . . . to discourse of the circulation of Blood, the valves in the veins . . . the Copernican hypothesis, the nature of comets and the possibility or impossibility of vacuities. . . . Some were then but New Discoveries, and others not so generally known and embraced as now they are, with others appertaining to what hath been called the New Philosophy which, from the times of Galileo at Florence, and Sir Francis Bacon in England, hath been much cultivated in Italy, France, Germany and other parts abroad, as well as with us in England.[3]

Bacon's literary vigour, his powers of controversy, and the vastness of his programme helped to weigh the scales in

favour of the scientific reform that took place in seventeenth-
century England. He was, in fact, responsible for a new intellectual attitude to science which the Enlightenment and Kant
—and later the positivists—maintained.

Logically enough Bacon—who had taken an active part in
the intellectual life of his time and had tried to prove the limitations of theologically inspired philosophy—was venerated
and reviled alternately. He was acknowledged by Leibniz and
Vico, extolled and defended by the Enlightenment. But when
the forms of culture he had most violently attacked were reinstated by the intellectual bourgeoisie, Bacon was naturally
among those held responsible for Europe's cultural 'degeneration' which culminated in the Enlightenment. Indeed, this
intellectual atmosphere fostered the biased and radical attacks
of De Maistre and Liebig. However Bacon was never more
unpopular than in the first decade of this century when attempts
were repeatedly made to reduce his philosophy to the sphere of
'gnoseology'. In a progressive historiography presenting Locke
as 'the precursor of Kant' and historical investigations as a
kind of 'geographical exploration of spiritual regions' it was
easy to 'fail' the Lord Chancellor's method. Thus Bacon was
conveniently classified in a 'dynastic' history of philosophy
besides being presented as no more than the inventor of a
gigantic and useless 'logical machine'. To make this task of
total annihilation easier, Bacon's whole *œuvre* was reduced to the
second book of the *New Organon*. It is hard to believe that a
number of distinguished scholars were among those who tried
to represent Bacon's plan as speculative when it had required
(apart from a profound knowledge of history) a departure
from all systematic or factional reforms, and an insight into
the relation of scientific progress to that of civilisation. However,
the validity of such an interpretation has recently been questioned and the case re-examined, so that it is now possible to
undertake an historical study of Bacon that will not necessarily be platitudinous or unproductive.

This book operates on that same level of re-examination to
which K. R. Wallace, B. Farrington, F. Anderson, and M. M.
Rossi in Italy, have made such valuable, if diverse, contributions. It is the result of a series of enquiries, begun in 1951, on

problems relating to the cultural environment that influenced Bacon's philosophy—and was in turn influenced by it. The aim of these enquiries is to integrate—and sometimes modify—the findings of other writers on Bacon. Thus, though it refers to all Bacon's philosophical texts, this book is not presented as systematic and has neither the qualities nor the pretensions usually associated with such works. I hope that it may, none the less, reveal some unsuspected aspects of Bacon's philosophy.

The first chapter studies the influence on Bacon of magical and alchemical traditions, his opposition to these traditions, and the way in which his appreciation of the mechanical arts influenced his views of science. The second chapter describes Bacon's attempts to substitute a new outline of history for that traced by Aristotle, to detect the historical and social sources of the doctrine he was opposing, and to discover the cause of the failure of traditional knowledge. In the third chapter I try to show how Bacon reacted to the idea of a secret wisdom contained in classical myths and the relation of these reactions to the different formulations of his scientific reform. I have also tried to detect the naturalist, materialist, and ethico-political patterns in his allegorical interpretations of fables, and his links with Vico. The fourth, fifth, and sixth chapters deal with Bacon's logic: the relation of logic to rhetoric; the connection of a form of logic that seizes the reality of 'things themselves' and a form of logic that lights up the 'magic glass' of the human mind; the links existing between Bacon's reform of logic and popular sixteenth- and early seventeenth-century rhetorical texts; Bacon's debt to the Ramistic dialectic and his attempts to adapt rhetorical methods to his new scientific logic for natural enquiries. May the content of this book make up for its size.

I wish to express here my gratitude to Professor E. Garin of the University of Florence; I am deeply indebted both to his teaching and to his writings. I am also very grateful to Professor A. Banfi of the University of Milan and to Professor B. Farrington of Swansea University who have been lavish with advice and encouragement.

University of Milan,
 September 1956.

Introduction to the English edition

Since this book was first published in Italy there has been no substantial addition to Baconian scholarship. J. G. Crowther's *Francis Bacon, the First Statesman of Science* (London, 1960), is an endeavour to bring the Lord Chancellor's ideas up to date and contributes nothing to an historical understanding of the question. On the other hand some useful studies have been published on particular aspects of Bacon's works: law, the problem of scientific unity, Aristotelianism, the notions of wit and wisdom, and the effects of Bacon's method on natural science.[1] B. Farrington, *The Philosophy of Bacon, an Essay on its development from 1603 to 1609* (Liverpool, 1964), gives the English translations of some basic texts and discusses some fundamental themes such as Bacon's views on the Bible, his ethical optimism, his appreciation of the mechanical arts, his attacks on the magical and alchemical tradition; it should be of great assistance to the Baconian scholar.

Here I have tried to examine Bacon's philosophy in the cultural context of its time; a number of comprehensive studies published after 1957 would have made my task easier had I been able to consult them. These include F. A. Yates, *Giordano Bruno and the Hermetic Tradition* (London, 1964); M. Boas, *The Scientific Renaissance* (London, 1962); A. R. Hall, *From Galileo to Newton* (London, 1963); N. W. Gilbert, *Renaissance Concepts of Method* (New York, 1960); and especially W. S. Howell, *Logic and Rhetoric in England 1500–1700* (Princeton, 1956), which was not available until I was correcting the proofs of the Italian edition.

When going over a work after the lapse of some years one is always tempted to rewrite whole passages and reorganise the whole book. However, I have resisted this temptation. The only alterations I have made are purely formal: a short passage eliminated here, a footnote referring to a particularly important study added there.

I wish to thank Professor George Boas who was kind enough to bring this book to the notice of English readers in *The Journal of the History of Ideas*, October 1958. And finally I thank my wife without whose valuable assistance and affectionate patience neither this nor my other works could have been written.

University of Bologna,
  February 1965.

I

The Mechanical Arts, Magic, and Science

The cultural significance of the mechanical arts

Juan Luis Vives in the *Diffusion of Knowledge* (*De tradendis disciplinis*, 1531) makes the statement that scholars would be well advised to study the technical methods of such trades as building, navigation, and weaving; they should, besides, observe the artisan at work and question him on the secrets of his craft. A couple of years later Rabelais, in *The Most Fearsome Life of the Great Gargantua*, numbered among the prerequisites of a complete education the study of the artisans' crafts. The young Gargantua was instructed by Ponocrates in the natural sciences, arithmetic, geometry, astronomy, and music; a variety of physical exercises were his only recreation. But on cold and rainy days he devoted himself to carving and painting and went with his tutor to observe

> the drawing of metals or the casting of cannon, or paid visits
> to jewellers, goldsmiths, and cutters of precious stones; or to
> alchemists and coiners; or to tapestry-makers, printers, musical
> instrument makers, dyers, and other craftsmen of that sort; and
> everywhere, as they treated to wine, they learned and considered
> the processes and inventions of each trade.[1]

This new interest in technical and mechanical methods, based on a belief in their educative powers, is typical of the sixteenth

I

and seventeenth centuries. The accomplishments of artisan, engineer, technician, navigator, and inventor were considered of equal importance to intellectual achievements, and Bacon, Galileo, and Harvey, among others, explicitly acknowledged their debt to the artisan.

Sciences such as chemistry, mineralogy, botany, and geology thrived on the fusion of scientific and technical knowledge.[2] Another consequence of the new status of technology and its methodological procedures was the realisation that theories should be tested before they could be accepted, and the lack of connection between traditional scientific learning and the practical potentialities of science was set in evidence by an increased familiarity with the mechanical arts.[3]

Much has already been said about the influence of this revaluation of technical knowledge on the expansion of overseas trade, the increase of commercial wealth, and the progress of the mining industry, as well as on the role of certain technical problems in the growth of theoretical and scientific research. Developments in hydrostatics, for instance, were linked to such problems as the increase of the speed of ships, the building of navigable canals and locks, the construction of pumps for mines, and water supplies for cities. Hydrodynamics were associated with enquiries into the handling of ships; the problem of calculating distances at sea was the starting point for enquiries in astronomy, chronometry, the theory of tides, and the construction of mechanical clocks. The printing and textile industries involved the solving of certain chemical and dyeing problems. And the demands of the art of war gave birth to the science of ballistics which, in turn, led to a new interest in dynamics.

This wealth of new interests—which was finally responsible for a radical change in social and economic life[4]—is reflected in the works of Biringuccio, Agricola, Besson, Ramelli, Veranzio, Zonca, Giacomo Strada of Rosberg, and Castelli[5] to name only a few. Yet the authors of these eminently technical writings do not seem to have been conscious of the revolution in traditional culture occasioned by the development of technology. They can only be distinguished from other scientific and philosophical writers of their time by a tendency to avoid the traditional magical and alchemical language of allegory, metaphor, and mysterious symbol; a tendency due in part to the need for clarity of expression intrinsic to the diffusion and progress of technology, and in part to their perception of the many discoveries still to be made before man's mastery of nature could be achieved.

George Agricola[6] is certainly the most typical, and also the most interesting, of the writers we have mentioned. He played an active part in social and political life as philologist, doctor, and technician; he was a friend of Erasmus and of Melanchthon; he was charged with various political missions at the courts of the Emperors Charles V and Ferdinand I. His *Origins and Causes of Subterranean Things* (*De ortu et causis subterraneorum,* 1546) and *Of the Nature of Fossils* (*De natura fossilium,* 1546) were the first systematic treatises on geology and mineralogy. His *Of Metals* (*De re metallica,* 1556) initiated, among other things, the study of geological strata and remained for two centuries the standard work on mining techniques.

Agricola's works show a profound awareness of the intellectual crisis whose symptoms, for him, are the general disinclination to study nature and the deterioration of scientific language. This last, he says, had become unfit for proper communication by its substitution of barbarisms for the lucid vocabulary of the classics.[7] But he saw the solution to this linguistic problem either in a revival of Latin, as in Italy, or in a return to eloquence such as the Humanists'.

> But the knowledge of Nature which is so vast that it embraces all that the senses and the mind can apprehend is still almost completely unappreciated. Because, besides other things, there are many particular species of animals, of plants, and various products of the earth which are yet totally ignored and undiscovered.[8]

Agricola felt that his mission was to reinstate the study of nature because it would enable man to achieve nobler and higher ends than those Nature herself had assigned him. In the preface to *Of Metals* he tells of the scrupulous accuracy with which he has carried out his work. This book, he says, describes in the minutest detail seams, implements, vessels, canals, machines, and furnaces; he had even employed illustrators at his own expense so that 'there could be no possible uncertainty in the minds of men either today or in the future'.[9]

3

This ideal of clarity and the conscious departure from the fabulous are what distinguish Agricola's treatise—and others of this kind—from medieval herbals, bestiaries, and encyclopedias as well as from those catalogues of animals, plants, metals, and stones that were so popular at the time. The accent in these encyclopedias of natural history is on the strange and the rare; living creatures and heraldic animals alike are classified according to the element in which they dwell: fire for the salamander, air for the birds, water for fishes. The material is drawn almost exclusively from classical sources with a few legends and fanciful etymologies thrown in.[10]

The *Riches of the World* (*La Minera del mondo*, 1589) by Giovanni Maria Bonardo[11] is typical of this kind of literature. Mountains, springs, lakes, metals, precious stones, trees, plants, worms, minute creatures, serpents, fishes, and birds are listed here in alphabetical order. Indeed, such books were more like collections of fairy tales than the collections of facts they were supposed to be:

> On the top of Mount Palombra there is a wonderful fountain and those that drink of its waters will never feel pain of any sort for as long as they live and will also preserve their youthful appearance for ever . . . In the copper forges of Cyprus a feathered, four-legged beast comes flying from the flames.[12]

Similarly, we have John Malpet's famous book published in England in 1576: *A green forest, wherein may be seen the sovereign virtues of all kinds of stones and metals: next of plants as of herbs, trees and shrubs: lastly of brute beasts, fowls creeping worms and serpents and that alphabetically.*[13] The term 'natural history' was used here for the first time in England but this book is no more than a medieval encyclopedia drawn in part from the *Of the nature of things* (*De proprietatibus rerum*) by Bartholomeus Anglicus and adopting Isidore's extravagant etymologies: 'The Cat in Latin is called catus, as if you would say *Cautus*, wary or wise.'

All this is very different from Agricola's lucid, exact classifications. Agricola's mistrust of alchemy proceeds logically from his fidelity to experiment and from his desire for accurate systematic investigations and a clear report of the latter. As he writes in *De re metallica*:

4

There is not a thing of which I have written that has not either been seen or read by me, or, if it was reported to me by others, examined with scrupulous diligence.[14]

He observes that there are very few studies on the art of metallurgy, whether it be on the properties of different metals, on methods for their excavation, or on soil formations, and the like.[15] It is surprising, therefore, he says, that 'there should be so many alchemists who have written on the art of changing one metal into another', and although it would be difficult to doubt the authority of so many:

> . . . no one of this calling has ever made a fortune in the past nor yet today, despite the fact that all over the world there are so many who all, I repeat all, by day and by night, with their hands and with their feet, vie with each other in their endeavours to make mountains of gold . . . They should have filled cities and castles with gold and with silver. . . . .[16]

Agricola attacks with even more vehemence the obscure and arbitrary alchemistic vocabulary,[17] and the practice of using natural research to 'dazzle the eyes of simple people with famous titles (taken from works of Plato and Aristotle) and with a great show of doctrine'.[18]

Agricola's defence of the art of metallurgy had a considerable cultural significance. This art, he says, has been accused of depending solely on chance, of having no scientific status at all, of being, in fact, no more than a form of manual labour. According to another tradition—deriving from Aristotle—metallurgy is a menial, shameful, degrading occupation, unfit for honourable gentlemen; here again it is compared to a manual labour and contrasted with the contemporary idea of science as detached contemplation of abstract truths. Agricola demonstrates the many ways in which technology is connected with various sciences. The technician, he says, requires a sound training in every sphere of knowledge. A metallurgist must be expert at identifying soils, at distinguishing seams, stones, precious stones, and metals, and he must be acquainted with 'every possible manner of experimenting with the materials at hand'. But he must also be versed in philosophy 'so that he may understand the origins, causes, and nature of subterranean things'; in medicine 'so that he may prevent excavators and

5

other workers from contracting the diseases to which they are more exposed in this labour than in any other'; in astrology 'so that he may know the quarters of the sky and from them judge the orientation of seams'; in calculating and architecture 'to be able to construct his own machines and props, or instruct others in doing so'; in the art of drawing and, finally, in law and jurisprudence.[19] Technical and scientific work are thus inseparable. On the other hand:

> Those who would denigrate the metallurgist's art say that there was a time when men were condemned to excavate metals as a punishment for their crimes and that slaves too were made to do this work, and that even now metallurgists are paid workers who dwell in filth and squalor like all manual labourers. Surely if this is enough to make the art of metals shameful and unfit for a gentleman neither will agriculture be proper because it was once the work of slaves and in Turkey it still is, neither architecture because some slaves were architects, nor medicine because many doctors also have been slaves; and what I have said of these arts could be said of many others which prisoners have been forced to perform.[20]

We should not forget that this attitude—arising from the needs of a specific phase of social and economic development in European civilisation—was common to many humanists and philosophers in the sixteenth century besides being that of most technical and scientific writers.[21] This tendency to replace a literary and theoretical education by a predominantly technical one is clearly expressed by Sir Humphrey Gilbert in England in his *Queen Elizabeth's Academy* (1562?)[22]. Gilbert— for obvious reasons—only stressed aspects of technical instruction that he believed would help form a new type of gentleman who would gradually redirect the course of English society. Culture and courtesy, an aptitude for politics and the arts of navigation and of war would, in this ideal society, be considered equal, if not superior virtues to those of blood and birth. Thus Gilbert's programme of education was designed for the ruling classes and more specifically for the younger sons of noblemen.

> Whereas in the universities men study only school learnings, in this Academy they shall study matters of action meet for present practice, both of peace and war. And if they will not dispose themselves to *letters*, yet they may learn languages or martial activities

for the service of their country. If neither the one nor the other, then may they exercise themselves in qualities meet for a gentleman. And also the other universities shall then better suffice to relieve poor schollars, where now the youth of nobility and gentlemen, taking up their scholarships and fellowships do disappoint the poor of their livings and advancements.[23]

In Gilbert's academy English is the language for instruction; logic and rhetoric, including exercises in political and military oration, are treated concurrently; political philosophy consists of history, systems of government and taxation, and the administration of law. The technological tendency is particularly evident in the field of natural philosophy and mathematics where only problems of fortification, artillery and strategy are considered. Geography and astronomy deal mainly with navigation, and the practice of medicine seems to have no purpose outside the battlefield. However the secrets of nature must be 'studied in every possible way' and the results of experiments 'reported without ambiguity or obscurity'. There will be a warship and an 'experimental' garden at the student's disposal and their education will be completed by the study of law, modern languages, music, fencing, and dancing.

Gilbert was better known as a pioneer of colonisation than as a pedagogue, so it is not surprising that his ideal citizen should combine the virtues of a *conquistador* with those of a courtier. In fact, like many an English humanist of his day, he tended to adapt the humanist ideal of courtesy to the demands of society. The aristocracy had come to see education as a last stand against the rising social class of lawyers and country gentlemen, and they found that the humanists were prepared to instruct them in those technical matters that a position at court or in society required.[24] If technology was now seen as a means of social advancement this only reflected the sixteenth-century tendency to consider practical sciences superior to theoretical knowledge; such an appreciation was, indeed, expressed by most English humanists. Thomas Starkey writes:

> The perfection of man standeth not in mere knowledge and learning without application of it to any use or profit of others, but the perfection of man's mind resteth in the use and exercise of all virtues and honesty, and chiefly in the chief virtue . . . the communing of high wisdom to the use of others.[25]

7

This attitude was responsible for the English humanists' intolerance of disputatious Scholastic learning and the Puritans' opposition to logical subtleties, and even for Ramus' great popularity in England. The burning of the texts of university debates in the market place, the pages torn from Duns Scotus' works and strewn over the quadrangle of New College, Oxford, in 1553[26] were more than political demonstrations against the abolition of monastic schools or against new religious jurisdiction. The concept of logic as a practical guide to the art of discussion which ensured success in religious controversies was being replaced by that of logic as an art and instrument for the purposes of natural research.

Bacon had read Agricola and certain aspects of his philosophy may well have been inspired by Bernard Palissy.[27] Palissy was an apprentice potter whose quest for a white glaze for ceramics had brought him a brief renown followed by almost total ruin. Sir Clifford Albutt, and later Farrington,[28] have suggested that Bacon—who was in Paris at the age of sixteen—might have attended Palissy's public lectures on agriculture, mineralogy, and geology, and that when he wrote in the *New Organon* that it 'occasionally happens that some workman of acuter wit and covetous honour applies himself to a new invention which he mostly does at the expense of his fortunes',[29] he was probably referring to Palissy who was, indeed, a typical example of such a workman. Significantly enough among the few books Palissy had read we find Vitruvius, a pamphlet by Paracelsus, and a treatise by Cardano.[30] Philosophy, he wrote, is the art of observing, which is not the prerogative of scholars: it is shared 'by all the inhabitants of the earth'. And he opposed the philosophical tradition in favour of a cult of nature:

How can a man understand and discuss the workings of nature if he has not read the Latin books of the Philosophers? So might it be said of me, for I prove by experiments that the theories of many philosophers are fallacious in many ways, even the most famous and ancient; and this can be seen and understood in less than two hours, by anyone who will take the trouble to come to my laboratory where he will see some wonderful things set up as examples and proofs of my writings, arranged by order and by degree, with labels attached so that everyone can learn for himself. I can assure you (reader) that in a very short time, namely in the first day, you will learn more of natural philosophy by the instances contained in this book than you could learn in fifty years reading the theories of ancient philosophers.[31]

Though crudely and ingenuously expressed, this passage contains two basic ideas of Bacon's philosophy:[32] traditional learning must be replaced by the cult of nature so as to re-establish the contact between man and reality; collections of facts are a means of study, an instrument for scientific research and not objects of pleasure and curiosity.[33]

Indeed Bacon was voicing the general opinion of his age, defining some of its essential demands, when he strove to rehabilitate the mechanical arts, denounced the sterility of Scholastic logic, and planned a history of arts and sciences to serve as foundation for the reform of knowledge and of the very existence of mankind. He constantly contrasted the fruit-lessness of traditional culture with the progressive nature of the arts. These, he says, unlike theoretical sciences, will not be set up as idols of perfection, for they are continually thriving, growing, advancing, and alive to the needs of humanity; we have already seen this happen in the case of printing, artillery, and navigation. These achievements were made possible because many minds collaborated to one end: in the mechanical arts there can be no dictators but only 'senates' of free and equal workers. Time, says Bacon, favours these arts but it saps the foundations of the great traditional monuments. There are many comprehensive works on methods of agriculture and other arts, but too many people think it is degrading for cultured men to study these methods. These men, in their foolish arrogance, are like the philosopher who fell into a pond because he was looking up at the stars—after which he could observe neither the stars nor the water—whereas if he had looked attentively at the water he could have seen the stars reflected in it. The new philosophy is based on a humble exact analysis of technical procedures; its function—besides transposing methods from one art to others and helping to advance technology—is to encompass in the sphere of technology sciences that had hitherto been excluded from it.[34] In fact Bacon sees the collective, progressive aspects of the mechanical arts as what finally distinguishes them from magic, as well as being a model for research in various fields of knowledge.

In 1609 Bacon, who was nearly fifty, decided to publish his third philosophical work, *De sapientia veterum* (*On the Wisdom of the Ancients*). Here he uses the classical Promethean myth to illustrate his theory of collectivity:

> The last point remains—namely the races with burning torches initiated in honor of Prometheus. This . . . alludes to arts and sciences, and carries in it a very wise admonition to this effect that perfection of the sciences is to be looked for not from the swiftness nor ability of any one inquirer, but from a succession. For the strongest and swiftest runners are perhaps not the best fitted to keep their torch alight since it may be put out by going too fast as well as too slow. It seems however that these races and games of the torch have long been intermitted. And well were it to be wished that these games in honour of Prometheus, that is of Human Nature, were again revived; that the victory may no longer depend upon the unsteady and wavering torch of each single man but competition, emulation, and good fortune be brought to aid. Therefore men should be advised to rouse themselves, and try each his own strength and the chance of his own turn, and not to stake the whole venture upon the spirits and brains of a few persons.[35]

Bacon was putting up a modern ideal of scientific research in opposition to the traditional ideals of magic and alchemy. To grasp the cultural significance of this ideal we must remember that the infiltration of technology into the different spheres of learning was no simple matter, in sixteenth- and seventeenth-century Europe and England.

In this respect Bacon's attitude was distinctive; and for this reason he has been so often and so completely misrepresented. Some—like Liebig for instance—stress only the errors and scientific absurdities that are certainly not lacking in Bacon's work.[36] Others, like Farrington, ignore the formative influence of Renaissance magical traditions on his mind.[37] Farrington's portrait, though basically correct, tends thus to distort the historical significance of Bacon's attitude; and Farrington's over-zealous followers make indiscriminate use of his intelligent formula—after cleverly distinguishing science from technology —to fit Bacon into their ready-made history. These representations of Bacon as philosopher of nature or pioneer in the application of science to industry are equally incomplete and misleading.

The basic themes of Bacon's philosophy are often biased and polemical. They were directed at specific objectives and may be ascribed to a definite phase of culture. This is a point that should be always kept in mind by the historian whose aim is to discover how certain traditional concepts are gradually remoulded by the demands of a given age. Bacon's appraisal of the mechanical arts and his concept of science must be seen in the light of his reaction to the Renaissance magical hermetic tradition; and his reaction to magic, his reasons for both acknowledging and rejecting it,[38] cannot be fully appreciated till we cease to misrepresent certain cultural manifestations as the relics of ancient or medieval superstitions. We should not forget that these problems enthralled such men as John of Salisbury, Albertus Magnus, Roger Bacon, and in the seventeenth century Bacon and Descartes, Kepler, Mersenne, and Gassendi.[39]

The heritage of magic

Bacon spent the last years of his life compiling a great encyclopedia of nature and of arts (or nature modified by man). It was to provide the material for a study of the New Science, and Bacon was convinced that its publication would finally establish his fame and his reputation. Assisted only by his secretary Rawley he worked for many years at a *Primal History* (*Historia prima*) to include material for all particular histories, which was published as the *Sylva silvarum* (*Forest of forests*) only after his death. But the particular histories came to assume an ever increasing importance for Bacon who made a 'sort of vow' to publish one each month for six consecutive months. Only two of these six histories were ever published in their entirety: the *History of Winds* (*Historia ventorum*) and a year later the *History of Life and Death* (*Historia vitae et mortis*) which was to have been the sixth.[40]

Bacon believed that a meticulous and exhaustive compilation of natural and experimental histories would rapidly change the destinies of mankind, so he discarded his logic[41] and gave up all his time to the realisation of this fantastic project, the greater part of which was never to be completed.

Thus the *Sylva silvarum* (a vast forest providing materials for future constructions) was written by a man who knew that he was working against time and who had besides to accomplish single-handed a job requiring a team of investigators and a complicated scientific equipment which he did not possess. These factors are mainly responsible for the dismissal of this work as unimportant and absurd.[42] It is true that Bacon, pressed by time, resorted to ransacking existing texts for his material: the *Sylva silvarum* includes borrowings from Aristotle's *Meteorological Problems* (*Problemata meteorologica*), Pseudo-Aristotle's *Of the wonders of accoustics* (*De mirabilibus auscultationibus*), Pliny's *Natural History*, Della Porta's *Natural Magia* (*Magic naturalis*), Sandys' *A Relation of a Journey*, Cardano's *Of Subtlety* (*De subtilitate*) and Scaliger's *Against Cardano* (*Adversus Cardanum*);[43] indeed the influence of magic and alchemical traditions on Bacon is nowhere more obvious. Thus the decomposition of bodies is explained by the tendency of the volatile spirits inhabiting them to escape and make merry in the sunshine; because dogs like bad smells their olfactory organs are said to be different from those of other animals; salamanders are described as being gifted with 'extinctive virtues'. This work also includes the theory of sympathies, and such beliefs as lunar influences, the evil eye, and the transmutation of metals. But such notions were widely held in those days even among the educated classes, and they survived for a long time; in 1646 the *Vulgar and Common Errors* by Sir Thomas Browne[44] (himself a firm believer, in a number of these errors) was an attack aimed not at popular superstitions, but at beliefs similar to Bacon's which were still current in cultured circles.

However, of far greater significance is the fact that Bacon adopted certain fundamental theories of Renaissance natural philosophy. This is particularly evident in the *Sylva silvarum* where they are applied to individual cases but they are not absent from his earlier works. According to these theories all substances are gifted with the power of discrimination, and when two substances are placed in contact a selection takes place by which what is pleasant is accepted and what is painful is rejected; if a substance is altered by another or alters it, discrimination invariably precedes the operation. A universal link exists between all beings perceived either as attraction or as repulsion (all the examples in the tenth Century of the *Sylva silvarum* are based on this theory). The powers of the imagination are of the utmost importance. Though Bacon had violently attacked Paracelsus for such notions, he proposed to test the powers of the imagination by trying to arrest the fermentation of beer and prevent churned milk from turning into butter. Indeed he exalts the occult powers of the imagination more than many a Renaissance naturalist.[45]

These theories, besides being typical of Renaissance vitalism, are a first step towards acknowledging the magical ideal that underlies it. Thus one of the major difficulties confronting the Baconian scholar is the presence of both mechanist and dynamic vitalist conceptions of reality in Bacon's physics.[46]

However, we are more concerned with the recurrence of vitalist, magical, and alchemical themes[47] in Bacon's earlier works which were written under more leisurely circumstances than the *Sylva silvarum* and with more clearly defined aims. For instance, in the *New Organon* and in the *History of Life and Death* Bacon declares that a spirit or spiritual (pneumatic) body is contained in all substances.[48] As the concept of decomposition originates in the spirit the only antidote to this process is the *detentio* or retaining of the spirit. Greasy, compact substances are better able to resist decomposition because they are less porous than others. In the *History of Life and Death* Bacon specifies that by spirit he means neither a virtue, a power, an entelechy 'nor any other such trifle' but a body, subtle and invisible yet situated in actual space.[49] And this is more or less the meaning alchemists gave to the term.[50] The spirit, as vital source of nourishment that must be retained in order to preserve life and that penetrates like a watery vapour into each elemental particle, forms the basis both for a mystical theory of reality and for the doctrine of the transmutation of metals.[51] For a given metal differs from other metals by virtue of a specific spirit which is no more than a variant or condition of the common metallic spirit; this in turn is an emanation of *anima mundi* or world spirit derived from the *spiritus universi* or universal spirit and, in the last analysis, from God. I do not think it is possible to find in Bacon either an explicit or an implicit espousal of these mystical aspects of alchemical tradition, but the influence of the hermetic doctrine of the transmutation of metals is clear. This last is based on the belief in a common metallic spirit entirely homogeneous except for unspecified impurities. To free a metal from these impurities is tantamount to making it perfect. This can be achieved by introducing into a basic metal the spirit of another metal. The process induced in the basic metal is called digestion.

Bacon's vocabulary bears the distinctive mark of this tradition: he speaks of the assimilation, nourishment, generation, and irritation of substances in the process of conservation or mutation; he makes frequent use of the term fixation with its traditional alchemical connotations.[52] These linguistic affinities reflect an ingrained affinity of outlook, especially pronounced where Bacon's physics are concerned. Here, however, Bacon's atomist and materialist leanings have sometimes led him to use certain alchemical terms in a context that alters their original meaning, and it will be necessary in the course of this study to determine the extent of these alterations. For the moment we need only remember that alchemical research was always related in some way to Aristotle's doctrine of matter. The alchemists saw it as a *continuum* or stream and also made use of the concepts of matter and form. Indeed, the transmutation of metals could only be possible if copper and gold, for instance, were not considered as two different matters but as different manifestations of the same matter; and Aristotle's theory of vapours with its implications of a total homogeneous identity for all metals gave further substance to this doctrine.[53]

In fact there was little connection between alchemy and traditional atomism, and the atomistic revival to which Bacon largely contributed completely redirected the course of alchemical research.[54] But here again Bacon's attitude is characteristic: his reappraisal of Democritean philosophy is known and he accepted most of the atomistic doctrine. However, his reservations were motivated by his alchemical allegiances; it was the problem of transmutation of metals which weighed the scales in favour of Democritus who believed in various forms of atoms, and against Pythagoras who maintained their absolute similarity. Bacon accepted Democritus' theory in so far as it stipulated an indirect transition from one substance to another in opposition to Pythagoras' theory of direct transition.[55] Research should, besides, be diverted from the *queta principia rerum* (passive principles of substances) to their appetites and inclinations.[56]

Bacon's attitude to the problem of vacuum was equally ambiguous. This may have been due to his uncertainty in the related problem of the continuity of matter, which brings us back to his interest in alchemy. For his whole theory of 'primal natures' (or simple natures), of 'latent configurations' and 'latent processes' stems from his belief in the transmutation of substances; thus his use of Aristotelian terms and of the distinction between matter and form are no mere coincidence. However, Aristotle's influence on Bacon was not direct; it affected him through the alchemists, so that the efforts of some scholars to find an absolute similitude between Bacon's texts and Aristotle's have rarely been crowned with success.

Bacon analysed substances to determine their primal natures or irreducible qualities, so that gold becomes a combination of yellowness, specific weight, a degree of pliancy, malleability and so forth. This process is akin to that of reducing a word to its component letters, and so these primal natures are 'nature's alphabet' and constitute the ultimate elements to which the whole of nature can be reduced. If one could discover a method for 'superinducing' upon a certain substance the correctly graduated natures of yellowness, specific weight, pliability and fluidity one could transmute it into gold. The method would be identical if one or more natures were to be superinduced but, adds Bacon, the difficulties would be greater in the second case, as it is not easy to assemble in a single substance a number of natures usually only assembled under natural circumstances. But there remains the fact that operations such as these are based on the constant, eternal and universal elements of nature and that they can immeasurably increase the powers of mankind.[57]

Indeed for Bacon mankind appears to have no greater purpose than to 'generate or superinduce' new natures on a given substance, and he tries to find a 'true and perfect rule of operation' for discovering primal natures for this end.[58]

Bacon's link with alchemical traditions is particularly evident here where he makes use of two typically alchemical notions; namely that transmutations from one substance to another can only be achieved by superinducing foreign elements upon a given substance—thus the alchemists often presented the trans-mutation of substance as a more pervasive form of dye;[59] and that the attributes of a substance are seen as 'specific beings' or separate independent 'natures', to be added, removed, or exchanged at will.[60] And when Bacon stresses the difficulty of introducing more than one nature into a single substance at one time, he does no more than echo a characteristic alchemical problem. He declares that fire can produce previously non-existent substances and this belief was also shared by the al-chemists. Further, he himself admits that, apart from their erroneous use of fire, their enquiries were directed towards the same ends as his own.[61]

Now that we have seen how greatly Bacon was involved with the alchemical tradition it will be easier to understand some of the better-known aspects of his alchemical tendencies such as his assumption that matter could be reduced to two elements: mercury and sulphur. Also the notion of the convertibility of air to water. His bent for astrology—an interest he would not give up though he condemned its effect. And his belief in the possi-bility of prolonging human life indefinitely.[62]

Two other basic theories of Bacon's philosophy can also be traced to Renaissance magical and alchemical sources: the ideal of man's scientific domination of nature, and the idea of man as nature's 'servant and interpreter', as opposed to the traditional definition of man as 'reasoning animal'; though he reshaped these concepts so that they assumed a very different significance in his philosophy. However, to appreciate their difference as well as their similarity we must recall the position held by magic in the Renaissance. Most of the important magi-cal texts were based on older writings: thus Agrippa's *Occult Philosophy* (*Philosophia occulta*) was indebted to *Picatrix*. Yet the evaluation of magic and of its human and social function under-went a radical change at this time. Cornelius Agrippa, one of the foremost Renaissance magical writers, describes this change in his *Dedicatory letter to Johannes Trithemius*:

> The outstanding question was this: why is it that although magic originally occupied the pinnacle of excellence in the judgement of all the ancient philosophers and was always held in the highest veneration by those great sages and priests of antiquity, sub-sequently (from the beginning of the rise of the Catholic Church)

it became an object of hatred and suspicion to the holy Fathers, and was at last hissed off the stage by the theologians, condemned by the sacred canons and, in fine, outlawed by the judgement of all laws?[63]

Three centuries earlier Roger Bacon—defending 'beneficial magic' against the theologians' attacks and claiming its right of citizenship to the realm of 'Christian Knowledge'—drew a very similar picture of the fate of magic: in the first three centuries of the Christian era, he said, three great powers contended the field: Christianity, philosophy, and magic. Christianity and philosophy then joined forces against magic, though still accusing each other of magical practices. The philosophers, in particular, committed the error of identifying magical illusions and Christian miracles so that a number of holy men were led to condemn magic, rejecting at the same time a lot of magnificent knowledge.[64]

Both Agrippa and Roger Bacon were aware of the gulf separating theology and philosophy from magic and alchemy in the middle ages. There is little point in enumerating instances where magic and demonology are identified as in Cyprian, Tertullian, Lactantius, and Augustine, but there is a certain relevance in the fact that magic was condemned for its sinful commerce with demons by Augustine and Hugh of St Victor as well as by John of Salisbury and Saint Thomas. Even William of Auvergne and Albertus Magnus—who advocated the distinction between natural and demonic magic—finally accepted the rulings of the Church and admitted the dangers of all magic and its implicit idolatry.[65] Indeed as Eugenio Garin has said, the magician of the Middle Ages was hunted and persecuted as the heretical disturber of godly order and reason; he was looked upon as a being who dwelt beyond the boundaries of the rational in contact with demons and the powers of evil.

Such accusations led to the confusion of magic with necromancy, of judicial with mathematical astrology and of ritualistic with experimental alchemy. Only the complete revaluation of man's significance in the world and of his relation to nature could reinstate magic as a 'human science' worthy of mankind and to be practised without shame. Thus magic ceased to be the disturber of universal order and of a fixed celestial structure when order and structure began to be contested from all sides; and in the Renaissance it acquired the status of an intellectual achievement praised by Ficino, Pico, Bruno, and Campanella.[66] This status was to be maintained till the beginning of the modern era of Kepler, Bacon, Gassendi, and even Descartes.

One of the basic theories of Renaissance philosophy was the absence of a specific nature in man and his ability to acquire the nature of his choice. This theory was adopted by Pico and Bovillus among others, yet it never took a substantial hold on Bacon. For him man's powers were not infinite but always subject to the laws of nature (*obsessus legibus naturae*) and he cannot break or loosen the causal ties that govern it.[67] Man's portion is neither to praise his infinite freedom nor to preserve his essential unity with the whole, but to realise that, in order to consolidate his limited power he must adapt himself to nature, submit to its commands and assist in developing its operations.[68] Only thus can he achieve the true mastery of nature, because to dominate nature man must be its servant and interpreter. That is why it is not only harmful but foolish to imagine that man can penetrate the divine spheres with his senses and his reason, for the possibility of freely operating upon nature does not in any way imply the possibility of doing so how and when he pleases, but only of knowing no limits to those operations that observe the laws of nature and are essentially no more than a development of natural operations.

This idea of man's position in the world gives a clue to Bacon's concept of science and to his interest in the objective aspects of ethical life, his interest in reading faces and in the art of personal success and his partiality to Machiavelli's naturalism.

Yet Bacon's idea of a science serving nature by speeding or delaying operations should not be seen as an historical novelty; if we open one of the most popular texts of Renaissance magic— a text on which Bacon certainly meditated—we read:

> Therefore natural magic is that which having contemplated the virtues of all natural and celestial things and carefully studied their order proceeds to make known the hidden and secret powers of nature in such a way that inferior and superior things are joined by an interchanging application of each to each; thus incredible miracles are often accomplished not so much by art as by nature,

to whom this art is as a servant when working at these things. For this reason magicians are like careful explorers of nature only directing what nature has formerly prepared, uniting actives to passives and often succeeding in anticipating results so that these things are popularly held to be miracles when they are really no more than anticipations of natural operations; as if someone made roses flower in March or grapes ripen, or even more remarkable things such as clouds, rain, thunder, various species of animals and an infinite transformation of things . . . therefore those who believe the operations of magic to be above or against nature are mistaken because they are only derived from nature and in harmony with it.[69]

This passage from Cornelius Agrippa shows clearly that the so-called miracles of magic are not, like the miracles of saints, a violation of natural laws, but the result of developing natural powers. They are miracles only in the etymological sense: things worthy of admiration. And this definition of natural magic is akin to Bacon's concept of an art following faithfully in the footsteps of nature,[70] incapable of miracles because it is a human art with human limitations.

This view was common to all Renaissance writers concerned with the significance of magic. Della Porta valued the practical nature of magical operations and inveighed against incantations of any kind. For him magic was the climax of natural philosophy;[71] magical operations only seem miraculous, he said, because the spectator does not understand how they are produced, they never overstep the limits of nature. He too wrote of magic as the 'servant of nature' and compared the magician to a cultivator: the operations of magic, he said, are no more than the operations of nature and the art from which they derive is nature's servant; the magician creates nothing.[72] Campanella writes that the aim of magic is to 'imitate and assist nature'. For him magic is the ruling science for it is a practical activity operating on reality; certain inventions had been described as magic until they were understood, when they became common knowledge; such were gunpowder, the magnet, and the printing press.[73] Even Cardano and Paracelsus, who considered magic absolutely essential to human existence, still presented it as the servant and not the oppressor of nature. For Paracelsus alchemy fulfils and perfects nature: 'the alchemist is he who helps to develop to the extreme limits intended by nature that which nature produces for the benefit of mankind'. Thus the weaver, the baker, the cultivator, are alchemists and the difference between the saint and the alchemist is that the operations of the one proceed from God whereas the other employs only natural powers. If the alchemist's work is inaccurate, planets and constellations will not assist him because, as such, they cannot add anything to natural art nor subtract anything from it.[74] Cardano boasts that he has taught 'the use of observing natural phenomena for practical ends', ignored palmistry, incantations and evocations —though he admits to having prophesied by astrology—and excelled in medicine, geometry, mathematics and natural magic or 'the study of properties pertaining to substances and similar problems'.[75]

The writers who made the distinction between true, sophistical, and false alchemy did so less as a precaution against the confusion of divine and human operations than as a warning to alchemists to enlist natural laws instead of ignoring them.

Thus Benedict Varchi,[76] in the *Questione sull'alchimia* published in Florence in 1544, wrote that false alchemy claimed to cure disease instantaneously, create talking statues, and bestow eternal youth; that it could 'not only imitate nature but master and surpass it, all of which is impossible and absurd'. Sophistical alchemy transmuted all metals to gold, committed forgery and brewed poisons, for which 'it is quite naturally banned and condemned by virtuous men in all well organized republics'. At one time alchemy was highly reputed but it had since been debased by unscrupulous adventurers. Yet the alchemist manufactured glass, mirrors, lead, steel, lime, gunpowder, oils, and spirits 'and many other things without which not only could we not live in comfort, but we could not live at all'. The true alchemist knew that:

> Neither art nor the alchemist can produce gold but only nature prepared and assisted by the alchemist and by art, just as health cannot be restored to an ailing body either by drugs or by doctors but by nature prepared and assisted by doctors and by drugs . . . as a good doctor uses drugs to purge the body of infected matter and matter liable to infection and then encourages and assists natural strength until . . . the patient is restored to his

former health . . . just so the good alchemist first purifies a substance . . . and then lets nature follow its course. Therefore it is
clear that art alone cannot transmute metals but that nature is at
least as instrumental as art. [77]

Although these notions had to be extracted from a medley of
instances, examples, and fantastic beliefs, their influence on
European civilisation was substantial. All the same, I agree
with Luporini in refuting Thorndike's systematic association of
magic with experimentalism, in favour of a case-by-case distinction between the practical and the metaphysical aspects of
the general world picture. Indeed, in the light of this distinction
'organicist or unitarian-immanentist attitudes usually transpire
through the magical disguise'. [78]

We have already seen that the metaphysical aspects of magic
and alchemy had little or no influence on Bacon; but he did
borrow from this tradition the idea of science as the servant of
nature assisting its operations and, by stealth and cunning,
forcing it to yield to man's domination; as well as the idea of
knowledge as power. [79] In fact Bacon's definition of magic is an
almost literal repetition of Agrippa's words in the passage
quoted earlier:

> I however understand it as the science which applies the know-
> ledge of hidden forms to the production of wonderful operations;
> and by uniting (as they say) actives with passives displays the
> wonderful works of nature. [80]

In a long list in the *Great works of nature for the particular use of
mankind* (*Magnalia naturae praecipue quoad usus humanos*) Bacon also
includes examples of 'anticipations' used by Agrippa:

> Acceleration of time in maturation.
> Acceleration of germination.
> Impressing of air, and raising of tempests.
> Making of new species.
> Altering of complexions, and fatness and leanness. [81]

It is not difficult to see why, in the fifth aphorism of the *Day
of preparation* (*Parasceve*), Bacon gives such prominence to the
art of operating on bodies and altering substances to force
nature into various unnatural forms. In the second chapter of
the *De augumentis*, Book II, we are again confronted with the

notion of a natural history assisting the passage 'from the wonders of nature to the wonders of art' (all that is required of the natural historian, however, is to observe the spontaneous development of nature so as to master it and use it for his own ends). And the opening paragraphs of the *New Organon* acquire a new significance beside the Renaissance texts quoted above:

> Man being the servant and interpreter of Nature can do and understand so much and so much only as he has observed in fact or in thought of the course of Nature: beyond this he neither knows anything nor can do anything.
> Towards the effecting of works all that man can do is put together or part assunder natural bodies. The rest is done by Nature working within.[82]

Bacon's partiality to magic and alchemy, his wish to see them reinstated as the ultimate aims of human effort, are proofs of the influence of this tradition:

> The aim of magic is to recall natural philosophy from the vanity of speculations to the importance of experiments. Alchemy aims at separating and extracting the heterogeneous elements latent and implicit in natural substances, purifying what is polluted, releasing what is obstructed and bringing to maturation the unripe.[83]

If Bacon had reservations about magic and alchemy they were not concerned with the experimental nature of their enquiries, for the idea of an active, inventive science was basic to his own method.[84]

The condemning of magic and the extolling of science

If we study the historical sources of a given idea and the recurrence of traditional concepts in even the more revolutionary contexts we may avoid the pitfall of taking all past philosophers for innovators or precursors, but we run the risk of making the opposite mistake and ignoring the novelty of traditional concepts refashioned by new interpretations to meet new demands. In this way scholars have successfully proved that Bacon was not the prodigy of the Encyclopedists but a product of his age, and then, without further investigation, have classed him among medieval or Renaissance thinkers.[85] However, Bacon definitely detached himself from Renaissance alchemical and scientific traditions when he set up as a model for his New Science the mechanical arts with their progressive collaborative procedures.[86] For he wanted science to depart from arbitrary uncontrolled personal research and turn instead to organised collaborative experiment, and he believed his logic would make the conquest of new truths possible. He was not interested in transmitting acquired truths and therefore refuted contentious Scholastic learning; because he saw science as a collaboration of seekers he stressed the importance of strict methods clearly and simply stated to provide rules for further experiments and ensure progress. Indeed, it has been rightly said, that if more attention had been paid to this aspect of Bacon's philosophy he would not have been so consistently misinterpreted.[87]

Bacon pursued his plan of scientific reform with astonishing perseverance and very little success. Apart from the actual re-organisation of research on a practical, collective basis he wanted to see it supported by the State or some public organ-isation, and he also dreamt of an international brotherhood of scientists. In his letter to Burghley dated 1591[88] he declared that he had 'chosen all knowledge for his Province', a Province he wanted to free from two enemies: those who made use of 'frivolous disputations and verbosities' and those whose arms were 'blind experiments and auricular traditions and impost-ures'. No one could deter him from his purpose to direct science towards careful observations and well-founded conclusions, useful inventions and discoveries. In an essay written in 1592 on the occasion of the Queen's birthday[89] we find already outlined certain theories of the *New Organon*: he wrote that a 'meeting between the mind of man and the nature of things' never yet achieved either by the Greeks or the Alchemists was essential, and he praised the inventions of the printing press, gunpowder, and the magnet. Man's supremacy is in knowledge, he ended, and knowledge includes much 'which kings with their treasure cannot buy, nor with their force command, their spies and intelligencers can give no news of them'. Two years later in a speech entitled *Gesta Grayorum* (*The Deeds of Gray*) Bacon gave a detailed description of his programme of reform: it was not concerned with individual discoveries and inventions but it required scientific establishments and institutions. Recalling the rulers of antiquity who had left their mark on civilisation by the building of monuments, Bacon begged the king to make four important donations: a library to house books from all the countries of Europe and the world; a botanical garden and a zoo filled with every species of plant, animal, bird, and fish; and finally a laboratory with mills, furnaces, and stills for the discovery of the philosophers' stone.[90]

Bacon's efforts, as we know, were unsuccessful—'My zeal was taken for ambition', he wrote in 1603.[91] But that same year his hopes were rekindled when James I came to the throne. In 1605 in the *Advancement of Learning* Bacon invoked the sovereign's aid once again. His programme had now assumed new proportions, for he not only clamoured for new institutions of learning but also for the reorganisation of the principal existing ones: the universities. He wrote:

> All works are overcomen by amplitude of reward, by soundness of direction and by conjunction of labours. The first multiplieth endeavours, the second preventeth error and the third supplieth the frailty of man.[92]

But in the universities scholars were content with new editions and more accurate reprints of classical works, and ever more abundant glossaries and notes. While students became expert at debating and formal reasoning they were wholly ignorant of vast spheres of knowledge. The art of argumentation was reduced to 'childish sophistry and ridiculous affectation' and study restricted to a handful of texts, or even to no more than those of Aristotle. There were few facilities for experiment and botanical gardens only grew plants for medicinal purposes. Responsible persons would have to be engaged by the universities to report on progress in all branches of learning and to encourage interest in unpopular branches. Finally relations should be established with scientific organisations all over Europe for an exchange of results and other information. Thus a brotherhood of scientists would develop, similar to the natural brotherhood in families.

When Bacon finally realised the impossibility of reorganising the universities to suit his purpose he still hoped to obtain the personal control of certain colleges: Westminster, Eton, Winchester; Trinity and St John's Colleges, Cambridge; and Magdalen College, Oxford.

There is an outline of Bacon's programme in the private *Free Commentaries* (*Commentarius solutus*) of 1608 and, under a slightly different form, in the long unpublished *Refutation of Philosophies* (*Redargutio philosophiarum*) and *Thought and Vision* (*Cogitata et visa*). It recurs with further alterations in the *New Organon* and *De augmentis*, but he did not set it down in its final consistent form till the *New Atlantis*, in a passage describing Solomon's house, where it is no longer presented as a project but as a Utopian dream. Indeed this plan, never realised during Bacon's lifetime, marked the birth of scientific humanism for the founders of the Royal Society and later for the Encyclopedists; and through humanism it has inspired some of the more progressive forms of European culture.

Bacon's plan for the reform of science was his great contribution to culture. It inspired the Encyclopedists' notion of the aims and purpose of man; indeed, their whole attitude bears its mark: they 'addressed themselves to the artisans of France' and visited laboratories to question technicians and workers and 'take down their replies'; they tried to find exact definitions for the ends and methods of each separate art so as to compile a complete *corpus* or encyclopedia of learning. Man, they claimed, must be conscious of the theoretical scientific principles implicit in his work and put theoretical scientific research to practical uses. Bacon's influence can be detected in d'Alembert's objections to the 'superiority of the liberal arts' and in his programme for a history of the arts 'a history of the uses to which man has put the products of nature to satisfy his needs or his curiosity'.

For Bacon science was not a luxury to be indulged in after human needs were satisfied, a detached contemplation, or an aspiring towards truth. This, however, was the picture which had come down through the centuries, and if the paint had worn a little thin in places it was still basically the same. Aristotle was the most coherent exponent of this view of science which stemmed from the economic structure of a society where slaves made mechanical devices unnecessary or even useless, and where contempt for the worker was extended to the work itself, depriving it of all cultural value.[93] Thus in Plato's *Laws* the artisan is not entitled to full citizenship, while Aristotle—who denies his right to any citizenship whatsoever—distinguishes him from the slave only in that he caters for the needs of more people. For Aristotle the aims of artisan and merchant alike are degrading because their occupations are base and require no special skill. Thus the contrasts between slave and free citizen, artisan and scientist, practical and theoretical knowledge became merged during the classical and medieval eras for most of civilised Europe.

But Bacon saw the development of the mechanical arts as a new and exciting cultural event, and his reappraisal of their social and scientific significance[94] and of their aims enabled him to disprove some of Aristotle's theories concerning the relation of nature to art.

For Bacon the 'history of arts' was but a section of natural history; by asserting this view he departed radically from the traditional opposition of art and nature where the former is only a vain attempt to imitate the latter. According to this tradition nature includes principles of infinite motion while the products of art, moved by exterior principles, can never successfully imitate the spontaneity of natural motion. Bacon exposed the relation of this doctrine to Aristotle's theory of 'species' where a natural product such as a tree is defined as possessing a 'primal form' while an artificial product such as a table possesses only a 'secondary form'. For Bacon natural and artificial objects possessed the same kind of form and essence, and differed only in their cause. Art was man added to nature, and if in one phenomenon the necessary conditions for its existence were naturally conjoined and in another they were conjoined by the art of man this did not make them incongruous. Man could only affect nature by joining or separating natural bodies. By distinguishing art from nature philosophers were led to consider art as a mere adjunct to nature and the consequences of this attitude were fatal, causing man to despair of ever being able to influence and improve the conditions of his existence.

Bacon voices his misgivings as to the practical consequences of Aristotle's theory in the *Masculine birth of time* (*Temporis partus masculus*), violently attacking Galen:

> Baleful star! Plague of the Human race! You would have us believe that only Nature can produce true compound. You

snatch at the notion that the heat of the sun and the heat of fire are different things and parade this opinion with the malicious intention of lessening human power wherever you can and bolstering ignorance to all eternity through dispair of any improvement.[95]

For Bacon science had a public, democratic and collaborative character, individual efforts contributing to its general success and the common good of all.

Further it will not be amiss to distinguish the three kinds and as it were grades of ambition in mankind. The first is of those who desire to extend their own power in their native country; which kind is vulgar and degenerate. The second is of those who labour to extend the power of their country and its dominion among men. This certainly has more dignity, though not less covetousness. But if a man endeavours to establish and extend the power and dominion of the human race itself over the Universe his ambition (if ambition it can be called) is without doubt a both more wholesome thing and a more noble than the other two.[96]

And if, he said, there are some men who take up science out of idle curiosity, and some to acquire a reputation, and others still to distinguish themselves in argument, there are yet a few who take it up for its real end which is the benefit of the entire human race. Thus there are men who see science as a bed to rest upon, or an arcade wherein to stroll, or a tall tower to satisfy their pride, or a fortress for warring, or a market place, but very few see it as it really is: a rich store for the glory of God and the good of humanity.[97]

Thus Bacon implicitly refuted the traditional image of the enlightened sage and the conception of scientific collaboration as a meeting of *illuminati* jealously guarding their precious, mysterious discoveries. The distinction between ordinary mortals and the enlightened genius is prevalent in all European cultures from the Pythagoreans to the Gnostics, from Averroes to Ficino, and is even to be found at the dawn of modern civilisation together with the new ideals of scientific technology, co-operative progressive science and the union of knowledge and action.

Roger Bacon's writings have been rightly seen as one of the most significant expressions of a medieval cultural crisis marking the turning point in scientific development—the affinities of his outlook with that of the Lord Chancellor are considerable. Roger Bacon favoured a division of labour (*manum industria*) to correct the inevitable errors of physics and mathematics; he compared science to architecture, an art requiring the collaboration of a number of workers; he suggested a reorganisation of scientific research with the help of subsidies and the co-operation of scholars; he drew attention to the increase of human knowledge with each successive generation, thus proving the superiority of his contemporaries to men of previous ages; and he urged the diffusion of learning.[98] But one cannot ignore, on the other hand, certain basic opinions by which Roger showed himself to be a man of his time, heir to the hermetic tradition.[99] He declared that wisdom should not be imparted to everyone indiscriminately; scholars, he says, have always kept the highest knowledge from the masses, and he quotes as examples the Greek philosophers meeting by night, wise men concealing the revealed truth in complex figures of speech, the Scriptures, Moses on Mount Sinai, and the three apostles who witnessed Christ's transfiguration.

As Thorndike points out Roger Bacon's 'experimental science' was really two-thirds hermetic; its aim was first to study established scientific methods, secondly to add to them new conclusions, and only thirdly to increase the powers of mankind by natural experiments; even this last (and only progressive) aspect of science bore the imprint of tradition, for the experimental methods employed could not be disclosed, being the prerogative of the initiated. Thus experimental science though claiming to be sovereign among arts and revealer of supreme truth still conformed to mysterious, hermetic, and esoteric regulations.[100]

The notion of learning as the prerogative of an élite was common to most hermetic and magical works but it was most prevalent in the western world after the end of the twelfth century.[101]

> But I ask and adjure all men of understanding in these matters into whose hands this precious, new-found pearl may fall that they pass it on to those whose energies are employed at full stretch by this question, who are hungry for art and accomplished in the principles of natural science, but that they should conceal it from fools and children since they are unworthy.

This is from the *Margarita preciosa novella* written in 1330 in Pela by Bono of Farrara.[102] Here is also the opening paragraph of *De magia veterum* printed in Basel in 1575:

> Who would know secret things, let him know also how to guard secrets with secrecy, reveal what is fit to be revealed and set his seal on that which should be sealed up; let him not give to dogs what is sacred, not cast pearls before swine. Observe this law and the eyes of your mind are opened to the understanding of secret things, and you shall hear all your heart's desire revealed to you through divine power.[103]

Ficino's translations of hermetic texts were very popular in the fifteenth and sixteenth centuries where culture was interwoven with hermetic, magical, and astrological patterns.[104] The sage, possessor of occult wisdom, was a familiar figure in the works of those philosophers Bacon had so bitterly attacked. Paracelsus writes:

> This arcane lore was kept by the ancient Fathers who were in possession of it in most careful concealment, lest it should fall into impious hands . . . therefore we ask you . . . that following the practice of those fathers, you be so good as to handle and preserve this divine mystery with the utmost secrecy.[105]

Even Agrippa—though familiar with technical problems and aspiring towards an international brotherhood of scientists— saw the language of science as that of an initiated minority.[106]

> Yet I advise you carefully to preserve this precept: that you communicate common matters to the world at large but higher mysteries to the higher sort and your chosen friends . . . I enclose the cabbalistic book you mentioned . . . my most eager and hungry Chrysostom, aspiring to try yourself in this, be sure you conceal so great a mystery in the secret, inmost room of your devout breast, and hide it in an unfailing silence, for it should be the work of an impious spirit to divulge to the many the words filled full of the majesty of divine power.[107]

And in the *De occulta philosophia* he declared that 'the first step and the key to magical operations is the ennobling of man' which consisted in renouncing the flesh so as to be uplifted in a sudden illumination to a god-like state in which the secret powers are revealed. Thus the highest doctrines must be concealed from the masses and the adept should 'disclose to no man either the place, or the time, or the ends pursued'. And finally he writes that nobody should take offence if he has been obliged to dissemble the revelations of science in ambiguous riddles dispersed through his pages, for they are not hidden from the wise but only from malicious fools 'so that we have written in a style to confound the ignorant and be understood by the enlightened'. These revelations cannot be transmitted by normal, public channels but require a special secret transmission, an 'infusion' from soul to soul by sacred words:

> For they do not commit these things to letters, nor do they write them down with the pen. Instead, they are infused from spirit to spirit in few and sacred words; and if it should happen to reach you. . . .[108]

What is true of Agrippa is equally true of Cardano—another of Bacon's Renaissance sources:

> Work has no need at all for partnership. So far as I am concerned not even twenty out of sixty discoveries owe anything to others. A great many of these discoveries have other sources, and some have mysterious sources like the 'glory', or even sublimer sources. So what have I to share with my fellows? Until now I have spoken of myself as an ordinary man, and even, as to nature and education, as inferior to other men; but now I shall speak of a wonderful gift I possess.[109]

What has such a quester to do with technical instruments, exact methods, or clear definitions? All he wants is to attain the essence of all things by supernatural powers unknown to ordinary human beings:

> I encompassed the sublime summit never attained since Plotinus —I mean the beginning and end of all things—in my seven books *Of Eternal Secrets*, and also the disposition of the Universe and every single thing contained in it, in my four books *On Fate*. The third kind of understanding . . . comes to me entirely from a tutelary Spirit who simply demonstrates, revealing cause and essence by means of an infallible proof.[110]

When we read Cardano we find that miracles were always happening to him; he describes his supernatural gifts, dreams, strange adventures, and the ministrations of his guardian spirit; we witness also his sudden furies and his pride. He wrote

'In my teachings I have preferred to use supernatural instances.'
This mystical attitude arrested the growth of his earlier empirical tendencies so that the only observations we find are
disconnected, gratuitious and unselective. For he was not interested in studying the regular course of events but in noting
the miraculous and the extraordinary.[111]

Bacon attacked pitilessly such attitudes and the ideals they
implied. In the *Temporis partus masculus* he describes Paracelsus
as a monster and a fanatical breeder of phantasms whose in-
quiries are surrounded by the trumpets of ostentation, the
subterfuge of darkness, and connivance with religion. He describes Agrippa as a clown who turned everything into a futile
joke, and Cardano as an untiring weaver of cobwebs, for ever
in contradiction with all things and with himself.[112] In the
Redargutio philosophiarum his attacks are more explicit: if magic,
encompassed in a framework of lies, is put to any use, it is only
for its novelty or to provoke admiration, never for its real worth.
A peculiarity of philosophical demonstrations, continues Bacon,
is that they make everything seem less admirable than it is; but
to make things appear more admirable is a form of deceit.

Bacon's target here was an attitude typical of all magic, but
of Renaissance magic in particular. Della Porta among others
describes the magician's aims:

> The magician who has an understanding of these matters mingles
> inferior things with superior qualities and extracts in this way
> from the very heart of nature the secrets enclosed therein—then
> he makes public the things he has found to be true so that all may
> know of them—and be full of good will towards the Artificer and
> praise him and honour his great powers.
>   . . . And if you should wish for more magnificent results and
> to be considered truly admirable . . . then take up the study and
> the understanding of causes.[113]

This is what Bacon had termed vulgar and degenerate ambition, the attitude to science which he compares to building a
tall tower to satisfy one's pride. For the ethics of his new scientific research were inspired from the much despised mechanical
arts:

> We have also houses of deceits of the senses; where we represent
> all manner of feats of juggling, false apparitions, impostures and

illusions and their fallacies. And surely you will easily believe that we that have so many things truly natural which induce admiration, could in a world of particulars deceive the senses, if we would disguise those things and labour to make them seem more miraculous. But we do hate all impostures and lies; in so much as we have severly forbidden it to all our fellows under pain of ignominy and fines, that they do not shew any natural work or thing adorned or swelling; but only pure as it is and without all affectation of strangeness.[114]

Bacon's reservations and his censures of magical and alchemical tradition concerned this one aspect only.

Astrology, natural magic, and alchemy, of which sciences nevertheless the ends and pretences are noble . . . but the derivations and prosecutions to these ends both in theories and in practices are full of error and vanity.[115]

According to Bacon, magic endeavours to dominate and to improve nature; and for this it should be imitated. Where it needs revising is in its claim to use one man's inspiration instead of the organised efforts of the human race, and to make science serve individual ends rather than mankind.

Bacon condemned magic on ethical grounds. He accused it of fraud, of a craze for genius, and of megalomania; he refuted its non-progressive, non-co-operative methods and especially its attempts to replace human sweat by a few drops of elixir or an easy combination of substances.[116] He was convinced that only infinite patience could unravel the 'riddles of nature'. Out of humility towards his Creator, affection for his fellows, pity for the sufferings of mankind, loathing of ignorance and love of truth, man should abandon or at least set aside those absurd philosophers who have trampled the works of God underfoot and claimed, on the grounds of a few hurried experiments, to have created a complete natural philosophy that no scholar could possibly take seriously.[117] The pages of nature's great book should be read with patience and reverence, pausing and meditating over each one and discarding all easy interpretations. The language of nature must be learnt anew: it had suffered the confusion of the Tower of Babel and man must come to it again, not searching for marvels and surprises but handling, like a little child, each letter of its alphabet.[118]

Bacon explicitly declared that his new scientific method

would leave little scope for individual talent for it was to be a leveller of intelligences.[119] Some scholars, showing a remarkable lack of insight, have taken this to indicate Bacon's optimistic faith in his method: that owing to its mechanical nature it would run, as it were, on its own steam once it had been instituted; and there have been violent objections to his so-called endeavours to make thought 'run on pre-established tracks'. However, it suffices to set Bacon's statement in its historical context for it to appear as no more than a reaction against magical and alchemical methods of research where results were entrusted to mysterious individual operations. Bacon opposed to this lack of method a system based on the division of labour and on a progressive continuity and it is to this aspect of his method that he alludes when he compares it to a ruler or a compass. In the absence of instruments we must rely on a steady hand and a sharp eye, qualities which are subjective and uncontrollable.

> For my part I am emphatically of the opinion that man's wits require not the addition of feathers and wings, but of leaden weights. Men are very far from realising how strict and disciplined a thing is research into truth and nature, and how little it leaves to the judgement of men.[120]

What debars magic and alchemy from the status of science, continues Bacon, is precisely the burden they entrust to individual judgement and skill. Alchemical and magical research make use of a minimum of rules that have never been properly integrated into the methods because their essential communicability has not been stressed. They are expressed in symbols—not to be confused with the symbols used in modern chemistry with which they have nothing in common—referring by analogy and correspondence either to the Whole or to a Universal Spirit, or to God.

In the *New Organon*, Book II, paragraph four, Bacon made a deliberate attempt to modify alchemical rules to meet the needs of technical science. Here he acknowledges the aims of the alchemist and uses almost exactly their own vocabulary, but he refutes their subjective methods with decisive arguments. Suppose we wish to induce a new nature upon a given substance, he says, let us see how to set about it: we must be provided with a set of well defined rules because for an operation such as this a method is required that is reliable and comprehensible and that uses only the materials of which one disposes and is less complex than the operation undertaken: an abstract model, in fact, reduced to its simplest expression. The alchemists instead refer to supposedly sacred texts. Thus they can only accuse themselves for their inevitable failure, and with increasing self-reproach they repeat the experiment over and over again, convinced that they have misinterpreted the wilfully equivocal instructions in some minute detail.[121]

Such were the views which distinguished Bacon from the great Renaissance thinkers. It is true that Della Porta, Cardano, Paracelsus and so many others stressed the importance of experiment, and, like Bacon, acknowledged the revolutionary significance of sixteenth-century discoveries[122] and insisted on the practical aspect of every enquiry. However, they persisted in seeing scientific realisations as the fruit of individual efforts, the privilege of exceptional gifts or the result of a secret collaboration between *illuminati*. These theories exclude Bacon from their ranks.

Bacon's attitude to science and nature finds its expression in a tone of quiet modesty prevalent in much of his writing:

> My motives in publishing are the following: I wish to spread among men all that makes intellectual relationships and freedom of thought possible, so that it may be passed from mouth to mouth; the rest, with discernement and common sense will be accomplished by hand. Verily, I am setting in motion something with which others shall experiment. Indeed it is not in my nature to be always preoccupied with external events, I am no pursuer of fame, neither do I wish to establish a sect like an heretic, and I consider that it would be despicable and ridiculous to try and obtain personal advantage from so noble an enterprise. It is enough to know that I have worked for a good cause and written my books—with this last, Fortune herself cannot interfere.[123]

It is only by wrenching this passage from its historical context that scholars have managed to give it an appearance of political scheming. The following is one of the many portraits Bacon draws of the scientist according to his own ideal:

> There were some fifty men there, all of mature years, not a young

man among them, all bearing the stamp of dignity and probity
. . . At his entry they were chatting easily among themselves but
sitting in rows as if expecting somebody. Not long after there
entered to them a man of peaceful and serene air, save that his
face had become habituated to the expression of pity. They all
stood up in his honour, and he looked round and said with a
smile: 'It is more than I can understand as I recognize you one by
one, how you can all be at leisure at the same time. How is it to
be explained?' Then one of the company replied: 'You yourself
are the explanation, for we all put what you have to tell us above
any other business.' 'Then, said he, I am incurring a heavy
responsibility for the total of time that will be lost here, during
which you might be all going about your several tasks serving I
know not how many men. I must not keep you waiting any
longer.' Which said, he took his seat, not on a platform or pulpit,
but on a level with the rest and delivered the following address.[124]

The scientist represented here is certainly more like Galileo
or Newton than Paracelsus, Cardano, or Agrippa, who was
known as 'philosopher, genius, hero, God and all'. Such classical
composure—reminiscent of the early humanist conversations—
is very different from the titanic bearing of the Renaissance
magician; and there is, besides, a quiet confidence that comes
from knowing the unlimited powers made available to man by
technology and collaboration. The theatre of human endeavours is no longer only the city but the whole world. This
portrait is inspired by a totally new idea of science. It is no
longer the haphazard jotting of random ideas but methodical,
systematic thought; it is more than experience, observation and
a rejection of authority; it is not the solitary inspiration of the
individual genius, but collaborative research institutionalised
in specific social and linguistic forms.[125] Above all scientific
knowledge is not the fruit of enlightened, exceptional wisdom;
it is a human product and tends to improve both the intellectual
and the material conditions of the human race. Bacon's contribution to the expansion of these ideas was considerable; they
are strikingly illustrated in his image of science as a relay race
of torch-bearers where no single runner can ever be a substitute
for the whole team. The aim of each participant is to free the
world from the domination of magic, and though Bacon was
finally entangled once again in its snares, the manner and rules
of the race had been changed for ever.

II

The Refutation of Philosophies

The break with tradition

For Bacon the purpose of scientific research was neither to acquire fame nor to produce miracles, but to improve the conditions of human existence, and he believed this could only be achieved by collaboration, the founding of adequate institutions, and the publication of results in plain exact terms. William Rawley, Bacon's biographer, writes:

> Whilst he was commorant in the university, about sixteen years of age (as his lordship hath been pleased to impart unto myself), he first fell into the dislike of the philosophy of Aristotle; not for the worthlessness of the author, to whom he would ever ascribe all high attributes, but for the unfruitfulness of the way; being a philosophy (as his lordship used to say) only strong for disputations and contentions, but barren of production of works for the benefit of the life of man; in which mind he continued to his dying day.[1]

Such a critical attitude, together with the notion of substituting practical for theoretical forms of enquiry, required an insight into past errors and a will to eliminate them which are surprising in a lad of sixteen. But Bacon had evidently seen from the very first that the new function he ascribed to knowledge involved a break with tradition; in the *Temporis partus masculus* (*The masculine birth of time*) written between 1602 and

36

1603[2] he states the fact quite clearly. The main themes of this short work are developed—in a rather different vein—in the *Valerius Terminus* (1603), the historical section of the *Advancement of Learning* (1605), *Filum Labyrinthi* (*Ariadne's Thread*, about 1607), *Cogitata et visa* (*Things thought and things seen*, 1607) and the *Redargutio philosophiarum* (*Refutation of philosophies*, 1608). Bacon maintains the same antagonism to tradition in the preface to the *Instauratio magna* (*The Great Instauration*, which is the first book of the *New Organon*, 1620) and in the historical sections of the *De augumentis* (*On growth*, 1623), though it acquires a greater astringency in these pages. And in the *De principiis atque originibus* (*Of birth and origins*, 1624) only a few years before his death, Bacon recapitulates some of his theories from *De sapientia veterum* (*Of ancient wisdom*, 1609)[3] and expands his views on the philosophy of Bernard Telesius.

This work of demolition on which all Bacon's great projects were founded—his reform of logic, his reorganisation of science —proceeds by first classifying all past philosophies and then analysing individual exponents and schools. Both methods are based on presuppositions which Bacon tested and consolidated while writing the *Temporis partus masculus*. Anderson has proved conclusively that this work belongs to an early period of Bacon's activity, but he also detracts from its significance, describing it as a manifestation of 'ignorance, disproportion, and philosophical ineptitude' later attenuated by a relative historical 'objectivity'. It is true that many of Bacon's theories underwent a number of modifications. However, I shall attempt to prove that he stood by this refutation of tradition and ancient philosophy first proclaimed in the *Temporis partus masculus*.[4]

Bacon's whole outlook was based on the belief that a new era in the history of mankind was at hand. If man, confronted by his new destiny, were to recall science from the gloom of antiquity rather than seek it in the bright light of nature, it would indeed be sinful; that which has been done is of no importance, but only what may yet be done.[5] When a country has been overrun by arms in a successful battle it would be vain to enquire into genealogies and to try to discover if our ancestors were there before. There is no need to refute each single error of tradition, searching as it were, by candle-light, for every crack or imperfection; but we must raise on high the flaming torch of truth to dissipate the shadows that have accumulated over the centuries. There is little point in hurling oneself into the fray to assist one side or the other, for the battle, though ruthless and bitter, is waged by phantoms and shades.

> Your philosophers are more fabulous than poets; they debauch our minds; they substitute a false coinage for the true; and worse still are the satellites and parasites of the great ones, the whole mob of professional teachers.[6]

Classical philosophers: Plato, Aristotle, Galen, Cicero, Seneca, Plutarch, and those of medieval and Renaissance times: St Thomas, Duns Scotus, Ramus, Cardano, Paracelsus, and Telesius were not accused of committing theoretical errors. But their philosophies, all comparable to some extent, deserved the same condemnation and the same fate because their ethics were at fault. This seems so monstrous to Bacon that he says 'such profane and polluted' subjects cannot even be discussed without shame. He does not wish to replace them by a new philosophy of the same kind with identical principles, arguments, and aims but by an entirely new attitude to nature involving new principles and a different kind of argument, and different aims: in fact a new concept of truth, a new ethic, and a new logic.

Thus Bacon opposed 'to the rubbish and bother of the schoolmen'[7] a logic of facts similar to the logic of those philosophers of the Enlightenment who were to see in Bacon their master. One should not attempt to anticipate reason in the form of a closed system, as Cassirer puts it, but:

> The mind must abandon itself to the abundance of phenomena and gauge itself constantly by them. . . . Only in this way can the genuine correlation of subject and object, of truth and reality, be achieved; only so can the correspondence between these concepts, which is the condition of all scientific knowledge, be brought about.[8]

Bacon proposed in the place of traditional learning a union 'with things themselves in a chaste, holy, and legal wedlock', that would change the destinies of man, increase his fortunes, and dissipate his general perplexities.

But here—as in his attacks on magic—Bacon's refutation also

takes the form of moral reprobation: sophistry, a combination of religion and science, and a few experiments decked out to gain applause had been substituted by the philosophical tradition for humility and reverence for the works of the Creator; this was the result of intellectual pride that uses philosophy for triumphs in the debating hall and deprives it of all fruitfulness. The Greek philosophers had bequeathed to mankind this sterility together with their dual claim to replace the patient perusal of nature's great book by artful sentences, and to encompass the whole of method and the totality of nature in a single principle and a single doctrine.[9] Thus it is not without reason that the affinities of Bacon's views with a religious conception of the reform of knowledge have often been observed.[10]

Now, Bacon's refutation of certain philosophies—or more precisely of certain interpretations of their aims and purposes—came to involve his refutation of the entire historical background of which, according to him, they were the inevitable result. When in the *Temporis partus masculus* he mentions 'the shadows thrown by words', 'a mixture of religion and science', and 'a few commonplace observations and notorious experiments tricked out to make a composition more fanciful than a stage play', he is not attacking tradition in general but three actual philosophical manifestations: the logical exercises of Scholasticism; the various rational theologies inspired by Aristotle and the religious themes in contemporary Platonic trends; the metaphysics of magicians, alchemists, and Renaissance philosophers and scientists.

Owing to the importance of sceptical, empirical and naturalist influences in sixteenth- and seventeenth-century England, the actual situation in the universities has too often been overlooked. Here, methods of instruction bore the distinctive mark of a Scholastic tradition emptied of all intellectual zeal and reduced to a dry academicism.[11] The reaction to this tradition, now accused of 'barbarism' and 'papism', was directly connected with the social and religious upheavals of the Reformation. In 1550 Duns Scotus' texts were publicly burnt and 'the funeral of Scotus and Scotists' was the signal at Oxford for a total repudiation of traditional philosophy. Representatives of scientific trends recalling Occam and Roger Bacon moved from Oxford to London where they found the support of members of the ruling classes; groups of independent philosophers were formed, old libraries and manuscripts consulted. Robert Recorde, John Dee, and Thomas Digges, who were members of these groups, brought about a revival of the characteristic medieval English interest in mathematics and science and were the first to be drawn to Copernicanism before the visit of Giordano Bruno.[12]

But if tradition and the spirit of Scholasticism had been banned from the universities, Scholastic methods of teaching and study were still prevalent, though the late Scholastic discussions of physics and logic had been replaced by a rigid Aristotelianism. According to the 1556 statute, the Oxford B.A. course required two terms of grammar, four of rhetoric, five of logic, three of arithmetic, and two of music. The basic texts were, for the study of astronomy Ptolemy, and for that of geography, Strabo and Pliny; Copernicus, Christopher Columbus and Vasco da Gama might never have existed! Regulations for the year 1585–6 stipulated that all bachelors and undergraduates 'should lay aside their various Authors, such that caused many dissensions and strifes in the Schools, and only follow Aristotle and those that defend him', Aristotle must be dissociated from 'all sterile and inane Questions disagreeing from the antient and true Philosophy'.[13]

According to Frances Yates, the spirit of this regulation, doing away with Scotist and Nominalist traditions, is typically humanist and not medieval at all. Her opinion is based on the text's apparent scorn for the 'sterile and inane Questions' of Scholasticism and on its identification of 'antient' with 'true' philosophy.[14] This is certainly correct, but on the other hand, a regulation such as this would, in this case, refer less to Scotists and Nominalists than to the anti-Aristotelian Ramists and Ramistic logicians. Already in 1574 the Ramist John Barebone was given the alternative of retracting or resigning his university post. In fact, this faith in the absolute truth of Aristotelianism should be seen less as a humanist reverence for antiquity than as an opposition of traditionalism to Ramistic doctrines. Though the latters' attacks on Aristotle were violent and superficial they possessed a form of logic—unencumbered by excessive subtlety—that was a useful instrument of research and

40

communication; and they claimed their superiority to traditional methods on these grounds. The title of Temple's book published in London in 1580 is significant: *From Francis Mildapet of Navarre to Everard Digby of England, an admonition that the single method of Peter Ramus be retained and the rest rejected.* The fact that a man like Everard Digby, considered to be one of the leading authorities on matters of logic, was influential at Cambridge between 1584 and 1588 shortly after his controversy with Temple, may give some measure of the Ramists' unpopularity in the universities. Indeed, his vigorous defence of Aristotle against Temple's attacks is more worthy of mention than his metaphysics of a universal correspondence and his logical assumption of a double method of approach to truth. His *Theoria analytica* (1597)[15] is a mixture of ideas from Aristotle, St Thomas, the neo-Platonists, pseudo-Dionysius, St Augustine, Cornelius Agrippa and Reuchlin; but the following year he published an attack on 'Ramistic infiltrations': *Two books concerning the double method, in refutation of the single method of P. Ramus*[16] in the form of a dialogue between an Aristotelian and a Ramist, where the former's arguments are clearly stated. Digby argues in favour of the Aristotelian synthesis, analysis, induction, and syllogism to reassert the validity of traditional teachings and the authority of Aristotle.[17] At Oxford, with John Case, author of *Lapis philosophicum* (1599), Aristotle is the 'Prince among philosophers', though Case's critique of the *Physics* contributes nothing to an understanding of Aristotle. In Case, as in many of his contemporaries, though Machiavelli is dismissed as an 'old atheist', Ramus vigorously attacked as a 'dangerous innovator', the alchemists mentioned and the philosophers' stone discussed, there is not the slightest allusion to the great sixteenth-century naturalists.

When in *Cogitata et visa* Bacon describes systems of education in the universities, he is referring to the existing conditions where outmoded methods did nothing to further observations, experiments, and the freedom of thought required for scientific knowledge.[18] The Scholastic method of *lectio, expositio, quaestio, disputatio* had been revived in the English universities with little or no change in the authorities referred to during *quaestio*. The problems discussed were very similar to those that the twelfth-century student had pondered: final causes, the subjection of secondary to primary causes, precedence, formal definitions, substantial forms, primary and secondary substances. Case's book, *Lapis philosophicum*, discusses problems such as: was matter created? are all natural substances composed of matter? is matter formless? In the 1630s books like Samuel Smith's *Aditus ad logicam* (1633) were mechanical repetitions of Aristotelian concepts. Further, examinations for a master's degree were based on the texts of Aristotle. Bacon says that education was 'so managed that the last thing anyone would be likely to entertain was an unfamiliar thought', and anyhow, no one dared exercise his own judgement because 'studies are confined to the works of certain authorities: a man who disagrees with them or raises awkward questions is censured as a disturbing and revolutionary influence'.[19]

In the preceding chapter I have tried to show the significance of Bacon's opposition to the 'fanciful compositions' of magicians, empiricists, and naturalists. Here I shall only recall the letter addressed to Lord Burghley in 1591 where Bacon tells of his objections to the 'frivolous disputations and verbosities' of Scholastic logic and to the 'blind experiments and auricular traditions and impostures' of the naturalists.[20]

We shall discuss later what Bacon calls in the *Temporis partus masculus* 'a mixture of religion and science', for the relation and distinction between scientific and philosophical research and religion is a central problem in Bacon's philosophy. But the historical facts he attacks are on the one hand the Aristotelian tendency to identify the First Mover of natural philosophy with the Christian God, and on the other that form of Platonism or 'superstitious philosophy' that mixes religion with science and mystical with rational elements. In Elizabethan England the first is an extension of the pre-Reformation Church and a distinct antithesis to those movements inspired by Augustinian humanism where the texts of the Fathers are contrasted to the 'integrity' of primitive evangelical religion and to rational Aristotelian theology.

Bacon's attacks on the Greek philosophers in the *Temporis partus masculus*, and especially his attacks on Plato and Aristotle acquire a new significance in this historical context. For Bacon Plato's theory of congenital truth is fallacious. Plato, says Bacon, also made use of religion to back his worthless theories;

in this way he both deprived men of reality by directing their gaze inwards towards contemplation, and favoured a mixture of science and theology which is fatal to the progress of science and to the power of religion.[21] As for Aristotle, he caused men to be the 'slaves of words' by awakening their passion for vain subtleties and sophistry; he was the originator of that verbosity which has become so popular with 'all the Scholastic dregs', he constructed hasty theories on insufficient facts, and he introduced a form of science that weaves theoretical cobwebs instead of determining causes.

However, a certain number of philosophers are spared in the *Temporis partus masculus*: Roger Bacon, who tried to extend the powers of mankind by mechanical devices;[22] Peter Severinus and, to a lesser degree, Paracelsus, who endeavoured to recall men to experience; Arnaldo of Villanova, and others like him, who made observations and experiments, though they detracted from the results by an over-refinement of argument. Even Heraclitus, Pythagoras, and Democritus strayed in some way from the beaten track of traditional philosophy; and Epicurus, however ingenuously, refuted final causes. The works of Tacitus have been unjustly overshadowed by those of Plato and Aristotle, for they contain a wealth of observations on human customs. Pyrrho and the Academicians revived the powers of the intellect, but their relations to philosophical errors are like those of a fickle lover to his beloved whom he repeatedly offends without ever achieving a final break.[23] But none of these thinkers is worthy of Bacon's praise; their half-truths are mere freaks, for 'everybody stumbles on some truth sooner or later'. Even the most far-fetched hypothesis can, at some point in the argument, intersect a reasonable one, and traditional philosophers, according to Bacon, never came upon the truth in any other way. One might as well say that a pig can write tragedies because it has accidentally traced a letter of the alphabet in the dust with its snout as compare the fortuitous truths of these philosophers to scientific truth.

Bacon's reasons for demanding a final break with philosophical traditions emerge from this brief summary of the *Temporis partus masculus*. Philosophy has turned man from natural investigations so that he has become introspective; it has substituted contemplation for action, and resignation for the hope and the will to improve the human condition; its evasion of problems of experience and reality are reflected in three of its characteristic features: the substitution of verbal for real solutions; the ambition to evolve doctrines in the form of systems that will solve, once and for all, every problem and explain all natural phenomena; the confusion of divine with natural things and of religion with science. This conception of knowledge inevitably leads to sterility and although attempts have, in fact, been made to establish a 'union with things themselves' these have been unmethodical, fragmentary, and uncertain, so that the transition from verbal projects to their realisation has never been accomplished. And here once again the cause of failure is none other than the fabrication of systems and the thirst for applause. Those who construct general theories and natural metaphysics are like men who hear a sentence in an unknown tongue and try to interpret it by ascribing to certain words the meanings of words in their own tongue that they accidentally resemble.

The function of history and the sociology of knowledge

In the years 1603 to 1608, though Bacon was involved in a number of serious political problems, he managed to elucidate his motives for totally refuting traditional philosophy. Where in the *Temporis partus masculus* he had done little more than oppose this tradition, in the *Cogitata et visa* and the *Redargutio philosophiarum* of 1607 and 1608 respectively he examined it historically, exposing its political and social shortcomings and the causes of its failure. This historico-critical operation was based on analyses and on a system of 'signs' or criteria.[24]

In 1603 Bacon began to write the *Advancement of Learning*—one of his major works—published in 1605. Book II opens with a discussion of histories, which Bacon divides into natural, civil, ecclesiastic, and cultural, deploring the total inadequacy of the last. No one, he says, has ever described the evolution of culture from age to age as natural, civil, and ecclesiastic progress has been described. So long as this was not done history would be as blind as the statue of Polyphemus and lack that which most enriches the mind and the very life of man. Particular histories of jurisprudence, rhetoric, mathematics and philosophy had indeed been written, but they were only memorials[25] concerned with individual schools, authors, books, or sects, whereas what was required was a true history of ideas and culture, a universal history examining the origins and development of science and scientific schools, their methods, struggles, decadence, and final disappearance, and determining the 'causes and occasions' of development and decadence. (When Bacon later translated and amplified the *Advancement* he defined these causes as the different character of countries and peoples, whether favourable or not to a given science, and accidental events furthering or hindering the progress of learning.) This history should also include a study of the relations between culture on the one hand and religion and law on the other so as to establish their influence on the advancement of learning. Such a history would consider the various circumstances that had played a part in the progress of culture. It would be a work compiled, not to satisfy the idle curiosity of amateurs, but to teach a conscientious use of knowledge: a 'more serious and grave purpose'.[26]

On this historical basis Bacon endeavoured, in the *Cogitata et visa* and the *Redargutio philosophiarum*, to define the historico-social causes of Greek philosophy's failure and of the failure of all philosophies derived from the Greeks. The history of all human culture, writes Bacon, covers no more than twenty-five centuries, of which barely five have been favourable to the advancement of learning. The only three productive periods have been those of the Greek, Roman, and western European civilisations. All other epochs were dedicated to wars and strife and were entirely devoid of cultural value.[27] Modern philosophy derives from Greek philosophy, or more precisely from that part of Greek philosophy which was 'not bred and nurtured in the glades and thickets, but in the schools and cells, like a domestic animal being fattened'.[28] The hopes and fortunes of mankind have been staked on six men, for there is very little either the Romans or the moderns can show that does not come from Aristotle, Plato, Hippocrates, Galen, Euclid, or Ptolemy. So that in all the wealth of scientific writings we find the same concepts constantly emerging. The whole civilised world is drunk with this philosophy; theology, politics, even language, are infected by it: its vocabulary has been adopted

45

not only by single individuals but by academies, universities, and governments.[29]

Bacon proposed to check the extraordinary diffusion of this form of culture by enquiring into its exact sources. It would then be possible, he maintained, to see the folly of blindly accepting the intellectual product of an age whose characteristics and purposes were entirely opposed to those of modern times. In other words, Bacon wished to return Greek philosophy to its historical context so as to reduce it to its just proportions. For him the best way to overcome the dogmatism of the various philosophical factions was to prove that Greek philosophy was an historical and not an eternal supratemporal phenomenon. To appreciate the importance Bacon's censures acquired in his own eyes, as well as their intrinsic validity and limitations, it is essential that we understand Bacon's position here. It will also help to clarify the statement—recurring in many of his works—that he does not seek to cast aspersion on the 'honour' of Greek philosophers nor to rob them of the 'palms of genius'. All he desires is that their authority and influence be completely eradicated. Their genius and skill are not questioned: should we try to follow in their footsteps we could never attain what they have attained, but their purpose, methods, and authority must be refuted because the main cause of man's poverty is the assumption that he is wealthy.

Such are the notions that distinguish Bacon's later attitude to traditional philosophy from that expressed in the *Temporis partus masculus* and other works anterior to 1605. But the change stems from what Bacon called in the *Advancement of Learning* the 'liberating function' of historical awareness, and not, as so many critics believe, from the retraction of an over-hasty unconsidered judgement. In the *Temporis partus masculus* the Greek philosophers were summoned to defend their guilt; in the *Cogitata et visa* and the *Redargutio* their guilt emerges as the result of an historical background evoked by Bacon. Direct violent attack is now abandoned for a cautious enquiry that might be described as 'sociological' or 'historicist' (not that I have any intention of tracing the origins of historicism back to Bacon).

An Egyptian priest is quoted by Plato[30] as saying that Greek civilisation had the prattling, bickering, unproductive qualities

46

of a child[31] and Bacon adopted this view, applying it more specifically to Greek philosophy. The Greeks, he says, were given to hasty judgements and 'professorial pomp',[32] two failings that stay the progress of learning. And the surest way of proving the limitations of their philosophy is to study the age in which it flourished; for Greek philosophy 'took its rise in an age that bordered on fables, was poor in historical knowledge, was little informed or enlightened by travel and knowledge of the earth'.[33] The minds of men living in such an age could not be other than mean and narrow, both for the epoch and the land in which they dwelt. They had no history: 'The Greeks knew (except fables) not much above five hundred years before themselves',[34] and how many parts of the world did these men know who called all peoples from the north Scythians and all those from the west Celts, indiscriminately? They had no knowledge of Africa beyond the Ganges; they had no idea of the existence of the New World and had dismissed as unfit for human habitation lands and climates where whole populations thrived.[35] The 'great expeditions' of Pythagoras, Democritus, and Plato were really no more than excursions into the suburbs.[36] Natural philosophy was unable to prosper because Socrates diverted men's minds towards ethical problems so that philosophy became an ambitious quest for new ideas. And before Socrates philosophers who tried to explain the natural causes of thunder and lightning were condemned as heretics.

Bacon ascribed the failure of natural philosophy in the Roman and Christian civilisations to the same political and social factors. In Roman times the best minds were intent on political matters 'when the size of the Empire claimed the exertions of many', and after the triumph of Christianity they turned to theology 'to which branch of learning the most handsome rewards and generous aids were directed' so that, once again, men were distracted from nature. In modern times theology is still in the ascendant because controversies have made it popular.[37] According to Bacon Aristotle himself owes his authority to a political hazard: Aristotle came as Antichrist preaching in his own name and referring to his predecessors only to refute them, but their works were not forgotten despite his attacks, for under Caesar Juvenal praised the wisdom of Democritus. Aristotle was finally victorious, thanks only to

Attila and the Goths, who totally destroyed civilisation, for his philosophy alone survived because of its very inconsistency.[38] However, Bacon's intention is to rescue the early naturalists from the unmerited oblivion to which the barbarian invasions had condemned them.

In the *Redargutio philosophiarum* and the *New Organon* Bacon expounded his doctrine of signs, in which he had elaborated a criterion to estimate the value of philosophical methods. In the *Redargutio* the doctrine is presented as a straightforward historical investigation; but in his 1608 masterpiece it includes his theories on Greek civilisation[39] and has a far greater significance; it is a system of valuation based on the intellectual portion common to all men regardless of individual gifts.

Bacon is quite aware of the fact that 'to justify . . . a debate there must be agreement about first principles . . . Even the hope of a basis of discussion is precluded, since I cast doubt on the forms of proof now in use.'[40] Because his conflict with the whole tradition of Greek philosophy arose from its basic conception of man and nature and their relation to each other, he considered it impossible, harmful, and unfair, as he had already declared in the *Temporis partus masculus*, to engage in single combat and try to refute individual errors. Such engagements would require precisely those 'rules of discussion' that were denied them in the absence of any agreement as to 'purpose' and 'principle'. Thus Bacon was led to 'reject the forms and deny the validity of their proofs and demonstrations' which had intoxicated all cultures and radically—and apparently irrevocably—conditioned contemporary reasoning. The only means of enlightening and persuading mankind—since demonstration is impossible without a norm for discussion—is an appeal to the regions of the mind as yet uncontaminated and open to the truth, neither dimmed by prejudice nor burdened with the weight of ancient knowledge. If we discard the baubles of erudition for the bare simplicity of innocence our minds will be prepared to receive the truth.

In the *Redargutio* the four signs which prove the inadequacy of traditional philosophy are its sterility,[41] its unco-operative, non-progressive, static nature as opposed to the thriving progressiveness of the mechanical arts,[42] its confessed impotence[43] and its lack of method and disregard for adequate intellectual tools.[44]

As to the first sign:

> There is no 'sign' more certain and more noble than that from fruits. In religion we are warned that faith be shown by works. It is altogether right to apply the same test to philosophy. If it be barren let it be set at naught. All the more should this be so if instead of the fruits of grape or olive, it bear the thistles and thorns of disputes and contentions.

In Bacon this is a basic theme: the validity of a philosophy is identical with its ability to produce works and contribute to the welfare of humanity. Philosophical speculation, says Bacon, has never at any time made a single genuine effort to improve the conditions of human existence, because according to Aristotle the main purpose of philosophy was to provide men with an answer to all problems and enable them to extract themselves from any embarrassment:[45] natural philosophies deriving from such a doctrine could only be obstacles to invention. Thus the Aristotelian theory of the four elements satisfied the demand for formal perfection, but when applied to medical research it produced the theory of four tempers, four humours, and four primary qualities and was of no practical use to experimental enquiry. Indeed if any progress were to be achieved in experimental research the whole system of natural philosophy must be revised. Instead of rejoicing in the perfection of final solutions we should see their value as merely verbal; preference should be given to empirical observations freed from the metaphysical presuppositions that condition research and impose limits upon it.

In the *Temporis partus masculus* Bacon had already censured— though less explicitly—this ideal of formal perfection for natural philosophical systems, which, according to him, deprived them of significance and hindered their progress. It was part of an uncritical method of education giving no scope to discovery and invention but fostering an attitude of 'professorial pomp' and reducing the history of science to a history of the relations between master and disciple. This closed systematic scientific tradition sacrificed everything to the immutable perfection of theories:

Their science having been established in this fashion, when a controversy arose over any example or instance, as being in contradiction to their views, they did not take steps to revise their theories. No; they retained the theory and brought the unruly facts into order. This they did either by some subtle dialectical distinction or (since they were not such bad fellows after all) they let it stand as an exception. At other times it was not the resolving of a contradiction but the explanation of some obscure fact that was required. This they managed either by ingeniously finding a place for it in their speculative scheme or by torturing it out of its true form. The whole of this enterprise and effort I regard as baseless.[46]

Bacon opposes to this method of 'formal perfection' the 'aphoristic' method used by the ancient questioners of nature. Its difference from the first is not merely verbal since it pinpoints deficiencies and omissions and leads to meditation, criticism, and discovery.[47]

In his discussion of the third sign Bacon expresses some interesting theories, which explain why he required that scientific research should be accomplished with modesty and humility. Those writers, he says, who have been the despots of science and the presumptuous arbiters of nature, have always accused the intricacy of nature, the mystery of reality, and the inadequacy of the human mind; but these accusations are not signs of modesty. On the contrary, they denote a boundless pride and arrogance; for such philosophers wish to imply that all scientific matters which have been dealt with by others than themselves or their masters are outside the sphere of research. Thus they translate their own incompetence into a senseless slander of nature.[48]

So between 1603 and 1608 Bacon consolidated his refutation of traditional philosophies by means of an historical enquiry and his system of signs. Reviewing the history of Greek civilisation according to rules he had set down for the *history of letters* in the *Advancement*, he proved that the limitations of Greek philosophy coincide with those of the entire civilisation. By a criterion drawn from the 'common portion of the human mind' he also showed the basic errors of this philosophy and of those derived from it. But all this was perfectly consistent with his previous attitude and the views he had expressed in the *Temporis partus masculus* on verbosity, systems, mixtures of science and religion, and contemplative philosophies which divert the minds of men from natural enquiries.

Bacon's attempt to rescue pre-Socratic philosophy from unmerited oblivion was intimately connected with this attitude. We shall see later that during this period he decided—for tactical reasons—not to publish his three more polemical works,[49] and turned to other matters. However, 'under the patronage of antiquity and the veil of allegory' his project of reinstating pre-Socratic, and particularly Democritean, philosophy was included in the *De sapientia veterum* (1609). But he had not given up the idea of a general attack on tradition and after ten years it was finally launched in the preface to the *Great Instauration*, the first book of the *New Organon*, and in the *De augumentis* (1623).

Naturalists ancient and modern. The responsibilities of Plato

Bacon's history of philosophy must be traced through a number of his works and is more flexible and complex than might be supposed. More so, indeed, than the unconsidered judgements of certain scholars would warrant. His criticism, though it refutes the principles of traditional philosophy, does not exclude an understanding of former doctrines; for, as we have seen, it was not the isolated theory or assertion of a philosopher that he rejected but a non-constructive philosophical attitude that reduced science to a series of professorial reports. Bacon attacked the aims of such philosophies and the purpose they assigned to learning, and his refutation included individual theories only in so far as they were expressions of such aims. His refutation was, in fact, the outcome of a belief in the imminence of a new era, confronting mankind with new purposes to which the duties of philosophy and the function of learning must be adapted.

According to Bacon, Aristotelian despotism had conditioned not only the progress of philosophical and scientific thought, but also the means of understanding this progress. Aristotle's intolerance of alien doctrines was a typically dogmatic attitude.

More ambitious than any man—except his own disciple Alexander—Aristotle opposed antiquity and tried to annihilate its culture. As a Turkish Sultan murders his brothers so that his reign shall not be contested, Aristotle attempted to destroy all rival doctrines with his reasonings.[50] When he considered that his campaign of extermination had been successful he set out to elaborate a system to solve simultaneously every possible problem.[51] He advertised his philosophy as the climax of historical thought—thus condemning the past to oblivion—and claimed at the same time its sway over future generations. The barbarians were his allies for their invasions razed culture to the ground and cloistered the medieval monk with nothing but Aristotle's texts upon which to sate his intellectual appetite.[52] Thus he became the supreme master of philosophy and it seemed 'that the course of philosophy could flow no further; fixed for evermore, all that was left was to worship it'. For Bacon such a conclusion denoted only ignorance and intellectual sloth. But the most relevant feature of all this is that Bacon's refutation of Aristotelian despotism embraced the whole historical outline by which Aristole had demonstrated his superiority to all past and present philosophers.

For Aristotle's universally accepted outline Bacon substituted one that, by classifying Greek philosophers in three groups, changed the entire framework of that philosophy. The Sophists (Gorgias, Protagoras, and Hippias) who travelled from town to town earning their living by teaching, constituted the first group. The second included Plato, Aristotle, and Epicurus,[53] and was made up of the more pompous and solemn philosophers who had disciples and were the founders of schools. The third group was that of Euripides, Heraclitus, Anaxagoras, and Democritus who shunned 'professorial pomp' and studied nature with unobtrusive diligence. For Bacon the first two groups really merged into one so that the term Sophist applied equally to Plato, Aristotle,[54] Theophrastus, Epicurus, and Carneades, indeed, to all Greek philosophers who possessed to a greater degree the distinctive qualities of Greek civilisation: 'professorial pomp' and 'sterile contentiousness'. Thus the Sophists' ambitious quest for novel ideas soon put an end to the brief reign of pre-Socratic natural philosophy.

Bacon declares that he has given much of his time to the

study of pre-Socratic naturalists in the texts provided by Aristotle, Diogenes Laertius, Plutarch, Cicero, and Lucretius. Their apparent insubstantiality, he says, is due to the fragmentary nature of these texts and the impossibility of acceding to their opinions directly. But he hopes that some day a complete edition of these sources will be available;[55] for the naturalists had been the victims of fate, though many of them had had insights into the mysteries of nature which had escaped Aristotle, and had possessed that 'taste' for nature, experience, and reality[56] which had been destroyed by the subsequent developments of Greek philosophy. Democritus, for instance, had gone further than any other philosopher in his approach to nature and was rightly called a magician.[57] He had realised the impossibility of perceiving with the senses the primary elements of matter and had therefore ignored any residue of seeming sensibility derived from vulgar experience. Instead of the Aristotelian method of abstraction, elaborating systems from superficial appearances, Democritus resorted to the more fruitful method of analysing (*secare*) nature by reducing it to its component parts.[58] Democritean mechanicism was by no means perfect: thus his penetrating investigations of principles was not backed by a convincing theory of the expansion or contraction of matter,[59] and his theories of the diversity of atoms and of the existence of a vacuum were, according to Bacon, untenable.[60] But he had tried to guard natural philosophy against the contamination of ideas such as final causes by which it had been turned into a form of theology.[61]

But even pre-Socratic philosophers, with their apparent positivism, were still within the boundaries of Greek civilisation, for they too were the prisoners of words. Their theories, says Bacon, are like the plots of plays, more or less persuasive, more or less consistent; for it is quite possible to elaborate as many theories as one pleases—all perfectly consistent and each one different from the other[62]—by interpreting experience in different ways, and using the evidence of experience to suit one's own ends. Indeed, Renaissance natural philosophy and especially that of Telesius, was not constructed in any other way.

A quick glance at the criticism Bacon directed at Telesius in the *De principiis* will help to clarify this assertion, and to explain his opposition to Renaissance naturalism and his censure of certain aspects of Democritean and pre-Socratic materialism. Bacon compares these natural philosophies to great metaphysical poems on nature; yet formal perfection and coherence are not really important: what matters here is their efficacy; and Bacon considered that it was impossible to have any effect on nature if one did not first acknowledge its objectivity, though this necessary acknowledgement was not sufficient in itself. Hence his rejection of such forms of naturalism as Telesius' which he calls 'pastoral philosophies'. If the purpose of philosophy were contemplation of the world these doctrines would all be true and, indeed, they all seem perfectly credible; their basic fallacy, however, is the assumption that the world is to be contemplated and not improved; they have forgotten the existence of man and the mechanical arts.[63] For these philosophies have organised nature to perfection (and there are many new ways of organising it) but these arrangements are like well-acted plays that console or amuse the spectators for the time being but have no effect on reality. Whereas the new philosophy, by acknowledging natural objectivity will attempt to adapt nature to the needs of man, for which purpose those technical tools—the mechanical arts—fashioned by man for such ends, cannot be overlooked.

Bacon's attacks on pre-Socratic naturalism are consistent with these views. The pre-Socratic philosophers, he wrote in the *De principiis*, were content to identify what was most immediately apparent in various substances with the principle of nature. This assumption of a first principle led them to believe that all natural mutations such as heat, cold, density, fluidity, dryness, humidity, were derived from this one substance. They did not bother to explain how this was possible nor to describe and follow up these mutations, so that further investigations were abandoned. They were the prisoners of a metaphor, holding forth on fabulous entities when they thought they were discussing air, water, earth, and fire.[64] They substituted a verbal solution for an analysis of nature, thus they too were victims of Greek civilisation, of the spirit of systems and the cult of words.

For Bacon the turning point of Greek philosophy was with Socrates and the Sophists[65] when speculation became purely ethical and interest in natural philosophy flagged. But it was Plato whom he held responsible for the ultimate sterility and verbal evasiveness of traditional learning. In the *Temporis partus masculus* Bacon accused Plato of diverting the minds of men from observation to contemplation and of confusing science and theology, and he never departed from this earlier judgement. Indeed, he reasserted it at the very end of his life in the *De principiis*. For the pre-Socratic philosophers, he wrote, 'reality ruled the mind'; for Plato 'ideas ruled reality'; and for Aristotle 'words ruled ideas'.[66] From this point of view even the positive aspects of Platonism are sterile because they stem from a false conception of philosophy. The purpose of science for Plato was the discovery of forms and he used induction, not only to detect universal principles, but intermediary propositions as well.[67] Only for him forms were abstract transcendental entities of matter and it is from this notion that the Scholastic 'forms' derived.[68] Moreover, he drew the material for his inductions from everyday events because, being more familiar to his audience, they could serve more aptly as examples in his discussions.[69] Here one of the accusations from the *Temporis partus masculus* recurs: for Plato natural philosophy was only a means of increasing his popularity by adding a certain grandeur to the moral and political doctrines that were his real preoccupation. Thus Plato's theories have at least:

> ... the merit of supplying table-talk for men of culture and experience of affairs, even indeed of adding grace and charm to every day conversation.[70]

This passage throws light on the following statement from the preface of the *New Organon*:

> Be it remembered then that I am far from wishing to interfere with the philosophy which now flourishes, or with any other philosophy more correct and complete than this which has been or may hereafter be propounded. For I do not object to the use of this received philosophy, or others like it for supplying matter for disputations or ornaments for discourse,—for the professor's lecture and for the business of life. Nay more, I declare that for these uses the philosophy which I bring forward will not be much available.[71]

Bacon also resumed and amplified his earlier censure of

the way in which, by mixing science and religion, Plato adulterated both. Plato's theory that forms were distinct from matter led him to speculations of a theological nature, which both irremediably corrupted his philosophy,[72] and led him to incorporate the notion of final causes into physics.[73]

It is easy to see why Bacon found in Plato an example of that most virulent of philosophical diseases: 'superstitious philosophy'. It is fabulous, inflated, poetic; it flatters the mind and captivates even the highest intellects, he wrote. Pythagoras also suffered from it, but in Plato it was more subtle and insidious; one of its most dangerous symptoms is the glorification of errors for there is nothing more contagious than fallacies when they have once succeeded in awakening admiration.[74]

Thus Bacon believed that he had traced back to Plato the historical origins of the use of a lyrical, rhetorical discourse in philosophy and the infiltrations of theology and religion into science. These two interrelated fallacies were equally dangerous for the future of humanity. Here again one must realise that Bacon was attacking two existing philosophical trends: that of magical naturalism mentioned in the previous chapter, and the attitudes and ideals of English humanism.

There is a definite parallel between Bacon's objections to magic and his rejection of religious trends in Renaissance Platonism, where the Hebrew *gnosis*, the Cabbala, and Hermeticism joined forces. We have already seen that Bacon's scientific ideal of co-operative, diligent research was opposed to esoteric philosophies thriving on allusion, ecstasy, intuition, mystery, and prophetic wisdom, and inspired by Moses, Zoroaster, Hermes, Plato, Plotinus, Proclus, and pseudo-Dionysus. The function of learning is to distinguish and isolate natural research from religious ecstasy and divinity, not to elaborate 'occult cosmologies' and 'interpret' the Book of Genesis.[75]

The historical significance of Bacon's refutation is not impaired by the fact that in his own philosophy science and magic overlapped, and that in his works there are definite traces of magical, hermetic, and Platonic influences. The situation is somewhat similar to that of Kepler, Gassendi, and Mersenne rejecting Robert Fludd,[76] and Fludd was a perfect example—in Bacon's own time—of a form of hermetic philosophy whose complex ramifications spread far into the seventeenth century.[77]

Thus Bacon rejected Cardano, that 'spinner of spider's webs'; Patrizzi 'who sublimated the fumes of Platonism'; Paracelsus 'who has made man into a Pantomime', mixed heresy and fable to desecrate science and religion, and replaced traditional philosophy by extravagant hypotheses; and Agrippa, 'a trivial buffoon relying on distortion and ridicule'. Even William Gilbert with his careful magnetic experiments was not spared, for he had erected on these experiments the crazy edifice of an arbitrary naturalism. All natural philosophy had been marred by extravagance and the infiltrations of theology.[78]

In the first book of the *Advancement of Learning* Bacon expounds his views on the rhetorical corruption of humanism, here again imputed to the influence of Platonism. There are, he says, three vices in contemporary culture: 'phantastical learning', 'contentious learning', and 'delicate learning'. The first (astrology, magic, and alchemy) gives rise to vain imaginations; the second (Scholastic philosophy) gives rise to vain altercations; and the third (Ciceronian humanism) gives rise to vain affectations. Though the ancestry of the last is lost in antiquity its immediate forebears can be traced to the Reformation: when Luther, in his controversy with Rome and the decadent Church, found no assistance in contemporary culture, he turned to the classics for help;[79] then books which had lain unopened for years were taken from the shelves of libraries and read avidly, because now it was of the first importance to understand these writers; scholars studied their language and their style and came in this way to admire also their subject-matter; and their admiration was increased when the humanists criticised the slovenly style of the Scholastics and the neologisms of medieval philosophers. Besides which, the 'new' culture was bent on 'winning and persuading' public opinion and found in eloquence and rhetoric exactly what was required for such a purpose. The four sources of humanist eloquence are, according to Bacon the cult of classical authors, loathing of the Scholastics, an exact study of languages and the efficacy of preaching. Men now began to value words more than truth, and to prefer a well-turned phrase to the importance of meaning, the weight of argument and the subtlety of invention. John Sturm and Ascham[80] glorified Cicero and were deservedly despised by Erasmus[81], for words are only 'the image of matter', whereas the humanists had bartered words for reality, and like Pygmalion, they had fallen in love with an image in the place of truth.

For Bacon this 'distemper of learning' spreads far beyond the age he was dealing with, both into the past and into the future. Xenophon,[82] Cicero, Seneca, Plutarch, and Plato himself used language to adorn philosophy. Bacon had, as we have seen, nothing against such a practice where learning serves a social or political purpose in persuading or advising; but he saw it as detrimental to the quest for truth, because it favours complacency and robs man of the desire to make further investigations.

Bacon's position and its link with the attacks he launched against Platonism become much clearer if we recall certain statements he had made. In the preface to the *New Organon* he distinguished his own from traditional philosophy which aims at 'supplying matter for disputation and ornaments for discourse for the business of life'. In the *Temporis partus masculus* he accorded to Platonic philosophy the merit of 'supplying table-talk for men of culture . . . and adding grace and charm to everyday conversation', and in the *Cogitata et visa* he called Plato 'a poet'. Again in the *Temporis partus masculus* Plato is 'the father of philologists' and of a facile, agreeable form of learning eminently deleterious to the discovery of truth, that was practised in turn by Cicero, Seneca, and Plutarch; indeed, accusations of verbalism are present in all Bacon's works, but especially in the *New Organon*. Thus, in the last analysis, it is Plato who is responsible for the vices of humanism: verbosity, slothfulness, and the desire to please.

It is true that Platonic mannerisms had been adapted to the uses of English society, and, merged with a taste for allegory and symbol typical of Florentine neo-Platonism, they played an even more important part in the English literary and theatrical world than in English philosophy. John Lyly's *Euphues or the Anatomy of Wit* (1597), Spenser's *Hymnes in Honour of Love and Beautie* (1596), Chapman's poetry and Sir John Davies'[83] rhymed philosophical and theological treatises are typical of this rhetorical Platonism where dissertations on love, mistresses, friendship, and God alternate with allusions to Plutarch's historical heroes and mythological figures from Ovid. Such themes—introduced into England with the works of Ficino—

inspired the humanist ideal of nobility and courtesy. More, Elyot, Sidney, Spenser[84] and indeed all humanist writers, though adopting Aristotelian ethics, were fascinated by the Platonic idea of an aristocratic republic governed by an élite of philosophers. Hence their projects for a new form of education that would add to the inborn virtues of the ruling classes the classical virtues of courtesy, taste, and tact. In English sixteenth-century social and political life such qualities were more fitted than chivalrous bravery to enable the men of a new social class trying to penetrate the higher spheres of society to earn the title of gentleman (with all the implications this term had acquired).[85]

The popularity of humanist ideals and of a form of education diametrically opposed to Bacon's own principles was one of the factors determining his attitude to Platonism. He certainly promoted, in England, an anti-Ciceronian prose aimed at clarity and concision and modelled on the Attic or Senecian style; his influence was comparable to that of Montaigne and Justus Lipsius in Europe, whose stylistic ideal, adopted by the seventeenth-century sceptics and libertines, coincided with the emergence of a new science.[86] On the other hand Bacon also supported a form of political realism and ethical naturalism reminiscent of Machiavelli and far removed from that which inspired humanist education. It is not surprising that the Puritan bourgeoisie should have referred to Bacon as their master, for they were a class of technicians and merchants who despised the 'abstract', 'useless', 'aristocratic' education and ideals of the early English humanists.[87]

Aristotle and scholasticism

Compared with the poetic vagueness of Platonic hermeticism 'the wisdom of Aristotle is worthy to be observed';[88] for where all other natural philosophers showed no discrimination in their choice of fable, myth, and legend Aristotle judiciously discarded those which seemed least trustworthy; thus they did not interfere with scientific research, but as he had wisely preserved them, neither were they lost to posterity.[89] So Aristotle's corrupting influence operated very differently from Plato's; according to Bacon he was an example of dogmatic philosophy

59

and of sophistic rationalism trying to solve all problems by mere verbal dexterity. In this respect Aristotle was wilfully obscure; he also made experiments fit his pre-established conclusions, and hoped to 'construct a world from categories' and solve the problems of matter, motion, density, and rarity by arbitrary distinctions such as those of potency and act. Though he tried to preserve the integrity of natural philosophy from the contamination of superstition he failed to see the equal dangers of dialectics and of subjecting science to logic. Further, he favoured contemplation and by destroying the past and foreclosing the future he tried to endow his philosophy with extra-temporal qualities.[90] Bacon opposed such despotism[91] by protesting the need for freedom from all forms of 'philosophical idolatry'. Aristotle's reputation was based on his disregard for past doctrines yet we are afraid to do to him what he did to others:

> But even though Aristotle were the man he is thought to be I should still warn you against receiving as oracles the thoughts and opinions of one man. What justification can there be for this self-imposed servitude? Are ye so inferior to the followers of the pagan monk, that they stopped affirming his *ipse dixit* after seven years, while you are content to repeat Aristotle's after two thousand?. . . But if you will be guided by me you will deny, not only to this man but to any mortal now living or who shall live hereafter, the right to dictate your opinions. . . . You will never be sorry for trusting your own strength, if you but once make trial of it. You may be inferior to Aristotle on the whole, but not in everything. Finally, and this is the head and front of the whole matter, there is at least one thing in which you are far ahead of him—in precedents, in experience, in the lessons of time. Aristotle, it is said, wrote a book in which he gathered together the laws and institutions of two hundred and fifty-five cities; yet I have no doubt that the customs of Rome are worth more than all of them combined so far as military and political science are concerned. The position is the same in natural philosophy. Are you of a mind to cast aside not only your own endowments but the gifts of time? Assert yourselves before it is too late. Apply yourselves to the study of things themselves. Be not for ever the property of one man.[92]

Fulton Anderson has made a detailed study of Bacon's relation to Aristotle and has shown remarkable insight in noting the two main features of Bacon's attack. In the first place it is not aimed so much at Aristotle's philosophy as at certain manifestations of medieval Aristotelianism. And in the second, it is impossible to separate Bacon's critique of peripatetic doctrines from the rest of his philosophy which is based almost entirely on the substitution of a new philosophy for the Aristotelian tradition.[93]

Bacon distinguishes three human faculties: memory, imagination, and reason, to replace Aristotle's three sciences: theoretical, practical, and productive; for the theory of physics and mathematics is put into practice in mechanics and in magic: speech is not distinct from action; thus Aristotle's classification is fallacious. Bacon also rejects the Aristotelian principle of 'abstraction' as a means of classifying knowledge, and the possibility of a transition from physics to metaphysics; for Bacon the function of metaphysics is to define the universal laws of natural phenomena; but he ascribes to physics a much more limited function than did Aristotle who, according to Bacon, expounded extravagant theories (matter-form, power-action), and treated physics as a form of logic, while logic itself was endowed with the power to create the world by a series of verbal definitions. Primary philosophy, as distinct from metaphysics, defines the principles or rules pertaining to the different spheres of physics; but these rules are not concerned with existence as such.[94] And a new theory of induction replaces Aristotle's. Logic as a method of verbal definition, a rational process, or a study of linguistic forms for the definition of existence, is replaced by a logic as the instrument and means of controlling a situation. It is possible, by a series of complex procedures, to control the various transitions from the empirical elements of natural history to the formulation of laws, and to a perception of forms permitting the execution of an unlimited number of operations. Finally Bacon substitutes his theory of the congruity of natural and artificial phenomena for Aristotle's theory of art as imitation of nature.

Thus Bacon's objections to Aristotelianism and the main themes of his own philosophy are identical. As these will be dealt with in detail in another section of this book, we need only discuss here Bacon's views on Scholasticism.

This doctrine was directly descended from Aristotelianism, according to Bacon, and presented a dual obstacle to the advancement of learning; for these philosophers 'have had the temerity to incorporate the contentious philosophy of Aristotle into the body of religion'[95] thus endangering natural philosophy more than by open opposition by favouring the acceptance of consecrated traditional theories and precluding invention and discovery.[96] Secondly, Scholasticism is the embodiment of a 'contentious learning', which emerges whenever a sound culture disintegrates into subtleties: 'vermicular questions' insinuate themselves from all sides with deceptive force to end up in 'vain altercations'. The Scholastics had 'sharp and strong wits, an abundance of leisure, and small variety of reading'; their minds were imprisoned in Aristotelian texts just as their bodies were imprisoned in monastic cells; they were ignorant of natural philosophy and history and they elaborated —with little material and great intellectual labour—the most beautiful spiders' webs, admirable indeed as to the fineness of the thread, but so fragile that they could serve no purpose.[97] Scholastic philosophy is, indeed, like the virgin Scylla, who was shaped like a lovely woman above her waist and from thence down was surrounded by hideous baying monsters; for the propositions are often ingenious and well expressed, but when we come to the distinctions 'instead of a fruitful womb for the use and benefit of man's life, they end in monstrous altercations and barking questions'. Besides which the Scholastics' contentiousness has deprived culture of its dignity and significance, for these endless controversies about truth have caused men to despise it, especially when they see learned scholars fighting 'about subtleties'.[98]

For Bacon the characteristics of medieval culture were the degeneration of classical soundness—which disintegration is the consequence of Aristotle's despotism and the illicit attempt to incorporate philosophy into religion by mixing theology and science—disregard for natural philosophy and ignorance of history. These shortcomings led the Scholastics to exert their brains in a vacuum.

The failure of Scholasticism was thus a consequence of the limited material at its disposal. If the Scholastics had possessed, in addition to their inexhaustible thirst for truth and their incessant spiritual agitation, a wider culture, they might have contributed considerably to the advancement of learning. But Scholasticism is in fact only an empty philosophy inventing new words to which reality is made to fit. Bacon later expanded his definition of the Scholastic method: it consists in advancing a theory, then advancing objections to this theory, and finally discussing these objections; but the result is most often a long list of distinctions. Such is the cause of its vanity. Bacon's judgement stems from the premiss that scientific learning should be based on unity and system. The house of science is symmetrical, he writes, and each part supports the others; like the old man's twigs in the fable, the strength of each branch of science is not in itself but in the whole.[99] No single scientific proposition is valid on its own, but only in connection with all the others contributing to a given scientific theory. Thus science can stand up to the 'smaller sort of objections' but will always succumb to attacks against a proposition singled out from its context, just as the twigs in the bundle can be destroyed easily one by one. The great store of Scholastic subtleties could be usefully employed in establishing axioms, for if they are used for obtaining results and not assent, they provide a good scientific tool.[100]

Bacon used to good purpose in this attack the main arguments of medieval humanist and Renaissance anti-Aristotelian and anti-Scholastic literature. With him as with Agricola, Vives, Nizolius, Ramus, and Patrizzi, Scholasticism is the outcome of Aristotelian despotism and the supremacy of a logic serving to make futile distinctions rather than as an instrument for discovery and experiment. Eminently preoccupied with educative and linguistic problems, this literature exposed the non-practical aspect of such over-subtle Scholastic logic. Thus Budé asserts that learning should be an instrument for the use of humanity, 'for a machine that no one can operate is no longer a machine but a heap of scrap-metal'; while Vives, reflecting the preoccupations of his age, compared the 'pseudo-dialecticians' to painters who spend their time mixing colours and trimming brushes, or to cobblers who are too busy furbishing their tools ever to get down to the job of making boots. Ramus, attacking the misuse of dialectics for sophist disputations, writes:

> Dialectic is the art of discussing well and is also called logic; for the two words come from the same root *logos*, or reason, and *dialegesthai* like *logizesthai* means to discuss or reason, that is . . .

to use reason whose true function must be shown and perfected in this art.[101]

Bacon also objected to Scholastic terminology since in his opinion this was a form of Aristotelian jargon. Like Ramus and some other rhetoricians and reformers, he wished to replace such a jargon by a clear efficient mode of communication more in keeping with objective reality.

But there is another no less significant link between Bacon's attitude and that of all anti-scholastic literature of the two hundred years that preceded him. Scholastic philosophy had repudiated, with theological ingenuity, the veracity and profundity of the Gospels' message, and Aristotle's physics, exalted to the status of metaphysics, had destroyed the meaning of divinity:[102]

> Indeed in the present age the Doctors of the Church do not just spawn and heap up opinion on opinion, but also darken and distort universal theology in a horrible manner.

The demand for a less 'quibbling' form of discourse reflected a yearning for integral texts and simple faith exemplified in England by Tyndale, Colet, and More,[103] but also expressed by Ramus and most critics of Scholasticism who said that scientific and religious renovation were inseparable, for the renewal of contact with nature through experiment coincided with a return to the true word of God.[104]

Bacon had attacked Scholastic philosophy as one of the three typical forms of religious imposture as early as 1597 in the ninth *Meditationes sacrae* (*Holy meditation*): the Scholastic 'trifles' were the outcome of a frenzied love for words and the reduction of all problems to a list of distinctions.[105] In the *Advancement of Learning* we find the same idea expressed more clearly; the following passage—omitted from the final edition of *De augumentis* for tactical reasons[106]—is important for the light it throws on the link between Bacon's refutation of Scholasticism and his attacks on all forms of rational theology and religious distortion:

> As in the inquiry of the divine truth their pride inclined to leave the oracle of God's word and to vanish in the mixture of their inventions, so in the inquisition of nature they ever left the oracle of God's works and adored the deceiving and deformed images

64

which the unequal mirror of their own minds or a few received authors or principles did represent unto them.[107]

Once again the reform of culture coincides with man's attitude to nature and to God; by distorting God's word the Scholastics distorted science. Bacon's discussion of the Scholastic method also refers to this correspondence. As we have seen, he asserts that each separate part of a scientific theory is related to the others and supports them all. The theologians committed the error of believing that religious discussions could follow the same pattern, and they tried to solve religious problems by systematic architectonic dissertations; but this attitude and the desire for perfection and finality, when applied to religion only distorts the true meaning of the Scriptures; the quest for clarity leads only to ambiguity; the desire for concision is the cause of obscurities that require elucidation; and the elucidations are then twisted and turned in an infinity of comments. Thus the early writings of the Fathers, instead of being explained are forgotten,[108] and the true faith has been destroyed by wordiness.

Ficino and Patrizzi countered the Paris Scholastics' Aristotelianism with the Platonic tradition; Rudolf Agricola stressed the importance of Lull; Nizolius distinguished the realism of Boëthius, Albertus Magnus, St Thomas, and Duns Scotus from Occam's nominalism, and openly declared his allegiance to the latter; a number of Renaissance anti-Scholastic works show a tendency to discover a diversity of patterns within the 'age of barbarism', and to stress the positive contributions of the Arabs or St Bonaventure or Roger Bacon. So the Renaissance did not refute indiscriminately Scholasticism and all intervening philosophies.[109] Bacon however seems to have ignored such distinctions; his condemnation of the Scholastics is more or less general and, apart from a single brief allusion to Roger Bacon in the *Temporis partus masculus*, it encompasses all that phase of history in which Aristotle's texts were the main subject of study in the schools. According to him even the Arabs only assisted the dialecticians' destruction of natural philosophy, and their medical research was a collection of extravagant fables.[110]

Among the reformers of classical logic Bacon only mentions

Ramon Lull. His method was seen as a fraud enabling men who were versed in the vocabulary of certain arts to pass for masters of the art in question; his attempts to symbolise the elements of nature and the categories, to establish laws governing all possible combinations of symbols, and thus find the answer to all questions was, according to Bacon, more 'verbalistic' even than Aristotle's logic.[111] In fact, though Pico, Cusanus, Bruno, and Agrippa were followers of Lull and his doctrine influenced even Descartes, it does not appear to have had any substantial effect on Bacon's philosophy, though his 'primary philosophy'—in so far as it was a study of the 'transcendental conditions' of bodies (the study of much, little, like, unlike, possible, impossible, etc.)—might offer a superficial resemblance to the general principles of Lull's doctrine (difference, harmony, discord, beginning, middle, end, superiority, equality, inferiority).[112] However the project (later adopted by Leibniz and Descartes) for a universal language or calculus to solve all problems was not included in Bacon's philosophy, and the study of much, little, etc., not belonging strictly to the sphere of physics was not considered by Bacon to be a matter of logic. He thought it an investigation into the reasons for some things being in greater supply than others in nature.[113] Possibly the relation between Bacon and Lull can only be grasped after a study of the latter's philosophy and an understanding of the link between his logic and his metaphysics:[114]

> That art is both logical and metaphysical . . . Logic is an unstable sliding science, but this art is permanent and stable . . . The logician has so far been unable to discover a true law with the aid of logic, but the master of the General Art discovers it.

Bacon's relation to Ramus is far more complex, as we shall see when we come to examine his logic. In the *Temporis partus masculus* he says that his refutation of Aristotelianism does not put him on a level with Peter Ramus 'that innovator . . . that most dangerous of all literary corroders who constricts and distorts reality with his narrow method and his summaries'. But already in the *Valerius Terminus* Bacon seems to have accepted two of the three rules of logic established by Ramus in the *Praefatio in scholas physicas*; and in the *Advancement of Learning* and the *De augumentis* he acknowledges—with some reservations —the substantial 'worthiness' of Ramus' endeavours.[115]

Bacon's critique of Telesius and Ramus, and his allusions to Kepler, Copernicus, Galileo, Gilbert, and Harvey are intimately connected with the basic problems of his method and his physics and suffer from the same limitations. His views were really a reaction to contemporary culture and cannot be understood outside the context of problems which will be discussed later. They were the restricted views of a 'buccinator' of science temperamentally and educationally unfit for the solving of scientific problems that were being raised in that dawn of modern times; for his attitude to such scientists and philosophers stems from his *Refutation of philosophies* and from his general outline of philosophical history.

Bacon's historical scheme

Bacon's history of philosophy has never been sufficiently appreciated; some scholars, shocked by his refutation of Plato, Aristotle, and the Scholastics, accused him of superficiality and injustice; while others—possibly in reaction to this attitude—deprived his refutation of all significance, either by stressing certain passages where Plato and Aristotle are commended, and interpreting them as a sign of retraction on Bacon's part, or by pointing out Bacon's derivation from these philosophers. The critics of the first group—though they include such names as De Maistre and Sortais—have not much historical relevance. On the other hand scholars bent on tracing Bacon's Platonic and Aristotelian sources could have contributed some interesting facts to Baconian scholarship. Unfortunately, however, Anderson is the only one to have pursued this course and he appears to have totally misunderstood or ignored the historical significance of Bacon's anti-Platonism.[116] Indeed, he commits the traditional error of seeing the *Temporis partus masculus* as a polemical outburst, and fails to see how pointless it is to search for Bacon's Platonic derivations if one does not consider simultaneously the historical importance of the hermetic and rhetorical Platonism Bacon was attacking.

As to the popular thesis based on Bacon's commendations of Plato and Aristotle, I have already shown that Bacon did not attack the arguments of traditional philosophy or try to replace them by others based on the same principles. In his new philo-

sophy such arguments had no place, for it implied a new relationship of man with nature, and its purpose was opposed to that
of traditional philosophy (such at least, was Bacon's intention).[117]
Traditional arguments, he submitted, were not fallacious, but
they were devised for a definite end which was not that of the
'new' philosophy; it is this end which Bacon attacks. Plato,
Aristotle, and even the Scholastics were therefore entitled to
Bacon's praise in so far as they were intelligent, witty, or able;
but such qualities could not make their influence less pernicious
in his eyes; if anything they made them more dangerous and
added weight to his attacks.

Be that as it may, commendations of Plato and Aristotle are
duly listed in almost every critical work on Bacon. Yet if Bacon
recognised the inner coherence of Platonism and Aristotelianism
he still denounced their aims:

> Two things occur to me of which, that they may not be over-
> looked, I would have men reminded. First . . . that the honour
> and reverence due to the ancients remains untouched and un-
> diminished; while I may carry out my designs and at the same
> time reap the fruit of modesty. For if I should profess that I,
> going the same road as the ancients, have something better to
> produce, there must needs have been some comparison or rivalry
> between us (not to be avoided by any art of words) in respect of
> excellency or ability of wit; and though in this there would be
> nothing unlawful or new (for if there be anything misappre-
> hended by them, or falsely laid down, why may not I, using a
> liberty common to all, take exception to it?) yet the contest, how-
> ever just and allowable, would have been an unequal one per-
> haps, in respect of the measure of my own powers. As it is however,
> —my object being to open a new way for the understanding, a
> way by them untried and unknown,—the case is altered; party
> zeal and emulation are at an end; and I appear merely as a guide
> to point out the road.[118]

These ideas expounded in the *Preface* to the *New Organon*—
but already formulated in the *Redargutio philosophiarum*—reveal
neither an alteration nor a retraction of the original judgement
pronounced in the *Temporis partus masculus*; for in granting certain virtues to these doctrines Bacon clearly establishes the
limitations of their achievements.

The word 'modern'—except when its use is restricted to
qualifying events taking place later than a pre-established date

in history—is one of the most equivocal of historiographical terms. Thus it has been applied of late to that Scholastic philosophy denounced by Valla, Ramus, Bacon, Descartes, and Galileo for its fallacious notions. A desire to elucidate the historical significance of the late Scholastic physical dissertations, and a no less worthy endeavour to free medieval historiography from the dual boundary-line of medieval darkness and modern light, too often result in a biased view of medieval culture which destroys all sense of historical perspective.[119] Thus the general outline of Bacon's history of philosophy and the controversial opinions it contains will have little success with scholars bent on exposing the decadence of the fifteenth and sixteenth centuries, for whom Galileo, Hume, and Newton are only exponents of late Scholastic philosophy: it will appear to be no more than an excuse for rhetoric based on false interpretations of history and a disdain—derived from Renaissance and humanist writers and rhetoricians—for the scientific acquisitions of late Scholasticism. However, if the historian is seen —not as a righter of wrongs—but as an investigator of the origins, meanings, and influences of certain attitudes, one can but acknowledge the 'modernism' of Bacon's historical panorama, where influences from the past are set in their historical context and the limitations of each age—and the effect of such limitations on the men of these ages—are defined.

Bacon's historical panorama is remarkable for its observations on Greek civilisation and on the politico-social reasons for the development of political philosophy in Rome, the success of theology in the early Middle Ages, and the survival of Aristotelianism. It is also remarkable for the stress it lays on the plurality of philosophical arguments, their diversity of significance and their various consequences; for pointing out the links between philosophy and civilisation, philosophy and history, and philosophy and geography. Indeed, it surpasses those compiled by men such as Roger Bacon who had succeeded, however, in depicting the crisis of Scholasticism and interpreting some of the essential needs of European culture. According to Roger philosophy was first revealed to Adam by God; it declined after the Fall when it was preserved by Zoroaster, Prometheus, Atlas, Mercury, Hermes, Apollo, and Aesculapius. In the days of King Solomon it was born again and grew to maturity with Aristotle.[120] But the Greek philosophers—heirs and disciples of the Hebrews—transmitted the divine revelation even though it was confused and imperfect in their interpretation. Thus Democritus, Plato and Aristotle participated in the Word's revelation and knew confusedly the mystery of the Holy Trinity; but Avicenna alone, —who likewise participated in the universal revelation—explicitly understood and acknowledged the supreme spiritual and temporal power of Rome's Bishop.[121] Though Roger Bacon stressed the limitations of Aristotle's philosophy ('he set in order all the parts of philosophy in so far as this was possible to a man of his time, but he failed to reach the end of wisdom') and conceived knowledge as progressing through a sequence of integrations and corrections,[122] in many respects he was still conditioned by those extra-temporal values which led to the one-dimensional medieval interpretation of human evolution, where time and history are superfluous. Thus Roger Bacon's interest in the Greeks, the Arabs and the Jews was the result of his desire to merge past and present and to reduce all beliefs to the unchanging unity of scriptural truths.[123]

But Francis Bacon had profited by the broader horizons of geographical discovery and the legacy of those humanist and Renaissance philosophers he had denounced, and the historical outline he traced was quite a different matter. It was the outcome of a philosophy opposing the medieval belief—revived by Pico and Ficino—in the unbroken chain of original revelation and *logos* running through history; a philosophy impartial and critical in the manner of the Italian humanists whose attitude had been enthusiastically adopted by the sixteenth-century rhetoricians.[124]

For example Peter Ramus, in the *Aristotelicae animadversiones* expresses a demand appropriated by Bacon for his own criticism: the origins of that wealth bestowed upon us by antiquity must be discovered, and Aristotle's claim to have been the *inventor* of logic and to have surpassed all his predecessors should not be accepted uncritically; his vanity and destructiveness must be exposed.[126]

The humanists and rhetoricians caused a cultural upheaval when they wished to teach a new form of worldly philosophy that aimed at serving mankind, conditioning human relations, and improving the efficiency of language. In a certain respect the attacks against Aristotelianism, Platonism, Thomism, neo-Platonism, and Averroism which they wanted to replace, took the form of attacks against philosophy itself, or rather against a particular attitude to philosophical research:

> Let us not be afraid to censure Plato, Aristotle, Galen, Porphyry, all the commentators on Aristotle, Greek, Latin and Arabic, and pretty well the whole of antiquity. . . . By the 'principles of truth' we understand simply certain precepts, or instructions, or lessons, or teachings—call them anything you like—which pertain to correct philosophising and investigation of truth. This meaning is flat contrary to that given to the phrase by the Pseudophilosophers.[126]

These are the words of Marius Nizolius, and his attack on the art of 'pseudophilosophers' came from a need that was later Bacon's own: to protect knowledge from barbarous subtleties and systems presuming to attain an immediate arbitrary unity;

> If I may divert you with a homely illustration; your learning is like the banquet of the Chalcidian host. When his guests asked where he had found such a variety of game, he replied: 'The variety is only in the sauces, the meat is a pig from my own back-yard'.[127]

Thus Bacon denounces the poverty hidden beneath the seeming diversity of such philosophies. His faith in the imminence of a new epoch of human culture led him to enquire into the cause of this poverty. In this respect his refutation differs from that of Descartes who wanted to abolish the whole past and start afresh with a 'universal science that would raise human nature to its highest degree of perfection'.[128] But Descartes too used the familiar Baconian formula that traditional philosophical arguments are not fallacious, but they correspond to certain aims which must be rejected. The acknowledgement of the doctrine's coherence and brilliance preserves the honour of antiquity; but Descartes wished to substitute for 'that which has been called philosophy' a form of culture where such arguments are useless:

> I do not wish to detract in any way from the honour due to each one; but I am forced to say, by way of consolation to those who have never studied, that if on a journey we set out in the wrong

direction, the longer and faster we walk, the further shall we be from our destination, so that, even when we have been redirected upon the right course, we shall arrive later than if we had not travelled at all; thus, the longer and the more assiduously we cultivate wrong principles, and believe we are reasoning correctly, so much further shall we be from truth and wisdom.[129]

What distinguishes Bacon from Descartes is that he demands for the purpose of his reform a thorough examination of past philosophies to distinguish their various positions, motives and influences. Thus in the *Advancement* and the *De augumentis* he evolves a method of historical enquiry presenting each philosophy *as a whole*, with its *developments* and its *relations to the age that produced it.*[130]

According to Bacon, if we wish to build a new philosophy answering contemporary needs we must first acquire a sound knowledge of the origins and beliefs of the philosophy we want to replace. Thus his critique of Platonism exposes those aspects which have reduced philosophy to a lyrical rhetorical argument and polluted scientific integrity with mystical and religious infiltrations. His critique of Aristotle exposes the origins of that contentious, arbitrarily systematic knowledge which obstructs the advancement of learning. Indeed, his attacks on Hermeticism, magical ideals, Scholasticism, and Ciceronian humanism are inseparable from his refutation of philosophies.

I have tried to show in this chapter how the whole framework of Bacon's refutation was based on the early accusations made in the *Temporis partus masculus*, and that these accusations acquire a particular significance when placed in their own historical context. It is no mere coincidence that those who, under varying circumstances, attack the rigidity of systems, the subjection of reality to words, and the rhetorical vagueness which pollutes human reason, follow, whether consciously or not, the basic arguments of Bacon's history of philosophy. Thus pre-Socratic naturalism is commended, the aristocratic tendencies of Plato's ideal are pointed out, Aristotle the 'naturalist' is distinguished from Aristotle the 'metaphysician', and the culture which dominated Europe during the late fourteenth and early fifteenth centuries is opposed to medieval Scholastic contentiousness.

III

The Classical Fable

Myth and allegory in sixteenth- and seventeenth-century literature

In the twenty-second chapter of *Don Quixote*, part II, Cervantes introduces a humanist:

> . . . he replied that by profession he was a humanist, and that his pursuits and studies were to compose books for the press, all of great profit and entertainment to the commonwealth. One, he said, was entitled *The Book of Liveries*, in which he described seven hundred and three devices with their colours, mottoes and ciphers. From these the gentlemen of the court could extract and use whatever they pleased at festival time and celebrations, and would then have no need to beg their liveries from anybody, or to rack their brains, as they say, to invent them to suit their desires and purposes.
> 'For', said he, 'I give suitable devices to the jealous, the scorned, the forgotten and the absent, and fit them out neat as a new pin. I have another book as well, which I mean to call *Metamorphoses, or the Spanish Ovid*, a new and rare invention. In it, parodying Ovid, I give an account of the Giralda of Seville and the Angel of the Magdalen, the Gutter of Vecinguerra at Dorcova and the Bulls of Guisando; the Sierra Morena; the fountains of Leganitos and Lavapies in Madrid, not omitting those of Piojo, of the Golden Gutter, and the Priora; all this with such allegories, metaphors, and transformations as will delight, surprise and instruct at the same time. I have another book that I call the

Supplement to Polydore Virgil which treats of the invention of things. It is a work of great erudition and research, for I elucidate and set out in an elegant style matters of great importance omitted by Polydore. He forgot to tell us who was the first man in the world to have catarrh, and the first to use ointments to cure himself of the French pox; but all these points I set out with the utmost precision on the testimony of twenty-five authorities . . . .'

Sancho declares that, according to him, Adam was the first man to scratch his head and Lucifer the first tumbler in the world when he was thrown out of heaven. To his master's reprimands he replies:

'Hush, sir . . . for if I take to questioning and answering I shan't be done by tomorrow morning, I promise you. Indeed, if it's a matter of asking stupid questions and giving foolish answers I've no need to go looking for help from the neighbours.'

'You have said more than you know, Sancho', said Don Quixote, 'for there are some who tire themselves out learning and proving things which, once learnt and proved, do not concern either the understanding or the memory a jot'.[1]

This conversation between 'cousin Humanist' Sancho and Don Quixote, besides expressing the author's critical attitude to a popular sixteenth- and seventeenth-century form of literature, depicts with consummate skill the three basic types of allegorical and mythographic traditions derived from Platonism, the Stoics, and neo-Platonism. These traditions were adopted by a number of medieval writers and attained their widest diffusion in the late sixteenth century, and, with Bacon and Vico, survived right up to the dawn of modern times.

The *Book of Emblems* is an allusion to iconographic and emblematic books like Alciati's *Emblematum Liber* (*Book of Emblems*, 1531) or the popular *Iconologia* of Ripa (1593), where philosophical and moral problems are disguised in complex images and which did, in fact, inspire certain forms of public entertainment in sixteenth-century Europe.[2]

Since the early fourteenth century, allegorical interpretations of classical mythology had always been popular in Europe. Thomas Waley's *Metamorphosis ovidiana moraliter explanata* (1510) was circulated from Milan to Cambridge and from Frankfurt

74

to Lyons. In 1595 *Las transformaciones de Ovidio en lengua española con las allegorias* was published at Antwerp, and Juan Perez Moya's *Philosophia Secreta*, published in Madrid ten years earlier, ran to at least three editions before 1611.[3] It was inspired by Boccaccio's *Genealogy of the Gods*, by Alberic's *Allegoriae poeticae*, and more directly by the *Mythologia sive explicationum fabularum libri decem* (Venice, 1551), which was to be one of Bacon's principal sources for the *De sapientia veterum*.

Cervantes—who, incidentally, had not escaped the influence of neo-Platonism which reached him through the Italian Leone Ebreus[4]—was attacking, besides these mythological allegorisations, a euhemeristic literary tendency to represent the classical gods as the forerunners of civilisation, and mythology as idealised history. The book to which his humanist was writing a supplement—*Of the Inventors of Things*—had been published in 1499. In it Bacchus is the inventor of wine, Mercury the creator of the Egyptian alphabet, Venus instructs in the art of love, and so forth.

This form of literature was a legacy from the Renaissance and from Italian humanism in particular. Marsilio Ficino writes:

> The theologians, to prevent the rash diffusion of divine mysteries, disguised them in mathematical symbols and in poetic images.

Landino, in the *Disputationes Camaldulenses*, interprets the *Aeneid* as an account of the soul's progress, and sees it as a eulogy of the contemplative life: Aenaeas stands for wisdom; Troy for sensuality; Juno for ambition; Dido for the active life; and the journey from Carthage to Italy for the transition from the active to the contemplative life. Pico's *Heptaplus* sees Genesis as an allegorical representation of the secrets of nature, the descent of Christ and the founding of the Church.[5] Poliziano's works are derived from Platonism.

But a concrete symbolism of abstract ideas—which according to Cassirer is typical of the Renaissance—was already present in the works of Valla, for whom Apollo was divine knowledge and Jove divine power,[6] and of Bruno, for whom ideas can only be communicated through concrete images. Cassirer says that in this form of culture allegory is not an adjunct, an occasional garment, but the vehicle of thought itself, and that for Bruno, classical mythology came thus to invade philosophical thought and to dominate it.

The Renaissance is certainly characterised by individualist, naturalist tendencies; but the picture is incomplete if one overlooks the typically medieval themes of classical inspiration which haunt the writings of the period; indeed, medieval mythological allegory flows in an uninterrupted stream right through the Renaissance.[8] The *Commentary* of Servius had six editions between 1470 and 1475; Macrobius' works five between 1522 and 1542; and those of Martianus Capella eight between 1499 and 1599. Thus the new culture was based on typically medieval texts.

But the change—as was usual with Renaissance culture—was one of form and not of content.[9] Medieval myths were given new interpretations that revealed a new attitude. The Promethean myth acquires for Bovillus[10] a totally different meaning from the one it had for Tertullian, Lactantius, or St Augustine; Cassirer says that the subject was the same but with the accent in a different place.[11] And even Seznec, a firm believer in the unbroken continuity of medieval and Renaissance cultures, has had to recognise a discrepancy in this particular respect: the medieval ability to conciliate, with unhistorical immediacy, pagan and Christian worlds, had vanished; the men of the Renaissance were now estranged from antiquity, but they yearned for this lost universe and sought to harmonise the two worlds.[12]

It is true that in certain spheres of culture the Renaissance attitude to antiquity was much more reactionary. Indeed, the importance of Valla and his followers resides in an acquired historical sense that enables them to establish culture in time instead of discussing it in the abstract. But this step was not, and could not be, taken in the sphere of mythology. Even before Bacon's allegorical interpretations of myths and Cervantes' satire of a fashionable form of traditional literature, the Renaissance mythological allegories had been criticised:

> But do you faithfully believe that Homer, in writing his *Iliad* and *Odyssey*, ever had in mind the allegories squeezed out of him by Plutarch, Heraclides, Ponticus, Eustathius, and Phornutus, and which Politian afterwards stole from them, in his turn? If you do, you are not within a hand's or a foot's length of my opinion. For

I believe them to have been as little dreamed of by Homer as the Gospel mysteries were by Ovid in his Metamorphoses.[13]

Is it possible that Homer meant to say all they make him say, and that he lent himself to so many and such different interpretations that the theologians, legislators, captains, philosophers, all sorts of people who treat of sciences, however differently and contradictorily, lean on him and refer to him: the general master for all offices, works, and artisans, the general counselor for all enterprises? Whoever has needed oracles and predictions has found in him enough for his purpose. It is a marvel what wonderful correspondences a learned man . . . draws out of him in support of our religion. . . . And what he finds in favor of ours, many of old had found in favor of theirs.[14]

However, one should not be misled by passages such as these: they had not enough weight to counteract the popularity of allegory in art and literature, and the views on the subject of the writers themselves were not without ambiguity. For Rabelais made use of Macrobius and Textor when writing his masterpiece[15] and Montaigne, besides commending the compilers of mythological manuals[16] finally adopted the very attitude he had satirised:

Most of Aesops Fables have many meanings and interpretations. Those who take them allegorically choose some aspect that squares with the fable, but for the most part this is only the first and superficial aspect; there are others more living, more essential and internal, to which they have not known how to penetrate.[17]

If Renaissance writers adapted mythological interpretations to the demands of their age, they still believed the myths to be the repositories of occult truths and of a vanished wisdom— even while doubting their historical authenticity. With Vico, however, these reservations and doubts disappear and the myth becomes the true expression of a primitive magical world. This notion, that gradually emerged after various phases of uncertainty and contradiction, was to prove invaluable for historical research into primitive societies:

Poetic wisdom which was the first pagan wisdom, sprang from a form of metaphysics, not rational and abstract like the metaphysics of the learned, but instinctive and imaginative, such as could be produced by the powerful instincts and imaginations of these early men . . .

... they (the philosophers) gave physical, moral, metaphysical or other scientific interpretations to fables, according to their zeal or inclination; thus, with their learned allegories they rather falsified than otherwise, the fables, for these learned meanings were certainly foreign to their first authors who had course, uncultured natures; indeed, because of their very natures they conceived the fables as true accounts of divine and human events ...

... This discovery, of the origins of poetry negates that notion of the ancients' unfathomable wisdom, which from Plato to Bacon of Verulam—with his *De sapientia veterum*—so many have attempted to fathom, when in reality it was no more than the common wisdom of the lawgivers who founded the human race, and not the secret wisdom of great philosophers.[18]

Vico's ability to free the past from present contrivancies and set it in perspective so as to discern its distinctive, autonomous quality, was in the true tradition of the 'philology' of Valla and the humanists.

Boccaccio's *Genealogy of the Gods* had been an important source of literary inspiration since the beginning of the fifteenth century, and Europe was flooded with works of Boccaccian and neo-Platonist derivation. The most noteworthy of these—as Seznec has pointed out—are Giraldi's *De deis gentium*[19], Natale Conti's *Mithologia*, and Cartari's *Imagini* which soon became manuals of allegorical interpretation so frequently quoted that references were no longer required.[20]

The mythological erudition of Elizabethan poets and writers owed a great deal to these Italian sources.[21] Francis Bacon and George Chapman were both influenced by Ficino and Conti,[22] while Robert Burton, whose *Anatomy of Melancholy* typifies the intellectual trends of his age, openly acknowledged the importance of Cartari's work. But in the poems of John Marston[23] we find the most striking evidence of this influence. Allegory, symbol and imagery invaded art, literature, poetry, and philosophy and were fast becoming the basic elements of Elizabethan culture. Spenser says in his prefatory letter to Sir Walter Raleigh, in the *Faerie Queene*:

Knowing how doubtfully all Allegories may be construed, and this book of mine ... being a continued Allegory or dark conceit, I have thought good . . . to discover unto you the general intention and meaning which in the whole course thereof I have fashioned.[24]

In the third book of his *Rhetoric* (1553) Wilson attributed moral and philosophical intentions to the classical poets.[25] Webbe, who believed in the educative and ethical potentialities of allegorical poetry, expressed a similar view in the *Discourse of English Poetry* (1586); while George Puttenham's theory of poetic wisdom in his famous *Arte of English Poesie* (1598) seems to foreshadow Vico's:

> The profession and use of Poesie is most ancient from the beginning, and not, as many erroniously suppose, after, but before, any civil society was among men. For it is written that Poesie was th'original cause and occasion of their first assemblies, when before the people remained in the woods and mountains, vagrant and dispersed like the wild beasts, lawless and naked, or very ill clad, and of all good and necessary provision for harbour or sustenance utterly unfurnished, so as they little differed for their manner of life from the very brute beasts of the field.

But the poets brought culture to this primitive world:

> Poets therefore are of great antiquity. Then forasmuch as they were the first that entended to the observation of nature and her works, and specially of the Celestial courses . . . they were the first that instituted sacrifices of placation . . . were the first Priests and ministers of the holy mysteries . . . the Poet was also the first historiographer . . . they were the first Astronomers and Philosophists and Metaphysics.[26]

In late sixteenth-century England the notion of poetry as a source of wisdom was linked to that of poetry and myth as a veil thrown by the sages of old over sacred truths to protect them from being profaned by the common people. Thus Sir John Harington in the *Apologie of Poetrie* (1591):

> It sufficeth me therefore to note this, that the men of greatest learning and highest wit in the auncient times did of purpose conceale these deepe mysteries of learning, and as it were, cover them with the vaile of fables and verse for sundrie causes: one cause was that they might not be rashly abused by prophane wits, in whom science is corrupted, like good wine in a bad vase.[27]

And in Bacon we find the notion both of a primitive race expressing itself by parable and symbol, and that of a mysterious allegorical meaning hidden in the classical fable. Indeed, such notions persisted in England well into the sixteenth century, though with Bacon's *De sapientia veterum* they underwent certain changes. In 1621, a year after the publication of the *Instauratio magna*, Thomas Lodge, in his *A learned Summary upon the Famous Poeme of William Saluste Lord of Bartas*, refers to Natale Conti and quotes him extensively. On the other hand Henry Reynold's *Mythomistes* (about 1633) is of unmistakable Baconian derivation; here the author, after the customary quotations from Conti, expounds an allegorical theory of poetry and attributes to classical fables, not only an ethical significance, but also, and especially, a naturalistic one. The influence of Florentine neo-Platonism, Poliziano and Bacon had merged significantly with cabbalistic esotericism.[28]

Five of Bacon's thirty-nine philosophical works are either directly concerned with the problem of a hidden wisdom in classical myths and fables, or at least refer to it explicitly. These works are *Cogitationes de scientia humana* (*Reflections on Human Knowledge*, a collection of miscellaneous fragments written in 1505); *The two Bookes of F. B. Of Proficience and Advancement of Learning Divine and Humane* (published in 1605); *De sapientia veterum liber* (*Wisdom of the Ancients*, published in 1609); *De dignitate et augumentis scientiarum libri IX* (*Nine Books of Proficience and Advancement of Learning*, published in 1623); *De principiis atque originibus secundum fabulas Cupidinis et Coeli, sive Parmenidis et Telesii et precipue Democriti philosophia tractata in fabula de Cupidine* (*On Principles and Origins, according to the fables of Cupid and Coelum, or the Philosophy of Parmenides, Telesius and especially of Democritus, treated in a Fable of Cupid*, a substantial collection of notes for the projected revision of *De sapientia veterum* written about 1623-4.[29])

De sapientia veterum is more directly concerned than the other four with the problems of myth and fable. Its intrinsic value, however, has only recently been acknowledged. Even Ellis, Spedding and Heath have shown their complete disregard for its philosophical significance in the context of Bacon's materialism and naturalism, by including it among his literary writings in their edition of Bacon. This mistaken classification has been responsible for its neglect, rightly described by Fulton Anderson as 'among the strangest phenomena in history of philosophical exegesis'.[30]

In this chapter I propose to outline Bacon's different attitudes to the problem of classical fables, and to explain how such attitudes were related to the various formulations of his plan for the reform of science. By analysing Bacon's interpretations of fables I hope to discern the naturalistic, materialistic, methodological, ethical, and political themes in the *De sapientia veterum* and to prove the significance of this work in the general context of Bacon's philosophy.

The interpretation of myths in the 'Cogitationes de scientia humana'

The *Cogitationes de scientia humana*, written probably around 1605, is a collection of fragments on a number of problems that were of perennial interest to Bacon: the limitations of human knowledge, the value of humility in natural research, motion, the static quantity of constituent matter in the universe, distinctions between the subject matter of science and that of faith, and the classical fable. In the fourth, sixth, seventh, and eighth of the Cogitationes—which form the nucleus of the *De sapientia veterum*—Bacon interprets the fables of Metis, *The Sister of the Giants*, Proteus, and Saturn.

The 'monstrous and at first sight very foolish fable of Metis', made pregnant by Jove and devoured by her husband Zeus from whose head Pallas Athene issued fully armed, symbolises for Bacon the mysterious power that preserves the sovereignty of kings and increases their authority. A king should consider the advice of his counsellors when making a decision; but once the decision is made its execution must appear to derive from the wisdom, prudence and will of the king alone.

Bacon's views on the relation of kings to their counsellors— reiterated later in the twentieth essay *Of Counsel*—denotes a political realism even greater than Machiavelli's. Indeed, in the twenty-third chapter of *The Prince*, the latter only required the king to

. . . adopt a middle-way, choosing wise men for his government and allowing only those the freedom to speak the truth to him, and then only concerning matters on which he asks their opinion, and nothing else. But he should also question them thoroughly and listen to what they say; then he should make up his own mind, by himself.

Bacon's interpretation of *The Sister of the Giants* expresses similar political views—inspired in this case most probably, from Machiavelli's *Discourses*, I, 7. These views—though clearer and more consistent—reappear in the fifteenth essay *Of Seditions and Troubles*, and in *Of Fame, a Fragment*.

Earth, mother of the Giants defeated by Jove, and begetter of Fame who avenges her murdered brothers, represents the mob 'ever rebellious and ill-disposed towards authority'. The mob gives birth to rebels, but when defeated, it becomes 'worse disposed and restless' and fills the city with murmurings, libel, and envy for those in power. Thus rebellion and fame do not differ in kind but only in sex; actions are male, words female.

The tenth of the *Cogitationes*—an interpretation of the Midas myth—is the only one that does not recur in the *De sapientia*. Midas cannot keep to himself the fact that his master has asses' ears; he whispers it into the earth from whence the swallows arise and spread the secret through the air. This is an image of those ministers who are incapable of keeping the king's secrets and betray them in some way, even if not in actual words. Libel and sedition then take wing like the swallows and spread the royal secret through the realm.

Bacon used these three fables—the last being only partly relevant—to express political opinions of Machiavellian inspiration.[31] However, his interpretations of the Proteus and Saturn fables are more philosophical. Here, alongside his adoption of a definitely materialistic attitude, we find a notion cherished by Bacon for many years and which he was to develop in the course of his works: the importance for mankind of the will to dominate nature, from which both the art of mastering it and the solving of its deepest mysteries should derive.

The shepherd Proteus who knows all things, past, present, and future, falls asleep after counting his flock; but it is no easy task to question him as he has the power to assume many different shapes. 'Under the person of Proteus, Matter, the most ancient of all things next to God, is meant to be represented.' His sheep are the different forms in which matter manifests itself; his slumber indicates that nature has ceased to produce new species. Proteus, however, can be forced into revealing the truth: nature, constrained by art can be made to assume shapes that are at variance with those of ordinary species. If we know the phenomena and procedures of nature we can attain the essence of things and grasp the outline of their past, present, and future development, even if particular instances may still elude us.

For Bacon the fable of Saturn, emasculator of his father Uranus and, in turn, emasculated by his son Jove who defeated the Titans and the Giants '. . . seems to be an enigma concerning the origin of things not much differing from the philosophy afterwards embraced by Democritus, who more openly than anyone else asserted the eternity of matter, while he denied the eternity of the world'. Saturn represents matter which has deprived its generator of the power to generate again, for 'the sum total of matter remains always the same and the absolute quantum of nature suffers neither increase nor diminution'. Matter's primal stirrings produced 'imperfect and ill-compacted structures of things that would not hold together: mere attempts at worlds'; then matter—symbolised by Jove, conqueror of the Titans—discards these transitory changes. Saturn's mutilated sex is cast into the sea and from it Venus is born, who represents the new and perfect harmony of all things: 'changes procede part by part only, the total fabric remaining entire and undisturbed'. But the danger is never completely eliminated: Saturn is mutilated but he is not dead: order could revert to disorder: chaos and confusion might return.[32]

Bacon's distinction between scientific and religious topics emerges clearly from the pages of the *Cogitationes de scientia humana* alongside materialistic tendencies and Empedoclean derivations. This distinction was to become the basic theme in *De sapientia veterum* and is also stressed in the *De augmentis*.

Human understanding can never penetrate the mysteries of God and the final laws of nature: these are matters for revelation and faith. On the other hand, man is gifted with the power to perceive the workings of nature and thus to dominate it. This is the way of salvation, of redemption from original sin. Notwithstanding Bacon's evident religious preoccupation[33]—

especially notable in the *Meditationes sacræ* and *Profession of Faith* of 1597—his distinctions between criteria of truth and his un-equivocal segregation of theology from philosophy were mainly actuated by the practical problem of realising his plan of reform in the cultural environment of his age.

However, Bacon was far from using these distinctions only as a means to an end. Not only was he a religious man, but in this particular phase of his development his views on the advantages of an active or a contemplative life were far from consistent. For instance, in the *Partis instaurationis secundae delineatio et argumentum* of 1607 he declares that the superficiality of em-piricism derives from the rigorous construction of its theories; while 'arbitrary rationalist theories' are condemned for their lack of rigour in the *Valerius Terminus* (1603) and in *Cogitata et visa* (1607). His changing views on the aims of knowledge coincide, in fact, with the successive reformulations of his pro-gramme of reform. In the third *Cogitatio* 'charitas' and religious inspiration are the aims of knowledge; in the interpretation of the Proteus myth, in the *Temporis partus masculus* and in *Cogitata et visa* he stresses the utilitarian function and the pragmatic value of science.

But such waverings did nothing to modify Bacon's basic aversion for Aristotelian and Platonic intellectualism and traditional philosophy, nor his partiality to pre-Socratic nat-uralism and Democritean materialism.

The theory of myths in the 'Advancement of Learning'

Bacon published the two books of the *Advancement of Learning* in 1605 while he was writing the *Cogitationes*. It is in this general encyclopedia of knowledge that he first attempted to determine the aims and significance of myths.

In the olden days, when men were predominantly instinctive, if they wanted to communicate some unfamiliar or abstract idea they had to stir the imagination of their audience by the use of varied and striking images. Aesop's fables and the aphor-isms of the Seven Sages are typical examples of such modes of expression: 'as hieroglyphics were before letters, so parables were before arguments'.

On the other hand 'the secrets and mysteries of religion,

policy, or philosophy are involved in fables and parables'. In other words, parallel to the revealing function of myths lies that of veiling acquired truths. To demonstrate how the hidden meaning of fables can 'with great felicity' be extracted, Bacon sums up the myths of the Giants, Briareus, and Achilles educated by Chiron ('ingeniously but corruptly' interpreted by Machiavelli[34], because there are times when princes must act the part of the lion, the wolf, or the man).

If we judge by these examples, says Bacon, the fables appear to be the fruit of fantasy preceding the interpretation rather than devised to veil occult mysteries. But whether this is so or the fable is, indeed, a conscious allegory, Bacon is unwilling to decide:

> I do rather think that the fable was first, and the exposition devised, than that the moral was first, and thereupon the fable formed. For I find it was an ancient vanity in Chrysippus, that troubled himself with great contention to fasten the assertions of the Stoics upon the fictions of the ancient poets: but yet that all the fables and fictions of the poets were but pleasure and not figure, I interpose no opinion.[35]

The theory of myths in 'De sapientia veterum'

Bacon's attitude changed considerably between 1605 when he published the *Advancement of Learning* and 1609 when *De sapientia veterum* came out:

> The most ancient times (except what is preserved of them in the Scriptures) are buried in oblivion and silence: to that silence succeeded the fables of the poets: to those fables the written records which have come down to us. Thus between the hidden depths of antiquity and the days of tradition and evidence that followed there is drawn a veil, as it were, of fables, which come in and occupy the middle region that separates what has perished from what survives.[36]

This is from the beautifully written preface of *De sapientia veterum*. Readers might suppose, continues Bacon, that his interpretations of fables are an agreeable recreation where he indulges in poetic licence. And could he be blamed if it were so, for mingling pleasant topics with arduous scientific and philosophical research? As a matter of fact, he is aware of the ever present danger of endowing fables with meanings they never possessed. Many are the writers who have wilfully done so, to add the glamour of antiquity to their own inventions and theories: thus Chrysippus 'interpreting the oldest poets after the manner of an interpreter of dreams' attributed to these poets the theories of the Stoics.

But though Bacon sees the dangers and the 'levity and looseness' that attend the interpretations of allegory, he will not desist from his purpose, first because the errors of some writers do not suffice to discredit parables as a whole, and secondly because he considers the shadows and veils which surround religion to be truly a link between the human and the divine. And apart from these considerations:

> I do certainly for my own part (I freely and candidly confess) incline to this opinion;—that beneath no small number of these fables of the ancient poets there lay from the very beginning a mystery and an allegory. It may be that my reverence for the primitive time carries me too far, but the truth is that in some of these fables, as well in the very frame and texture of the story as in the propriety of the names by which the persons that figure in it are distinguished, I find a conformity and connexion with the thing signified, so close and so evident, that one cannot help believing such a signification to have been designed and meditated from the first, and purposely shadowed out.[37]

Anyone, however blind and unintelligent, will perceive at once that the tale of Earth giving birth to Fame after the death of the Giants refers to the seditious murmurings which follow upon a failed revolution, and the same applies to the myth of Typhon and that of Silenus' ass.

Bacon elaborated three distinct arguments in defence of this theory. The first was based on the 'conformity of names': Pan means universe, Metis counsel, Nemesis vengeance, etc. The second was based on the apparent absurdity of certain myths which clearly indicates an underlying, hidden meaning: a logical fable might well have been invented for the mere pleasure of telling a story, but when we hear, for instance, that Pallas Athene issues fully armed from the head of Jove, the very unnaturalness of the image precludes the possibility of its having been invented without some definite idea in mind, and we instinctively search for this deeper meaning. The last argument was based on the fact that most myths do not seem to be the creations of the teller: if we could attribute to Homer and Hesiod the fables they have written we would not worry about origins. But a careful study will show that they are told 'as stories already received and believed' and not 'as new inventions then first published'. Further, these stories being told differently by each writer, we may distinguish that which pertains to tradition from individual embellishments and additions:

> The fables . . . must be regarded as neither being the invention nor belonging to the age of the poets themselves, but as sacred relics and light airs breathing out of better times, that were caught from the traditions of more ancient nations and so received into the flutes and trumpets of the Greeks.[38]

Bacon opposed yet another argument to those who persist in denying the allegorical value of fables and for whom, in consequence, all interpretations are adventitious: fables may serve 'to disguise and veil the meaning, and also to clear and throw light upon it'. Even if we refuse to admit the first use and see them only as the fruit of fantasy, we cannot ignore the importance of the second, where the fable becomes 'a method of teaching' by which the most difficult and unfamiliar conceit 'may find an easier passage to the understanding'. In the depths of antiquity, says Bacon,—enlarging upon some of his ideas from the *Advancement of Learning*—that which now seems natural and obvious was strange, unfamiliar, and fantastic: men's minds were rude and simple and they could only grasp things with their senses; all was enigma, parable, and simile, and the fable was then more an instrument of learning and enlightenment than a veil. Thus Bacon, defending his theory of allegory, was drawing a very schematic outline of an age of fantasy where truth is expressed allegorically in myths, and foreshadowing a notion that was to become a turning point in the development of European thought: the notion that religion stems from fantasy. ('As hieroglyphics were before letters, so parables were before arguments.')

The motives for Bacon's change of attitude

In the preface to the *De sapientia veterum* Bacon's uncertainties disappear. They are replaced by a firm belief in the allegorical significance of myths. Indeed, his views here are often completely opposed to those he expressed in the *Advancement of Learning*.

For instance, in the earlier work the function of myths was primarily pedagogical, and the possibility of an allegorical meaning was considered problematic and subordinate; obversely in the *De sapientia veterum* the pedagogical function is brought in only as an additional argument against the obstinate refuter of allegorical significance. Again, the interpretations in the *Advancement* tend to stress the fact that more can be gleaned from myths than they actually contain; while those in the *De sapientia* would prove the exact correspondence of names to concepts and the presence—evidenced by the tales' absurdity—of a hidden meaning. Lastly, whereas Bacon admits in the *Advancement* that he 'rather thinks . . . the fable was first and the exposition devised' in his later work he repeatedly asserts the contrary.

Though in the preface to the *De sapientia* Bacon concedes the 'levity and looseness' of many existing interpretations, such shortcomings are imputed, not to the intention—which is praiseworthy—to extract ethical or philosophical meanings from myths and fables, but to the ignorance of the interpreters.

It is impossible to understand the particular significance of the *De sapientia veterum* in Bacon's *œuvre*, or indeed the different phases of his intellectual development, if one does not elucidate the motives for his change of attitude. This requires a re-examination of the years immediately preceding 1609.

We have seen that in his writings of this period Bacon opposed the pre-Socratic philosophers—and Democritus in particular—to Plato and Aristotle. For him, they represented the type of the serious, unassuming questioner of nature, unencumbered by the characteristic 'pomposity' of Greek philosophers in general. They heralded the 'chaste, holy and legal wedlock with nature' that Bacon dreamt of substituting for Platonic 'evasions' and Aristotelian 'formalism'. This plan of substitution was outlined in the *Temporis partus masculus* (1603), in *Cogitata et visa* (1607) and in the *Redargutio philosophiarum* (1608). Though Bacon admitted that the pre-Socratics had been tainted by Greek civilisation and suffered from its limitations, he wished to reinstate some of their theories which were truly worthy and he saw their attitude to natural research as a model for the scholars of his day that would help to counteract the pernicious influence of the Platonic and Aristotelian tradition.

In the *Temporis partus masculus* Bacon's attacks were violent; they were moderate in the *Cogitata et visa* and in the *Redargutio*; yet in all three works his project for a reform of science was identical. In 1607 he sent the manuscript of the *Cogitata et visa* to Sir Thomas Bodley, founder of the famous Oxford library, and two years later he sent a revised copy to Lancelot Andrewes, who was one of the foremost figures in the Anglican Church. In the accompanying letter he wrote:

> My request to you is that, not by pricks, but by notes, you would mark unto me whatsoever shall seem unto you either not current in the style, or harsh to credit and opinion, or inconvenient for the person of the writer.[39]

Andrewes' answer has not survived, but Bodley, after a preliminary eulogy, criticised Bacon's refutation of traditional culture, adding:

> Although I am convinced as to the contents and subject of this admirable work, in no place of learning would you find a tribunal which would be able to acquit you of error.

These lines undoubtedly impressed Bacon, who had already begun to feel the hostility of scientific circles to his programme and to suffer from intellectual isolation:

> While I was immersed in the business a friend came to see me who had just returned from France. When we had exchanged greetings and personal news: 'Tell me', said he, 'what are your writings in the intervals of public business, or at least, when public business is less pressing?' 'Your enquiry is timely', said I, 'for just in case you think I have nothing in hand, I am planning an Instauration of Philosophy, containing nothing empty or abstract, but designed to improve the conditions of human life.' 'A noble task', said he, 'who is helping you?' 'You must understand', I replied, 'that I am working in complete isolation.'[40]

So Bacon abandoned the idea of publishing his three most polemical works, and, indeed, renounced violence altogether.

In 1604, in the *Cogitationes de natura rerum*, Bacon had attempted another form of persuasion. It was a simple, straightforward exposition of Democritean philosophy, starting thus, 'The Doctrine of Democritus concerning atoms is true or useful for demonstrations.' Some theories from this short work were incorporated the following year into the interpretation of the Saturn myth in the *Cogitationes de scientia humana*: the eternity of matter and the unvarying quantity of constituent matter in the universe. Besides these Bacon discussed here the problem of the function of motion in the formation of the universe, simple movements seen as the 'alphabet of nature'; and refuted the distinction between perfect and imperfect movement. But the work was never completed, Bacon having possibly found this method no easier than the first.

In 1605, however, when Bacon began to write the *Cogitationes de scientia humana*, he conceived the strategem of presenting his chosen doctrines 'disguised in the veils of allegory and crowned with Antiquity'. Thus his interpretations of the myths of Proteus and of Saturn convey some of the notions that were dearest to him. But this method required more than an hypothetical suggestion that truth might have been concealed in myths; the time of waverings was ended and the scales—if only for practical purposes—were heavily weighted on one side. The philosopher's aim was to uncover the hidden truth concealed, unquestionably, in the fables of the poets.

A few quotations from Bacon's writings of this crucial period may help to illustrate our theory. In the *Temporis partus masculus* he wrote:

> You would wish to know what I think may be hidden behind the silence and the reserve of antiquity? . . . But as for the writings which have vanished without trace, I know your modesty well enough to be assured that you will not misunderstand me if I suggest that this hunting after guesses is a wearisome business and that it would not be a proper thing for me, who am preparing things useful for the future of the human race, to bury myself in the study of ancient literature . . . science is to be sought from the light of nature, not from the darkness of antiquity. It matters not what has been done; our business is to see what can be done.

If a kingdom won in victorious fighting were offered to you, would you refuse it unless you had followed up the clues of ancient genealogies to prove that your ancestors had held it before? So much for the remote fastness of antiquity.[41]

Bacon expressed very similar views in the fifth chapter of the *Valerius Terminus* (1603). Of remote antiquity he says 'I cannot presume much of it' without fear of imitating those cartographers who cover their ignorance of distant, unknown lands by indicating deserts on their maps where these lands should be. Of the ancients, 'I am not apt to affirm that they knew little, because what they knew is little known to us', says Bacon, yet he accepts Aristotle's judgement on the ignorance of primitive civilisations.

In the *Advancement of Learning* (1605) his attitude to the significance of fables was more guarded, though still inclined to scepticism. But in 1607 and 1608 a reversal is perceptible. The passage quoted below is from the *Redargutio philosophiarum*, the phrases in italics having already appeared in the *Cogitata et visa*:

Your education, my sons, might be compared to a conducted tour through a portrait-gallery of the ancients. Very probably you have not failed to observe that a certain portion of the gallery was cut off by a curtain. Behind that curtain lie the secrets of that antiquity which preceded the learning of the Greeks. But why should you wish to direct my attention to those remote ages, of which the true history and even the traces of that history have vanished? Is not that remote antiquity like the poet's description of Fame, hiding her head in the clouds and relating wonders, singing in the same breath of what was done and never done. *Well I know, if I wished to be insincere, that it would not be difficult to make men believe that among the sages of old, long before Greek times, philosophy and the sciences flourished with greater value and less noise. If I did this I could, by referring my present proposals to those ancient times, invest them with a certain solemnity, as self-made men do, who attach to themselves the nobility of some ancient stock by means of genealogical hints and conjectures. But my resolution is fixed, to rely on the evidence of facts and avoid any sort of imposture,* however convenient or attractive. Accordingly I shall not interject into the present discussion my judgement on those centuries. I shall just remark in passing that, though the fables of the poets are of a nature to lend themselves to many interpretations, I should be loth to draw recondite meanings out of them, if they were invented by those who have handed them on to us. But this, I think, is not so. They are not offered to us as new inventions now for the first time brought forward, but as things formerly believed and known. This circumstance increases their value in my eyes, since it suggests that they are the sacred survivals of better times. But, however that may be, it has no vital bearing on the matter in hand. It may well be that my project, and much greater projects than mine, were really known to remote antiquity. But *this is of no importance for the business in hand. Similarly no practical importance attaches to the debate whether the New World is the old Atlantis and was known to the ancients or whether it has now been discovered for the first time. Truth must be discovered by the light of nature, not recovered from the darkness of the past.*[42]

Though this passage lacks, on the whole, the unwavering conviction expressed in the *De sapientia veterum* the following year, some of the views are identical. Bacon has, for instance, already taken up arms against the insincerity of men who try to invest their theories with a 'certain solemnity' by referring them to ancient times. But he attempted here the practically impossible feat of denying the importance of fables while admitting that they were the 'sacred survivals of better times'. But many years later, in the *New Organon*, the last part of the passage, from the words 'the matter in hand', was almost literally reproduced.[43]

The theories forming the philosophical loom upon which Bacon weaved his interpretations of myths in the *De sapientia veterum* are those he had expounded in the *Temporis partus masculus*, the *Cogitationes de scientia humana* and *Cogitata et visa*: the distinction between philosophical and theological topics; the importance of materialistic naturalism, of methodical, experimental science, of a scientific mastery of nature, and of a realistic Machiavellian policy. Bacon's aims are unchanged; only his attitude has altered.

Bacon's obsession with a plan of cultural and social reform is apparent in his *Commentarius solutus sive pandecta, sive ancilla memoriae*, a curious collection of personal notes, accounts, private meditations, philosophical speculations, and political reflections jotted down at random in the summer of 1608 and edited and published by Spedding.[44] This plan involved the founding of institutions for scientific research, the reorganisation of the English universities, and the collaboration of European scholars, some of these enthusiastic projects anticipating his description of Solomon's house in the *New Organon*.

Indeed, if Bacon did not publish his most virulent attacks on tradition, it was precisely because he was so anxious to realise his plan of reform and saw that this could only be achieved by outwardly moderating his antagonism to obtain, not only the support of his king, but also the sympathies of intellectuals all over Europe.

In the *Commentarius* the entry dated 28 July 1608 reads:

> Discoursing scornfully of the philosophy of the Grecians, with some better respect to . . . the utmost antiquity and the mysteries of the poets.

The first part of this entry corresponds to Bacon's theories expressed in the *Redargutio* (1608) which remained unpublished; the second foreshadows an attitude that became familiar to the readers of the *De sapientia veterum*.

Bacon's acceptance of the allegorical significance of fables and his interpretations of the latter show more erudition than originality. Pan, Prometheus, Paris, and the Sirens symbolising respectively nature, the saviour of mankind, the champion of love, and the dangers of lust, figure in the works of Boccaccio, Conti, and Alciati, all inspired by Plutarch, Lucian, Cornutus, Servius, Macrobius, Fulgentius, and the neo-Platonists. The treatises of Giraldi, Conti, and Cartari were widely circulated in the sixteenth and seventeenth centuries and mythological symbols acquired a new popularity through their use in alchemical writings. Lemmi has shown that Bacon borrowed extensively from Natale Conti's *Mitologia*—one of the most popular manuals of the time—for the *De sapientia veterum*.

Bacon was nearly fifty in 1609 when the *De sapientia veterum*—a beautifully printed duodecimo—was published. This was his third philosophical work to appear, the other two being the *Essays* in 1597 and in 1605 the *Advancement of Learning*. The latter was a conventional book compared with the *Temporis partus masculus*, *Cogitata et visa*, and the *Redargutio philosophiarum*, and described by Bacon himself as 'a mixture of new conceits and old',[45] but a valuable 'key' to the *Instauratio magna* where new 'conceits' were unadulterated and old conceits refuted.

The *De sapientia* was prefaced by a letter of eulogy to the

Count of Salisbury, Chancellor of the University, and obse-
quiously dedicated to the 'renowned University of Cambridge'
—one of those, it will be remembered, which figured as
'obstacles to scientific progress' in *Cogitata et visa*. This work, like
the *Advancement*, was compounded of new and old conceits, such
a compromise being the method temporarily devised by Bacon
for publishing his theories without alienating public opinion.
And though his allegiance to an allegorical tradition may not
have been dictated by cold-blooded calculation, neither can it
be seen as an enthusiastic conversion. In the *Valerius Terminus*
and in *Cogitata et visa* Bacon had commented upon the two
major obstacles to the introduction of new ideas into a given
culture: public opinion and common sense. In his preface to the
De sapientia he writes:

> I mean the employment of parables as a method of teaching,
> whereby inventions that are new and abstruse and remote from
> vulgar opinions may find an easier passage to the understanding.
> On this account it was that in the old times, when the inventions
> and conclusions of human reason (even those that are now trite
> and vulgar) were as yet new and strange, the world was full of
> all kinds of fables, and enigmas, and parables, and similitudes:
> and these were used not as a device for shadowing and concealing
> the meaning, but as a method of making it understood; the under-
> standings of men being then rude and impatient of all subtleties
> that did not address themselves to the sense,—indeed scarcely
> capable of them. For hieroglyphics came before letters, so parables
> came before arguments. And even now if any one wish to let
> new light on any subject into men's minds and that without
> offence or harshness, he must still go the same way and call in the
> aid of similitudes.[46]

Bacon was aware, however, of the possible ambiguity of his
attitude. A few lines later he stated that he was confronted with
the choice of 'throwing light either upon antiquity or upon
nature itself'.[47]

In this detailed analysis I have tried to show Bacon's varying
attitudes to classical myth and the relation between these
attitudes and the different formulations of his programme for
the reform of learning. For me this relation is crucial because
it proves the absurdity of seeing the *De sapientia veterum* as a
'literary exercise' of secondary importance, irrelevant to the

evolution of Bacon's philosophy. The following summary will help to make this clear:

(1) *Temporis partus masculus* (anterior to 1603, unpublished): violent attack on traditional culture. The possibility of the ancients possessing occult wisdom is of little interest to those 'preparing things useful for the future of the human race'.

(2) *Cogitationes de natura rerum* (1604, unpublished): a direct presentation of Democritean materialistic naturalism.

(3) *Cogitationes de scientia humana* (1605, unpublished): Bacon develops two theories expounded in (2) in his interpretations of fables of Proteus and Saturn.

(4) *Advancement of Learning* (published 1605): 'a mixture of new conceits and old', according to Bacon, that may serve as a key to the *Instauratio magna*. He suggests here that the fable preceded the interpretation and criticises Chrysippus for reading stoical interpretations into the classical poets. But he will 'interpose no opinion' as to whether 'all the fables and fictions of the poets were but pleasure and not figure'.

(5) *Cogitata et visa* (1607, unpublished): a reversal to attitude (1) but less violent and with greater historical awareness. Bacon attacks those who 'insincerely' refer their theories to ancient times in order to 'invest them with a certain solemnity'.

(6) *Redargutio philosophiarum* (1608, unpublished): to the attacks of (5) Bacon adds 'in passing' the hypothesis of ancient fables being 'sacred survivals of better times'. But he denies the importance of such an hypothesis.

(7) *De sapientia veterum* (published in 1609): the waverings of (4) and the hypothesis of (6) have become firm convictions: the veil of fables is a link between ancient wisdom and the later centuries. The attempt initiated in (3) assumes here vast proportions. The philosophical theories of (2), (3), (5), (6) and earlier works are woven into Bacon's interpretations of classical myths.[48]

In this section we have tried to expose Bacon's motives for modifying his views on the allegorical value of myths between 1605 and 1609—or more precisely between 1607 and 1608.

After wavering in the *Advancement of Learning*, in the preface to the *De sapientia veturum* he finally asserted his allegiance to the allegorical tradition.

The four philosophical themes in the 'De sapientia veterum'

Apart from a number of psychological and moral reflections— some of which were later expounded in the second and third editions of the *Essays*—there are four main philosophical themes in the *De sapientia veterum*:

(*a*) the importance of distinguishing philosophical from theological enquiry and matters of science from matters of faith;

(*b*) the advantages of materialistic naturalism;

(*c*) the function of philosophical research and the need for method;

(*d*) the defence of a political realism, inspired by Machiavelli.

Though these themes were present in Bacon's earlier works, in the *De sapientia* they are curiously interwoven and acquire a new significance.[49]

The myths of Pentheus and of Prometheus or the distinction between science and religion

Bacon interpreted the myths of Pentheus and of Prometheus as illustrating his earlier theories on the distinction between religion and science and the notion expressed in *Cogitata et visa* that the mingling of things human and things Divine prompted by the alliance of Aristotelianism and theology was more pernicious than an open warfare between science and religion; that the inevitable offspring of such an alliance were spurious sciences and religions; that theology tended to invest scientific inventions with a religious significance; and that scientific research was diverted from its true path, attempting the impossible, for 'God is only self-like having nothing in common with any creature other than in shadow and trope'.[50]

In the myth of *Acteon and Prometheus or Curiosity* Prometheus, spying from the branches of a tree, discovers the secret rites of

Bacchus, and is deprived of his reason and condemned to wander aimlessly between twin visions of Thebes and of the sun without ever reaching the former. This symbolised for Bacon the punishment that awaited those who ignored their mortal condition and tried 'by the heights of nature and philosophy' to attain the divine mystery. They were chastised by their own greed which rendered them prone to inconstancy and indecision, so that their works and their thoughts were vain: 'since the light of nature is one thing and the light of Divinity another they are as men that see two suns'.[51]

In the myth *Prometheus or the Human Condition* the same moral was more vividly stressed. Among other crimes Prometheus would have done violence to the divine Minerva and his terrible fate was that which attends the over-ambitious scientist who would penetrate the divine mysteries with sense and reason.

> Men must soberly and modestly distinguish between things divine and human, between the oracles of sense and of faith: unless they mean to have at once a heretical religion and a fabulous philosophy.[52]

Materialistic naturalism in the myths of Pan and of Cupid

In the *Advancement of Learning*, Bacon placed next to the aspect of physics concerning 'all variety and particularity of things'—later expanded in the *De augumentis*—the doctrine 'touching the contexture and configuration of things' and the doctrine 'concerning the principles and originals of things'.[53] The fables of Saturn (discussed above) and of Pan (*Pan sive natura*) illustrate the first doctrine, that of Cupid (*Cupido sive atomus*), the second.

'Pan, as the word declares, represents the universal frame, or Nature.' Pan was variously described as the son of Mercury and the issue of Penelope's 'promiscuous intercourse' with the suitors. Likewise the universe was thought to originate from the Divine Word or from the 'seeds of things mixed and confused together'. According to a third source, however, Pan was the son of Jove and Hera—(the Greeks here seem to have been influenced by the Hebrew mysteries which may have reached them through the Egyptians)—and this refers to an image of the world subjected, by the Fall, to corruption and death. Thus Pan, said Bacon, was born of the Word of God, and of matter—

created by God—to the confusion of which the Fall contributed.[54]

Pan's relationship to the Parcae symbolises the sequence of natural causes: birth, continuation, and death, that are the fate of all things. His pointed horns, touching the sky, represent the pyramid of the universe. His partly goat-like form indicates the difference between celestial and terrestrial bodies,[55] and also the dual nature of all living matter that is always made up of two species: man and beast, beast and plant, plant and inanimate object. The meaning of the fable is finally made clear by the fact that Pan is the god of the hunt: every natural process, each movement and development 'is nothing else than a hunt. For the sciences and arts hunt after their works.'

Pan's discovery of Ceres, for whom all the gods had searched in vain, shows that for useful discoveries abstract philosophers—symbolised by the greater gods—are less helpful than Pan, or experience and knowledge of nature. Unlike the other gods, Pan has no amorous relations outside his union with the nymph Echo, and no descendants. This is because nature, being all things, can neither love nor desire anything, with the one possible exception of 'discourses'. Of all the many 'voices' of the world Pan elected Echo for his wife, who stands for that philosophy which faithfully reproduces the voice of nature, is only a reflection, a resonance, with no additional ornament. Pan's sterility is proof of the perfection and self-sufficiency of nature, whose parts generate one from the other, but who, as a whole can generate nothing. The maiden Iambe, sometimes erroneously presumed to be Pan's daughter, is a symbol of these false, hybrid doctrines of nature that overrun the world and which, though sometimes amusing, are more often irksome.

Bacon's interpretation of the Cupid myth—later expanded in the *De principiis*—presents three points of interest: an emphasis on mechanistic views that were already present in the fables of Saturn, Proteus, and Pan; a critical tendency towards Greek—and more especially Democritean—philosophy; a definite allegiance to atomism. Cupid is the most ancient of all the gods, and thus of all things except for Chaos, his coeval, who was never promoted to the state of a divinity. Though he was thought by some to be the son of the Night, he had no parents. He is a symbol of 'the appetite or instinct of primal matter

. . . the natural motion of the atom; which is indeed the original and unique force that constitutes and fashions all things out of matter'. The movement of atoms is not generated and is, after God, 'the cause of causes, itself without cause'. Thus Cupid was said to have been hatched from an egg by the impenetrable Night, because it is probably beyond human power to understand the 'summary law of nature', for which Cupid stands, whose repetition and multiplication is the source of all natural things.

Though the Greek philosophers had no amount of insight into material principles they were 'negligent and languid' in their investigations of the principles of motion. The peripatetic theory of stimulus as 'deprivation' 'is little more than words, a name for the thing rather than a description of it'; Democritus' theory does not explain the rotation of celestial bodies; and the theory of Epicurus about the 'decrease of atoms' is a gratuitous assumption equivalent to a confession of ignorance.

Cupid is represented as a young boy to indicate the simplicity of the 'seeds' of things; he is naked to show that atoms have no physical qualities perceptible to the senses; he is armed with arrows because of the atom's long-range action in space; and lastly he is blind like Providence and all the more wonderful on account of this infirmity that also precludes final causes from the sphere of natural philosophy.

In the *Cogitationes de natura rerum*, where Bacon first opposes his materialism to Platonic and Aristotelian physics, he had already suggested that atomism and atomic movement might account for the infinite diversity of nature, though he refuted the Democritean theory of a diversity in the configuration of atoms. The choice here between Democritus and Pythagoras— for whom this diversity did not exist—was determined for Bacon by his 'alchemistic' attitude to the problem of transmutation. He believed that all substances being composed of identical particles, enquiries should be made into the 'appetites' and 'inclinations' of things, not into their static principles.

In his interpretation of the Cupid myth Bacon's reservations concerning Democritean physics are based on its failure to explain the contraction and expansion of bodies. Such reservations were related to Bacon's belief in a *vacuum commistum* (or 'interspersed in the pores of bodies') accounting for the contraction, expansion, and variations in the space occupied by bodies. Indeed, this theory—which is attributed to Eronus of Alexandria—appeared to Bacon to be the only possible explanation of all movement, and was implicit in his interpretation of the 'archer' Cupid. His views on the *vacuum coacervatum* (or 'collected in one place') were not explicitly defined:

> Whoever maintains the theory of the atom and the vacuum—even though he suppose the vacuum not to be collected by itself but intermingled through space—necessarily implies the action of the virtue of the atom at a distance.

Bacon never took up a definite position as to the existence of a vacuum,[56] and this uncertainty was reflected in his contradictory theories of physical reality. From 1604 to 1609 he saw movement as the primal quality of bodies. In the *Filum labirinthi sive inquisitio legitima de motu* (1607) it was the key to nature's most hidden secrets. In the *Cogitationes* primal movements were nature's alphabet. Even in the *De sapientia veterum* traces of this attitude can be found. But later, Bacon's appreciation of movement—where the principles of natural structure are concerned—underwent a notable change, and with the elaboration of his doctrine of forms the departure from atomism became more pronounced. A comparison of his interpretation of the Cupid myth in the *De sapientia veterum* with that in *De principiis* sets the radical modification of his views on atoms and motion clearly in evidence.

In fact, the earlier interpretation bridges the gap between Bacon's atomistic tendency and a new naturalism. Cupid represents the appetites, stimulus and natural atomic movement, but he also stands for the supreme law of nature. In the *Cogitationes* this same identification of appetites and natural law had been less explicitly stipulated; it was however, an anticipation of the notion—expressed later in the *New Organon* and in the *De augumentis*—of component natural forms regulating the activities of nature.

Bacon's uncertainties concerning the problem of the existence of a vacuum[57] stemmed from this ambiguous attitude which was compounded equally of his juvenile atomism and his later theory of forms. The postulation of a spacially conceived 'intermingled vacuum' could be only temporarily consistent with the essentially qualitatively formulated idea of vacuum. Little wonder therefore, if in the *New Organon*[58] and more decisively in the *Historia densi et rari* Bacon finally denied the existence of a vacuum of any kind.

The myths of Atalanta, the Sphinx, Orpheus, Prometheus, Dedalus, and Icarus, or the aims of philosophy

For Bacon, Pan's chosen bride Echo represented a chaste and humble philosophical attitude conforming faithfully to reality and experiment; and Pan the hunter was a symbol of the questing nature of art and culture. But such contrasting images really stood for the same notion if the hunt was seen as a methodical, persistent pursuit rather than as a casual adventure.

Bacon interpreted the Proteus myth as expressing the idea of nature forced into new shapes by art. In the myth of Erichthonius (*Erichtonius sive impostura*) he explained how this art should operate in order to achieve success. Vulcan, he said, attempting to violate Minerva and giving birth to the deformed Erichthonius, presented an image of a form of art which violates nature, producing imperfect and useless objects. This, said Bacon, was often the case 'among chemical productions and among mechanical subtleties and novelties', when those who strived for immediate success chose to oppose nature rather than humbly beg her assistance.

The fable of Atalanta (*Atalanta sive lucrum*)—outrun by Hippomenes who cunningly places three apples in her path knowing that she cannot resist stopping to eat them—was for Bacon another illustration of art's contest with nature. It attacks the foolish habit of abandoning the natural course of scientific enquiry for experiments aiming at immediate results.

The characteristics of scientific research are further outlined by Bacon in his interpretations of the Sphinx and the Orpheus fables (*Sphinx sive scientia, Orpheus sive philosophia*). Science, he wrote, besides being the exhausting race described in the fable of Atalanta, was also a riddle, ever to be solved anew. The Sphinx is depicted as proteiform to indicate science's numerous aims; the claws represent penetrating arguments; the importuning of travellers indicates the many occasions for scientific research that occur in the normal course of life. The 'questions and riddles' of science are inspired by the muses, and so long as they do not depart from them they can do no harm, because when science is purely contemplative 'the understanding is not oppressed or straitened by it, but is free to wander and expatiate' and uncertainty itself becomes a joy and a delight. But when riddles are appropriated by the Sphinx—that is by practical science—they become a cruel torment to the mind. Only he who, like Oedipus, solves the riddle of the Sphinx, can rule over nature and mankind, 'for the command over things natural—over bodies, medicine, mechanical powers and infinite others of this kind—is the one proper and ultimate end of true natural philosophy' and 'whoever has a thorough insight into the nature of man, may shape his fortune almost as he will, and is born for empire'. To attain this double end it is necessary, like Oedipus, to be lame so as to avoid approaching the Sphinx with undue haste.

Orpheus' two songs, one to gain the favour of the Manes, the other to charm wild beasts and forests, symbolised the twin aims of natural and moral philosophy. Bacon thought that the 'restitution and renovation of things corruptible' could only be achieved 'by due and exquisite attempering and adjustment of parts in nature as by harmony and perfect modulation of a lyre'. Orpheus' doomed quest for Euridice was a symbol for the impatient haste of those who abandon the beaten track of experiment. When philosophers perceive that they have been ousted in the contest with nature, like Orpheus after his discomfiture, they retire in solitude, then found cities and exert a civilising influence over mankind. The laceration of Orpheus by the bacchantes represented for Bacon the destruction of civilisation by wars and revolutions, entailing the destruction of literature and philosophy; little indeed of ancient cultures had survived the barbaric invasions.

Bacon's interpretation of the myth of Prometheus (*Prometheus sive status hominis*) as depicting the central position of man in the universe and his constructive powers, is of distinctly humanistic derivation.

He believed that all things were at man's service. Man uses the movements of the heavenly bodies to measure time; he harnesses the winds to his ships and machines; from plants he extracts clothing, food, and medicine; the beasts assist him in his labour and provide exercise and sport.[59] Man is the most complex of all creatures and justly called by the ancients *mundus minor*. The alchemists—too literal in their interpretation of this definition—distorted its original meaning; yet the extraordinary wealth of the human faculties undoubtedly derives from man's infinite complexity. On the other hand, man is born naked, defenceless and incapable of fending for himself: his revolt against this condition is symbolised by Prometheus' stealing fire from heaven, a theft which made human operations—such as the mechanical arts and science—possible. Man responded to Prometheus' gift with abject ingratitude, denouncing him to Jove who, in exchange, allowed mankind to preserve the use of fire; those who exalt human arts and sciences are debarred from further progress; it is only by denouncing science, as Prometheus was denounced, that invention and discovery are stimulated; the gods rejoice in hearing nature and science accused, and they respond with new gifts. Thus it was more profitable to mankind to denounce Prometheus than to extol their acquisition, for faith in one's own wealth is the cause of most poverty. Jove's gift was strapped to the saddle of a slow-plodding ass, and this represents the slow and methodical type of experimental research as opposed to the hasty procedure of abstract philosophy—for empiricism and dogmatism can never be reconciled. The torch-races in honour of Prometheus have long been discontinued, but it would be well if they were resumed, for progress can only be achieved by teams of scientists and not by solitary seekers: it is high time that men discard the leadership of an élite to work in co-operation.[60]

Farrington is right in observing that the numerous critics of Bacon's enthusiasm for the mechanical arts as such cannot have read his interpretation of the myth of Dedalus (*Dedalus sive mechanicus*) which he saw as a censure of 'illicit artificers' and of the evil and distorted uses to which the mechanical arts had sometimes been put.

For Bacon, technology and the mechanical arts were of infinite value to humanity, but also able to produce instruments of death and destruction surpassing even the legendary Minotaur in their ferocious cruelty. The thread devised by the builder of the labyrinth represented precisely that fidelity to experiment which would lead the scientist along the right track.

Lastly Bacon stressed the advantages of moderation in scientific research in his interpretation of the myth of Icarus, Scylla and Charybdis (*Icarus volans, item Scilla et Charybdis sive via media*). According to Bacon, except in the sphere of politics moderation was always to be recommended; it was the only means of achieving a truly ethical life; and it would save science and technology from shipwreck on the rocks of over-nice distinctions or in the whirlpools of universal abstractions.

Proserpine and Deucalion and the magico-alchemical tradition

There were already traces of an alchemical influence in Bacon's interpretation of the Proteus myth where the transmutation of matter depended upon a process of 'isolation'—to which matter reacted marvellously. But in the fables of Proserpine (*Proserpine sive spiritus*) and of Deucalion (*Deucalion sive restitutio*) the influence is predominant.

For Bacon, Proserpine, wife of Pluto and queen of the Underworld, besides representing the force governing all stages of vegetation, was also the hidden power by which all earthly things are generated and to which they return. She was the 'spirit' of all substances; which in metals and minerals is imprisoned, or 'detained', by constraint and obstruction of the sheer mass; while in vegetable and animal bodies, because of their lesser density, it must be induced to remain 'by the assistance of adequate nourishment'. Proserpine was represented as the queen of the Under-world who was raped by Pluto, because the spirit is not progressively, but violently joined to a substance as the great billows of the sea disintegrate into foam when the air is raped by the waters.

Here too, however, Bacon appended a warning against the presumption of alchemist and magician. In the olden days, he said, the preservation and resurrection of bodies was not considered impossible, but only extremely arduous and very rarely achieved. The ancient allegory of a golden bough hidden among the branches of an impenetrable forest signifies precisely that this sort of thing could not be brought about by a simple drug or by any easy and natural means. Thus those—alas too numerous—who believed that a substance could be miraculously renewed by its very decomposition were doomed to failure and disappointment. The myth of Deucalion and Pyrrha, sole survivors of the flood, who, advised by an oracle to throw over their shoulders 'the bones of their mother', finally realise that these are the stones of Mother Earth, attacked, according to Bacon, the absurd belief in a miraculous renovation of bodies rising, like the phoenix, from their ashes. Indeed, the majority of alchemists—for whom the discovery of the philosophers' stone, capable of arresting the effects of death and decomposition, was indispensible for the fabrication of gold—openly acknowledged the art of resuscitating organic substances from their particular elements in decomposition. Bacon categorically denied the possibility of a philosophers' stone and of a regeneration of this kind. The latter was in complete contradiction to his physical theories, where the loss of spirit and 'humidity' entailed a change of molecular structure which, in all probability, modified the atomic structure as well. We must realise, wrote Bacon, that the corrupt parts have completed their circuit and are entirely inapt for regeneration.

Bacon's interpretation of the myth of Erichthonius now becomes clear. When Vulcan vainly attempted to rape Minerva his seed was spread on the earth and generated Erichthonius, a beautiful child down to the waist from whence his body tapered away in the shape of a worm; when art violates nature, striving against her, it cannot achieve its aims but brings forth monsters. The basic error of chemical and mechanical productions is not that they strive to dominate nature, but the method by which they attempt to do so; they rape Minerva instead of winning her over.

Bacon opposed to the alchemists' impatient, dogmatic and illusory methods of research, an attitude of humble respect for nature, patient and plodding (see the myth of Atalanta). He had nothing against the *aims* of such violations, nor against the premiss of a substantial identity and correspondence between the elements of a living substance. What he attacked was a presumption to dominate nature by extrinsic, miraculous interventions that would by-pass human labour and spare the sweat of the human brow. To attain true results, said Bacon, a happy medium is required between the arrogance of miracle-makers and the slothful unadventurousness of those who are content with the human lot.

Ethico-psychological themes in the myths of Cassandra, Nemesis, Memnon, Tithonus, Dionysos, the Sirens and Pandora's box

Bacon used the following myths to outline a psychological phenomenology and to illustrate, by a portrayal of distinctive characters, certain basic aspects of his ethics. Unlike the preceding interpretations, these passages from the *De sapientia veterum* recall the *Essays*—where indeed many of the themes were enlarged in the later editions.

The myth of Cassandra (*Cassandra sive parrhesia*)—on whom Apollo bestowed the gift of prophecy, but made it useless by causing her prophecies never to be believed—illustrated for Bacon the futility of advice given at random by those who could not adapt their speech to their audience and ignored the fact that there is a time to speak and a time to be silent. Cato of Utica was an example of this type of individual.

For Bacon Nemesis (*Nemesis sive vices rerum*) was a symbol for the ever-changing destiny of man. She was the child of Ocean and of Night, that is, of eternal change and of the mysteries of divine judgement. She was crowned by popular malice that always rejoices when power is brought to its knees. Those who attained a lasting felicity were exposed to her unrelenting attacks; she spared only the young dead, who form the subject of the fable of Memnon (*Memnon sive praematuras*), son of Aurora, killed by Achilles. Like him, those who died in adolescence had had to contend with things greater and stronger than themselves and had succumbed. The lamentations for the premature death of these youths were like the song of the birds sent by Jove to Memnon's funeral.

Three fables served to illustrate human passions: *Tithonus sive satias*, *Dionysus sive cupiditas*, and *Sirenes sive voluptas*. Tithonus was loved by the dawn goddess who begged Jove to make him immortal but omitted to obtain eternal youth for him. Thus Tithonus became the most unhappy of men till Jove, relenting, turned him into a grasshopper. According to Bacon this fable was a clever representation of pleasure, for when man is a prey to pleasure he tends to believe his condition will be everlasting and to forget all else; but satiety soon sets in, pleasure has no more charm, and all that remains are memories and tales of pleasures past. Old men and warriors love to recount their prowess, but like grasshoppers, their only liveliness is in their voice

Bacon declared that the fable of Dionysos, referring to custom had nothing to equal it in moral philosophy. Dionysos was the son of Jove and of Semele who, after conceiving him was consumed by Jove's lightning when he appeared to her in godly form. The unborn child was rescued from the ashes by his father who placed him in his thigh until his birth, when he handed him over to Proserpine, queen of Hades, to bring up. Dionysos was of effeminate appearance; he died, was buried, and rose again; he was the god of the vine and of wine; his conquests spread to the confines of India; he married Ariadne who had been abandoned by Theseus; the muses were of his escort, but he was the object of a fanatical, corrupt, and sometimes cruel cult; Pantheus and Orpheus were killed and dismembered by his followers; he is sometimes confused with Jove. Dionysos stands for passion; Semele, his mother, for superficial good. Passion is bred in the nether parts of man—like Dionysos in Jove's thigh—and torments those who harbour it, thriving in darkness and gloom as he did in the Under-world; it is masculine in its urgency, but feminine in its helplessness, and when spent it will rekindle itself. Inventions and discoveries are often the fruit of passion, as with the vine and wine—and its empire is for ever increasing. Passion covets that which man has rejected —thus Dionysos marries the abandoned Ariadne—and there is always a doctrine to justify it (the escort of Muses). The murders of Pentheus and Orpheus represent passion's antagonism for learning and advice. The confusion of Dionysos with Jove shows that great things are sometimes accomplished by latent passions and secret covetousness as well as by real virtue and greatness, so that it is not always possible to tell what comes from Dionysos and what from Jove.

Finally, interpreting the myth of the Sirens, Bacon exposed the dangers of lust and proposed three ways of resisting temptation. When Odysseus' ship was about to pass the island of the Sirens he stopped up his companions' ears with wax so that they should not hear their song and be lured to destruction; but he had himself bound to the mast, for he wished to hear them without risk. Orpheus, on the other hand, was saved by music, for he went among the Sirens playing his lyre and singing songs

of praise to the gods and so heard them not. The first two instances represent philosophy, the third religion. Only lowly
spirits, however, follow the companions of Odysseus and use
philosophy to shut out the world and avoid the dangers of sin;
but the strong-minded, like Odysseus himself, can approach
temptation as observers without being ensnared. But the best
and surest protection is that of religion, for like the song of
Orpheus, meditation on holy matters overcomes temptation by
its beauty, and there is no need for violent measures.

Thus philosophy enables man to resist his passions either by
ignoring them or by acknowledging their existence and overcoming them ethically and rationally. The myth of Pandora's
box—incorporated by Bacon in the fable of Prometheus—
illustrates these two attitudes, stressing their respective limitations.

Jove, wishing to punish Prometheus' arrogance through the
sufferings of mankind, instructed Vulcan to fashion the lovely
Pandora to whom the gods entrusted a little box containing all
possible ills and misfortunes, and lastly, beneath the rest, hope.
The wary Prometheus refused to open this box when Pandora
proffered it, but not so his brother, the rash Epimetheus; so
evil was spread over the earth and only hope remained for
Epimetheus. Then Jove, infuriated by Prometheus' wariness,
bore him off to the Caucasus where he was chained to a pillar
and an eagle each day devoured his liver, which was restored
each night. In the end Hercules, crossing the ocean in an earthen
vessel, set Prometheus free.

Pandora stands for the passions that bring all evil in their
wake and are a menace to individuals and states alike. Epimetheus is the unwary man who thinks only of present pleasures
and suffers in consequence all kinds of misfortunes with vain
hope his only consolation. Prometheus, on the other hand,
represents prudence and a stoic resistance to the onslaught of
evil; yet such an attitude implies the sacrifice of many pleasures, and those who adopt it are tormented and consumed
with anxiety, as Prometheus was by the eagle, and have peace
only in their nightly slumber. Hercules is strength and consistency, uniting the daring of Epimetheus to Prometheus' wariness. He 'foresees without fear, enjoys without fastidiousness and
bears without impatience'. But his strength is not congenital:

it derives from the sun beyond the oceans, and is born from reflections on human inconstancy; he crosses the ocean in a fragile earthen vessel so that man's relative frailty may not be invoked as an excuse for his failings. The ideal attitude for which Hercules stands was epitomised in the following lines by Seneca: 'It is true greatness to have in one the frailty of man and the security of god.'

In 1603, in the *Valerius Terminus*, Bacon had already stated the advantage of replacing traditional disputations on the nature of the highest virtue by a moral naturalism based on realistic historical and psychological research into moral phenomena. And once again he stressed the distinction between the aims of revealed theology and those of philosophy. The task of defining the highest virtue—identified by Bacon with the Christian ideal of 'charitas'—devolved to theology; while realistic philosophic enquiry should concentrate on the discovery of a realistic virtue upon which human society could be established. The first law of nature, *bonum communionis*, was thus identified by Bacon with the first law of the Christian faith; indeed, for him this last had an essentially moderating function. The best proof of his rigidly empirico-phenomenological interpretation of ethics is his allegiance to Machiavelli's conception of moral politics and his gratitude to the latter expressed in the *Advancement of Learning*.

In the sphere of ethics as in that of theoretical science Bacon strove to replace traditional philosophy by a practical method dealing directly with reality. He wrote in 1605 that in matters of morals, philosophers had behaved like a teacher of caligraphy who shows his pupils the shapes of letters without instructing them in the art of wielding a pen. These philosophers had exhibited wondrous models and elaborated vast programmes for the virtue and well-being of humanity: they had placed in the hands of man a well-designed target, omitting to instruct him in the art of taking aim. The new philosophy must concentrate, on the other hand, on the training and drill required to achieve public and private good. Moral, like scientific, theories are vain when they are not directed towards practical issues and when they ignore those all-important facts that traditional philosophers considered unworthy of their attention. Bacon's *Georgics of the Soul* aspired to just such a practical, concrete attainment of virtue. This doctrine, strongly influenced by the ethics of Aristotle, excepting where moralistic theories are concerned, is in three parts: a study of characters (where poets and historians had been more successful than philosophers); a study of human passions; a method for the control of passions.

The typical mixture of psychological and moral themes in the group of myths examined above was not the result of a mere literary preoccupation, since the study of human nature was an essential factor of Bacon's ethics. He refuted the strict coherence of transcendental ethics, declaring that the primal preoccupation of any moral doctrine should be human nature, which is responsible for all actions whether good or evil. The only way of attaining the third part of the *Georgics*—the control of passion—is by a form of analysis which ignores a priori theories of virtue.

With characteristic clarity Bacon interpreted the myth of Dionysos as representing the importance and the function of the passions, seen here as a basic element for the evolution of man. The aim of moral science is primarily, for Bacon, to understand how certain passions can be employed to overcome others and thus lay the foundations for a moral individual and social existence: by exalting such passions as hope and fear society curbs and subdues the more dangerous passions; and here moral and political research coincide. And Bacon's allegiance to a form of naturalism strongly reminiscent of Machiavelli's was most evident precisely in the sphere of politics.

Political realism in the fables of Metis, the Cyclopes, Juno's suitor, Endymion, Narcissus, Actaeon, Perseus, Achelous, Diomedes, and the Styx

Bacon's interpretation of the Cyclopes fable (*Cyclops sive ministri terroris*)—like that of Metis, whose Machiavellian derivations have been discussed earlier—illustrates the art of ruling and the relations of ruler and ministers. The Cyclopes assassinate Aesclepius at the bidding of Jove who does not attempt to protect them later from the avenging thunderbolts of Apollo. Thus ruthless ministers are employed by their sovereign in times of crisis when sanguinary measures are required; but once their task is accomplished they are left to the mercy of the avenging mob which, unaware of the sovereign's true responsibility, acclaims and honours him. It is interesting to note the parallel between this interpretation of Bacon's and the following passage from Machiavelli's *The Prince*, where he describes Cesare Borgia's method of pacifying the province of Romagna:

> . . . and found . . . that the province was rife with brigandage, factions, and every sort of abuse. He decided therefore that it needed good government to pacify it and make it obedient to the sovereign authority. So he placed there messer Remirro de Orco, a cruel, efficient man, to whom he entrusted the fullest powers. In a short time this Remirro pacified and unified the Romagna, winning great credit for himself. Then the duke decided that there was no need for this excessive authority, which might grow intolerable, and he established in the centre of the province a civil tribunal under an eminent president, on which every city had its own representative. Knowing also that the severities of the past had earned him a certain amount of hatred, to purge the minds of the people and to win them over completely he determined to show them that if cruelties had been inflicted they were not his doing but prompted by the harsh nature of his minister. Cesare waited for his opportunity; then, one morning, Remirro's body was found cut in two pieces on the piazza at Cesena, with a block of wood and a bloody knife beside it. The brutality of this spectacle kept the people of Romagna for a time appeased and stupified.[61]

The theories of Machiavelli and Guicciardini seem to have contributed in as great a measure as his own experience at court to Bacon's realistic interpretations of myths, illustrating the more intimate relationship of a sovereign to his minister.

The Moon's passion for the sleeping Endymion (*Endymion sive gratiosus*) represents the attitude of kings who are always diffident and wary of men 'that are perspicacious and curious', preferring those with a less lively intelligence who support their every whim without question, and are blind to their misdeeds as though their eyes were closed in slumber. It is only in the presence of such men that the king can occasionally discard his mask and be himself. They will never attain the high posts of government, but they have gifts and honours showered upon them. Thus Tiberius' favourites were those wise enough to ignore his conduct; and the same applies to the favourites of Louis XI of France.

Bacon's interpretation of the myth of Actaeon (*Actaeon et Pentheus sive curiosus*) depicts the fate that befalls those who attempt to penetrate state secrets: Actaeon, chancing to see Diana unclothed was turned into a stag and devoured by hounds. Thus he who discovers the secrets of state is condemned to a life of fear and foreboding until his own servants, turned traitors to please the king, falsely accuse him, and his fate is sealed.

The best way to succeed with those who are in power is that followed by Jove (*Procus Junonis sive dedecus*) who took the form of a 'wretched cuckoo drenched with rain' to gain the favours of Juno: one should renounce all public acknowledgements, discarding every symbol of status and standing. The powerful are usually ungifted, malicious, and vain, and any attempt at approaching them by other means is doomed to failure; it is not enough to honour them outwardly, total subjection is generally required.

In his essay *Of Nobility* Bacon declared that a 'commixture of good and evil art' is essential to those who wish to reach the top of the social scale. But in the myth of Narcissus (*Narcissus sive philautia*) he saw the portrayal of a type of beautiful, gifted individual who is so enthralled with himself that he has no need for public acknowledgement. Indeed, the rebuffs and hardships with which political life is fraught could only unsettle their fragile and tender souls. In their solitary, sheltered lives, flattered and encouraged by a few chosen friends, they become enamoured of their own image, and any vigour or creativity they may have possessed dwindles away. Narcissus, taking the form of that flower, sacred to the gods of Avernus, which bears his name, is an image of such men, who, after a vain and futile existence, disappear without trace.

Thus the life of a Narcissus is opposed to that 'commixture of evil and good arts' required for social success. Even in the sphere of politics Bacon turned from Aristotelian ethics and the primacy of contemplation towards action. All Aristotle's arguments in favour of the contemplative life concern the dignity and satisfaction of the individual and not the good of the community, said Bacon, for whom public has precedence over private life, since no one is entitled to the role of spectator in the theatre of the world. The only commendable reason for desiring power is that it makes good actions possible; for good intentions—though welcome to God—are of no more advantage to others than mere dreams if they are not put into action, and this can be done more easily by those who hold responsible and powerful positions.

This is how Bacon, in his essay *Of Great Place*, settled the old moral controversy on the advantages of public or private life and the philosopher's role in politics. But, he added, this position of power has also its share of dangers, suffering, and threefold servitude to the king, public opinion, and business. The powerful can only imagine that they are happy by trying to see themselves through the eyes of others, but deep down they will always know it is an illusion. Even in this essay, however, though he admitted the dangers and difficulties of public life, Bacon persisted in denying the advantages of a self-centered existence that is socially unfruitful.

The myths examined above show very clearly how Bacon's ethics and politics overlap. In his *Faber fortunae* (maker of fortune, i.e. achievement of personal success) he endeavoured to encompass private as well as public affairs in his theory of action, the realism of which ranks him unequivocally beside Machiavelli and Guicciardini.

Bacon expressed his personal views on offensive, defensive, civil, and religious wars, in a group of four myths: *Perseus sive bellum, Achelous sive proclium, Typhon sive rebellis, Diomedes sive zelus.*

In his interpretation of the Perseus myth Bacon declared that to extend an empire is very different from increasing one's private fortune. For instance, it is a mistake to attempt the invasion of neighbouring states, for against the often illusory advantages of accessibility one must consider the favourable occasion and the ease and profit of an enterprise. Thus if one attacks a distant nation the enemy is unacquainted with the invader's arms and methods and cannot easily retaliate by an invasion. Besides, where neighbouring states are concerned the choice of an occasion is far more restricted than if one goes further afield where there are better chances of finding a state whose military discipline is lax, whose strength is spent, or that is divided by civil discord. On the other hand the motives for starting a war should have every appearance of honour and justice, because this increases the fighters' impetuousity and helps the civil population to bear hardship and want. In this respect the best wars are fought for the overthrow of tyranny. Lastly, before launching an attack, one's own strength should be carefully estimated to avoid the danger of attempting more than one can realise. Victory depends upon speed, the art of disguising one's intentions, unity of command, and a fore-knowledge of the enemy's plans.

The defensive tactics used against the invader of a country are illustrated in the myth of Achelous, who, wrestling with Hercules for the possession of Deinira, changed himself into a bull. For the assailant has always but one form, while he who awaits the enemy must be ever prepared to assume new and different forms. The defender of his land, building fortifications, directing the peasants to the cities, blowing up bridges, storing provisions, and placing his men at strategic points, is like a mad bull preparing to strike. The invader prefers an open battle for he dreads to be stationary and idle in a hostile land; if he is victorious the horn of plenty is his, as he sacks the provinces and the cities abandoned by the terror-struck population that has fled to the strongholds. And this is why Hercules broke off one of Ache-lous' horns.

The story of Typhon is about civil war and the changing fortunes of princes. Juno, jealous of Jove who had given birth to Pallas Athene, wanted to have a son without Jove's participation. She shook the earth and brought forth a monster, Typhon, with a hundred heads, and claws of iron, who was suckled by a snake. When Typhon grew to manhood he declared war on Jove, was victorious and cut off the tendons of his victim's hands and feet. Mercury stole the tendons from Typhon and returned them to Jove who struck Typhon with a thunderbolt, then hurled Mount Etna at him, crushing him to death. Kings, said Bacon, should always be as one with their subjects, like Jove and Juno. But they are sometimes so intoxicated with power that they become despots, deaf to the wishes of the assembly, and acting only according to their own inclination. However, their subjects will not stand this for long, and rallying under some leader begin to revolt (Typhon's childhood).

Murmurs of discontent soon find substance in the mob's malevo-
lence and lead to open rebellion and disaster for subjects and
sovereign alike. The division of power (Typhon's hundred
heads), pestilence (the belt of serpents), massacre and rape (his
iron claws), force the king to flee from his country, renouncing
his power and might (Typhon's theft of Jove's tendons). With
the help of wise men (Mercury) who rekindle the people's
sympathies, kings may regain their power (the restitution of
Jove's tendons). Kings always try to avoid an open conflict and
to discredit the rebels, and if they are successful in doing so these
are reduced to vain threats (the hissing of serpents) and then, in
their turn, to flight. Now is the king's chance to crush them and
stifle the rebellion (the hurling of Mount Etna).

With the interpretation of the fable of Diomede Bacon took
his place among the supporters of religious tolerance. But
whereas, from Aconcio to the Socinis, those who opposed the
dogmatism of the established church did so either because they
believed in the triumph of a higher religious truth for which
trifling controversies were 'stratagems of the Devil', or for an
ideal of tolerance inspired by the Enlightenment or liberalism,
Bacon's motive was simply the futility of religious oppression.[62]
And here again the parallel with Machiavelli is evident: the
mob soon tires of cheering the persecutors of a religious creed,
for if the followers of this creed increase, the persecutors, from
being defenders of the one and only truth, become figures of
infamy and horror. Indeed, the lamentations of the martyrs
survive in men's souls for generations. It is more politic, therefore
even where the creed is depraved, to oppose it with logic, doctrine, and example rather than with fire and the sword.

But Machiavelli's influence is strongest in Bacon's interpretation of the myth of the Styx (*Styx sive foedera*) with its analysis
of international relations. In the olden days oaths were sworn
by the Styx—the winding river of the Under-world that en-
circles the realm of Dis—and not by the gods. Thus the treaties
of kings, solemn and sacred as they seem, are seldom more than
a mere formality, not a pledge of mutual trust. Even the ties of
mutual favours or of kinship cannot withstand the kings'
thirst for power, and as there is no authority above their own to
which they must refer their actions, there is never any lack of
pretexts for transgressing a pact and imposing their will. In

such circumstances the only guarantee for the fulfilment of a treaty is necessity (the Styx) and the mutual dependence of the contracting parties.

This notion of necessity and mutual dependence was expressed by the Athenian Iphicrates. In answer to the Spartans' proposal of innumerable precautions and sanctions to ensure the execution of a treaty he said, 'There is only one bond and security that can hold between you and us: you must prove that you have yielded so much into our hands that you cannot hurt us if you would.' According to Bacon these words sum up the requirements of interdependence and balance of power that are essential to the relations between states: only when a state is endangered by its own violation of a pact, is a pact truly a pact and an oath an oath.[63]

Bacon's attitude to allegory in the 'De augumentis'

During the eleven years that elapsed between the publication of the *De sapientia veterum* (1609) and that of the *Instauratio magna* (1620) Bacon—involved in political affairs where his ascendency had reached its peak—continued to work for long spells at the composition of the *New Organon*, but only published the second volume of his *Essays*.

As we have seen, the vast programme of works outlined in the *Distributio operis* of 1620 was never completed. After publishing the *New Organon* which formed the second part of the *Instauratio magna*, Bacon felt compelled to dedicate all his time to defining and classifying the arts and sciences, as a first step towards his reform of learning (*Partitiones scientiarum*). He was then sixty and, faced with the tremendous task of collecting material for the 'natural histories', he decided to make use of his previously published work *Of Proficience and Advancement of Learning* (1605). This book was written between 1603 and 1605— just after James I ascended the throne and while Bacon's hopes of enlisting his support were still fresh. It was divided into two parts, the first in praise of science; the second a classification of the arts and sciences. Originally conceived as 'some preparative or key for the better opening of the Instauration', the *Advancement* was thus integrated into the Great Reform itself— though Bacon describes it as 'a mixture of new conceits and old' in contrast to the novelty of conception of the *Instauratio magna*.[64]

In the process of rewriting and translation, this work underwent certain changes.[65] The second book was expanded to eight books in the *De augumentis* (II–IX); all the passages that might be offensive to Catholicism were either suppressed or attenuated; the sections on English history were curtailed; the treatment of mathematics was substantially altered; as to the interpretation of myths and allegory—with which this chapter is primarily concerned—a brief examination of those passages from the *De augumentis* dealing with parables, set beside the corresponding passages from the *Advancement of Learning* and the preface to the *De sapientia veterum* is well worth undertaking.

In the eighteenth chapter of the *De dignitate et augumentis scientiarum*, Book II (1623)[66] Bacon discussed the parable, comparing it favourably to narrative and drama, and stressing its sacred, venerable character. Religion, he said, makes use of the parable that establishes a manner of kinship between things human and things divine; it is not without faults, however, arising in most cases from a too easy-going interpretation of allegory. The ambiguity of the parable lies in its twofold function. It is at once a veil for hidden truths and a light thrown on truths already discovered: it is both 'the art of concealing' and a 'method of instruction'. In the latter guise it was much used in the olden days when even concepts that are now familiar were new and strange and had to be made accessible to the minds of men by example and image. In those days there were therefore many fables, parables, enigmas, and similitudes: the numbers of Pythagoras, the riddles of the Sphinx, Aesop's fables, the similitudes of the ancient sages; one, Menenius Agrippa, even told a fable to quell a rebellion as hieroglyphics were before letters, fables were before arguments, and to this day arguments lack the persuasiveness of the parable.

The other function of the parable—the art of concealing—is the exact opposite of the first, said Bacon, for it veils those things which are too awesome to appear undisguised. Thus the secrets of religion, philosophy, and politics are swathed in the veils of fables and parables. He went on to state his belief in the hidden meaning of many ancient fables. Though a similar

117

faith has been degraded by the allegiance of grammarians and simpletons, he wrote, this cannot make him waver or doubt. Indeed, it is certain that these fables are to be found in the most ancient of scriptures after the Holy Scriptures, and that they have not been invented by the authors themselves but received and transmitted from others and that they are as a gentle air blowing from the remotest past and caught up by the flutes and pipes of the Greeks.

In the past, he continued, fables have been interpreted by men who were unqualified for the task; for this reason the study of that philosophy which lies hidden in the classical fables is among the desiderata or gaps which must be filled by the new encyclopedia of learning. Bacon proposes three samples of interpretation to prove, that he could follow the paths he had mapped.

Such theories add little to those contained in the *Advancement of Learning* or the preface to the *De sapientia veterum*. However, these earlier texts, it will be remembered, were often contradictory where mythological tales were concerned, and at this point it may be opportune to summarise these contradictions. In the *Advancement* Bacon's attitude was basically undecided; he stressed the precedence of the fable to its allegorical content and condemned the 'vanity' of Chrysippus who asserted the contrary. In the *De sapientia*, on the other hand, Bacon's attacks on former interpreters of fables were aimed at their ignorance and inaccuracy. He admitted the possibility of a deep allegorical meaning around which the fable, in certain cases, was originally woven and therefore thought that there was some justification in trying to discover its hidden moral.

In this analysis of Bacon's evolution from 1603 to 1609 we have endeavoured to show the reasons for his change of attitude. But where his treatment of the parable in the *De augumentis* is concerned, it may be of interest to note that it is more a paraphrase of the theories contained in the *De sapientia* than a translation of passages from the *Advancement*. Indeed, the reservations and doubts expressed in the *Advancement* find no place in the *De augumentis*, while his belief in the hidden meaning of ancient fables is expressed here in almost identical terms to those of the *De sapientia veterum*.

It seems clear from what precedes that when, in the *De*

sapientia veterum, Bacon declared his allegiance to the 'allegorical' theory, he was not motivated solely by a desire to use a fashionable form of literature as a means for popularising his ideas of reform and his naturalism. Fourteen years later—after the publication of the *New Organon*—Bacon's attitude was unchanged, and in a work that was to be included in the *Instauratio magna* he reaffirmed his faith in the hidden wisdom of classical mythology.

Myths in the 'De augumentis': Pan, Perseus, Dionysos, Scylla, Atlas, Ixion, and Aesculpius

The three samples of interpretation given by Bacon in the *De augumentis*—Pan, Perseus, Dionysos—are amplified versions of interpretations figuring already in the *De sapientia veterum*. Apart from these he refers to four more myths which had not been mentioned previously.[67]

Scylla has the body of a beautiful young woman, but she is girded, from the waist down, by baying monsters. She therefore stood for those quibbling doctrines by which knowledge disintegrated in subtle probings and non-existent problems. Such doctrines found favour with the Scholastics whose knowledge was restricted to the writings of very few authors, and more particularly to those of Aristotle, who were ignorant of nature and of history and who laboriously wove an ornamental but valueless network of groundless theories. In their thirst for over-nice distinctions that were the death of truth, Bacon thought that these philosophers might be compared to one who, wishing to light up his hall, instead of raising high in the centre a powerful torch, creeps round the walls and into every corner with a flickering taper. Scylla, image of false science, had been made to stand for unfruitful, unrealistic intellectualism in the *Valerius Terminus*.

Bacon's attack on Scholastic subtleties was linked to the attack in the fifth book of the *De augumentis* on those who claim that wisdom is based on supposedly indisputable first principles. Man, wrote Bacon, desperately needs to find in himself something stable on which to build his intellectual edifice. Thus, like Aristotle who tried to discover the still point at the centre of all movement, he goes in search of a mythical Atlas to bear the burden of his unceasing waverings. But overhastiness leads to doubt and disappointment; certainty is only achieved by a suspension of judgement. The quest for Atlas ends in syllogistics: the art of finding, by way of intermediary terms, first principles considered as data and thus unassailable—while the intermediary terms are made accessible to all and sundry.

Bacon, we have seen, opposed a form of magic seeking for reality, to a form based on gullibility and superstition, extolling individual talent and secret gifts and diverting man from reality. For him Ixion—who, desiring Juno the goddess of power, begot the centaurs and the chimaera upon an elusive cloud— is a symbol for those who indulge in superstitious magic. How often are not men in their quest for power deluded by the clouds and vapours of their imaginations into forming vain hopes and monstrous aberrations!

In the second chapter of Book IV Bacon uses the myth of Aesculapius, son of Apollo the sun god, to define his attitude to medicine. He compares the delicate, varied structure of the human body to a fragile musical instrument whose harmonic power suffers from the slightest mishandling. From this image he passes to that of Apollo, god of music, and discusses the part played by conjecture in medicine and in politics. These arts, he says, unlike all others, must be judged only on results and on their immediate success. Hence the great number of impostors in medicine and politics. The poets were well aware of this when they gave Aesculapius Circe, the deceiver, for sister, who was also a child of the sun.

The 'De Principiis' and the myth of Cupid

Bacon wrote *De principiis atque originibus secundum fabulas Cupidinis et Coeli, sive Parmeniis, et Telesii et praecipue Democriti philosophia tractata in fabula Cupidine* in the last years of his life, after the announcement of the *Instauratio magna* and while he was striving, against time and circumstances, to complete his great plan of reform. It was certainly written after 1609, for it contains amplified versions of myths interpreted in the *De sapientia veterum* (the twelfth, *Coelum sive originis*, and the seventeenth, *Cupido sive atomus*); and as it contains some theories which are to be found in the *New Organon* it is probably ulterior to that work too. Further proof of its chronological position lies in the fact that it is not listed by Rawley among Bacon's works. He mentions, however, 'his revising his book *De sapientia veterum*'. Spedding interprets this—to our entire satisfaction— as referring not just to the three fables included in the *De augumentis*, but to a later and more complete revision of the whole work that was to have been incorporated—for surer preservation—in his *Moral and Civil writings*.[68] Thus the *De principiis*— unfinished and showing definite signs of hurried composition— was probably written as a series of notes for the revision of the *De sapientia veterum* around 1623–4.

In the *De principiis* Bacon, as we have seen, reinterpreted the myth of Cupid previously included in the *De sapientia veterum*. Chaos, coeval of Cupid, stands for 'the rude mass or conjugation of matter'; Cupid is 'matter itself and the force and nature thereof, the principle of things'; he is without parents for 'it is a thing positive and inexpliciable and must be taken absolutely as it is found and not judged by any previous conceptions'. Nothing has been more detrimental to natural philosophy than the search for Cupid's parents, for the searchers did not accept the principles of things that are in nature, receiving them as a positive doctrine based on experience, but vainly attempted to deduce them from the laws of discourse, dialectical or mathematical conclusions, or from fabrications of the mind that have nothing in common with reality. They believed that by casting these fabulous shadows they would discover a greater causal and demonstrative truth than that offered by the principles of reality which are revealed by simply observing nature.[69]

As in the *De sapientia veterum* Cupid is hatched from an egg by Nox, or Night. His essence—'the summary law of being and nature', or 'the force implanted by God in those first particles'— is a thing which 'the thoughts of man may graze but can hardly take in'. But:

> . . . That point concerning the egg of Nox bears a most apt reference to the demonstrations by which the Cupid is brought to light. For things concluded by affirmatives may be considered as the off-spring of light; whereas those concluded by negatives and exclusions are extorted and educed as it were of darkness and night. Now this Cupid is truly an egg hatched by Nox; for all the knowledge of him which is to be had proceeds by exclusions and

negatives; and proof made by exclusion is a kind of ignorance and, as it were, night, with regard to the thing included.[70]

Thus the theory of principles or elements is based on a method that proceeds by negatives and exclusions similar to that proposed in the *New Organon* for the discovery of form. If the mind tries to detect form by the method of affirmatives, wrote Bacon, it will only achieve phantoms, dubious principles, and ill-defined notions. God alone—who created them—and perhaps the angels, can know forms by the method of affirmatives. But such perceptions are beyond human power; man must start by the way of negatives and exclusions, and only after following it to its end may he at last define in the affirmative. Translating an abstract process into an alchemical image, Bacon adds that the form 'affirmative, solid, true and well defined' will be found at the end of the operation, as it were, at the bottom of a crucible.[71]

Thus the same method applies to the detection of the concept of form and of Cupid—the summary law of nature. The proof made by exclusion is like the Night, 'a kind of ignorance'; and, Bacon continues, Democritus rightly declared that atoms and their 'virtues' are like nothing that can be perceived by the senses, and he conceived them as 'of a dark and hidden nature'; they are not like sparks of fire, nor drops of water, nor bubbles of air, nor yet specks of dust; their virtue and form have also nothing of weight nor of lightness, of cold nor of heat, of density nor of rarity, of firmness nor of pliability, as such qualities appear in greater or compound substances. In the same way the movement of atoms is unlike the movement of compound substances: falling, expansion, contraction, impetus, attraction, and rotation. Yet 'in the body of the atom are the elements of all bodies and in the motion and virtue of the atom are the beginnings of all motions and virtues'. Thus the wisdom of the fable surpasses that of Democritus who is in contradiction with the fable and with himself. For he declared that the atom had two movements: descent and ascent, having picked these from among the characteristic movements of larger bodies. But as the atom is unlike all other bodies in virtue and in substance, so also is it unlike them in movement—and the fable, showing greater consistency than Democritus, conforms to this principle.[72]

However, the fable says, this process of negatives and exclusion does not last indefinitely, but only for as long as it takes Nox to hatch the egg; when Cupid emerges the time for affirmatives has come. Exclusions do not lead to affirmatives if we attempt to grasp the nature of God by means of the senses, but in the case of Cupid, we may achieve positive results. And it is not only the egg we must bring forth from the darkness of Nox, but Cupid must also emerge from the egg; the god is not an abstraction but a being who must be known individually.

The ancient philosophers saw matter—represented by Cupid —as possessing a form and positive qualities, not as a formless abstraction, which is how Plato and Aristotle came to see it. Plato and Aristotle's distinction of matter and form is a purely arbitrary notion giving rise to vain disputations and opening the way to such widely accepted abstractions as pure form, essence, or idea. Nearly all the ancient philosophers—Empedocles, Anaxagoras, Anaximenes, Heraclitus, Democritus— though they disagreed on other subjects, believed that matter was active and possessed a certain form, and that it imparted this form and included within itself the principles of motion.

In the fable Cupid is shown as a person to signify that matter has a form; and this notion tallies with the Holy Scriptures where God did not create matter but made heaven and earth out of unorganised matter.

Cupid, in the fable, is unclothed; therefore—as well as those who see matter as a formless abstraction—there are others who err in conceiving it as clothed, investing the principles of things with the qualities of objects that are perceived by the senses. Of these there are four different schools: the first believes in a single principle, or element, whose various manifestations are due to its inconstancy; the second sees it as basically single, fixed, and unvarying, and explains the variety of natural objects by their different sizes, shapes, and positions; the third talks of two or more elements variously compounded to make for a diversity of objects; while the last has solved the problem of natural plurality by an infinity of elements.

The first group clothed Cupid in veils: Thales' water, Anaximander's air, and Heraclitus' fire are either fabulous beings or compound substances presented as first principles. The third group, clothing Cupid in a tunic, goes even further astray: amongst them was Parmenides with his two elements, air and fire, and Telesius, his modern disciple. The fourth group (Anaxagoras), besides covering Cupid with a mantle, conceals his face under a mask; only the second group, which includes Democritus, shows Cupid in his natural unclothed form. Bacon's critique of the first group only is complete; he had postponed that of the fourth and, for the third, after offering four objections to the theory of Parmenides and Telesius, only discussed the first.[73]

Between Bacon's theory of physics in the *De sapientia veterum* and that contained in the *De principiis* there are certain discrepancies worthy of note. In the earlier work Cupid stood for 'the appetite or instinct of Primal Matter' or 'the natural motion of the atom', the 'impetus' in the elements of matter. In the *De principiis* he is only the 'virtue' or 'action' of matter, but he is the actual *matter* or *nature* of the atom. Motion, in the *De sapientia*, is the summary law of nature; in the *De principiis*—as in all the works included in the *Instauratio magna*—the concept of motion, stimulus, and action do not account for reality on their own, but are subsidiary to natures (or qualities) and 'forms'. Bacon's departure from dynamism is set in evidence by the following instances from the *De principiis*. In a passage suggesting the 'bisection' of nature as a means to avoid vain abstractions, though he maintains that the notion of matter is inseparable from that of motion, the former is presented as something already distinct from the latter: essence, action, and motion are here *consequences* and *emanations* of matter. In the *Historia vitae et mortis* Bacon had already described the *spirit* as 'having place, dimension, reality', and in the *De principiis* he says that 'a necessity plainly inevitable drives men's thoughts— if they will be consistent—to the atom' adding that the atom is 'a true being having matter, form, dimension, place, resistance, appetite, motion and emanation'.[74] The method of 'negatives and exclusion' mentioned in the *De principiis* recalls, as we have seen, the method proposed in the *New Organon* for the detection of forms as distinct from motion. It is interesting to note, therefore, that here he distinguishes the *nature* of atoms and germs from their *virtues*.

One cannot ignore the contradiction of Bacon's insistence on the 'inevitability' of accepting atomism in the *De principiis*, with his refutation of Democritean atomism in the *New Organon*:

> Nor shall we thus be led to the doctrine of atoms, which implies the hypothesis of a vacuum and that of the unchangeableness of matter (both false assumptions); we shall be led only to real particles, such as really exist.[75]

The 'real particles' can hardly refer to the 'principles of things', but the vagueness of Bacon's concept of a changing fluid matter is to be noted, as also his typical uncertainty as regards the existence of a vacuum:

> I am not prepared to say for certain whether or no there be a vacuum, either collected in one place or interspersed in the pores of bodies.

This is from the *New Organon*; but even in the *De principiis* Bacon mentions the difficulty of this problem without offering a solution. It is only in the *Historia densi et rari* that he declares unequivocally, 'There is no vacuum in nature, either collected or interspersed'.

However, owing to the fact that the exact date of the *De principiis* cannot be ascertained—though it was probably later even than the *Historia*—it is unjustifiable to see in this last statement, as Levi does,[76] a final expression of Bacon's views.

Furthermore, Bacon's hesitations were connected with his doubts as to the validity of a doctrine of first principles; in the *New Organon* he wrote:

> Nor again is it a less evil, that in their philosophies and contemplations their labour is spent in investigating and handling the first principles of things and the highest generalities of nature; whereas utility and the means of working result entirely from things intermediate. Hence it is that men cease not from abstracting nature till they come to potential and uninformed matter, nor on the other hand from dissecting nature till they reach the atom; things which, even if true can do but little for the welfare of mankind.[77]

Yet in the *De augmentis*, as in the *Advancement*, the doctrine of first principles occupies a prominent position in natural science, and even in the *New Organon* Bacon recognises the importance of atomism as a method for the dissection of nature:

> To resolve nature into abstractions is less to our purpose than to

dissect her into parts; as did the school of Democritus which went further into nature than the rest.

However, even in the *De principiis*—where the main object is precisely that quest for first principles condemned in the *New Organon*—Bacon wrote that it was better to renounce the solution of such problems than to run the risk of referring to some far-fetched principle.[78]

When Bacon identifies *simple natures* and *virtues*; when he conceives motion as an active virtue corresponding to the appetites and inclinations of matter; when he grants to all substances the power of perception, he is consistent with his theories of the *Cogitationes* and of the Cupid fable in the *De sapientia veterum*.[79] But when, in the *De principiis*, he stresses the realistic nature of the principles of things, he moves away from the typically vitalistic significance he had hitherto assigned to Cupid, and asserts his faith in a doctrine of reality based on a geometrico-mechanicist definition of the first principles. Only an analysis of Bacon's doctrine of forms could explain this co-existence of dynamic and mechanistic conceptions of reality; but this would entail a different enquiry altogether. However Bacon's doctrine of first principles was not so much a metaphysics of nature as a signpost directing science towards the goal he had assigned it. His last years were dedicated to the compilation of his natural history because he believed that an 'immersion' in this science would do more for the advancement of learning and man's domination of nature than arguments over first principles. In 1612 he had written:

> These then are the things I see, standing as I do on the threshold of natural history and philosophy; and it may be that the deeper any man has gone into natural history the more he will approve them. Nevertheless, I repeat once more that I do not mean to bind myself to these; for in them as in other things I am certain of my way, but not certain of my position.[80]

Recapitulation

For the reader of today the main interest of the *De sapientia veterum* consists in the range and variety of its enquiries. In just over sixty pages Bacon outlines with considerable art and dexterity the basic aspects of an organic world picture. Though the parable style he adopted may not appeal to modern taste, it answered the needs of his day and, in fact, was responsible for the wide diffusion of his philosophy.

Apart from such problems as the substance of matter, atomism, and the reform of philosophy and science, Bacon tackled here a number of minor problems still connected with his general plan for the reorganisation and advancement of learning. Youth and old age, kings and courtiers, aristocrats and favourites, revolutions and the expedients of government, public opinion and war, religion and international relations, are among the questions discussed. And in these pages his personality comes over with an intensity that communicated itself to the public he was so anxious to impress and persuade without antagonising.

This too may probably account for the extraordinary popularity of the *De sapientia veterum* in seventeenth-century Europe; and also for the attitude of certain critics who saw it only as the systematisation of induction. We have tried to show the significance of this work in Bacon's *œuvre*. Though his attitude to the problem of classical mythology changed frequently, he never ceased to appreciate the instrumental value of the parable form for the diffusion of his philosophy. However, this does not explain Bacon's ambiguous views on the 'remote' past. Outweighing his critical reservations and uncertainties was the belief in a distant almost forgotten age of wisdom and bliss that must be re-exhumed. The very title he gave to his basic work, the *Instauratio magna* expresses the desire for a renewal of the past.

The apparent complexity of Bacon's attitude was further enhanced by those aspects of his philosophy which influenced Vico. In the *Advancement of Learning* Bacon describes a primitive humanity governed by instinct and inclination and communicating by images rather than by rational discourse. This theory of an age of fantasy preceding the age of reason—later adopted by Vico—was supported by a comparison with hieroglyphics, a form of writing appealing to the imagination rather than to logic; fables precede arguments, as hieroglyphics precede letters.

The elusive ambiguity of Bacon's attitude to classical mythology derives then: from the value he attributed to fables as a means of popularising his plan for scientific reform; from his belief in an ancient, forgotten wisdom that must be recaptured; and from his notion of the fable as a primitive form of expression used by an uncivilised humanity incapable of rational thought. And this confluence of variously inspired motives can only be reconciled in the light of Bacon's pragmatism.

Bacon's belief in a primeval bliss that philosophy must strive to recapture was also connected with the idea of the Fall. He stressed the virtue of exact methodical research and reverence for the laws of nature, and condemned the lack of moderation shown by alchemists and magicians who claim to lead man to the conquest of the world by miracles and not by the sweat of his brow. Also on ethical grounds, Bacon refuted the Greek philosophers—and especially Plato and Aristotle: Aristotle's fruitless philosophy is the main obstacle to man's regaining of the prelapsarian bliss and control of the universe. The sin of traditional philosophy was intellectual pride: it claimed to impress its own stamp upon reality rather than to discover the stamp of God; that is why men should discard philosophies which try to put experience behind bars and trample underfoot the works of the Creator, and should instead learn humbly to read the great book of the world.

Bacon's theory of present-day man's superiority to past generations was related to his refutation of traditional philosophy in which he saw a form of pride akin to the original sin of the old Adam:

> For the old age of the world is to be accounted the true antiquity; and this is the attribute of our own times, not of that earlier age of the world in which the ancients lived; and which, though in respect of us it was the elder, yet in respect of the world it was the younger. And truly as we look for greater knowledge of human things and a riper judgement in the old man than in the young, because of his experience and of the number and variety of the things which he has seen and heard and thought of; so in like manner from our age, *if we but knew its own strength and chose to essay and exert it,* much more might fairly be expected than from the ancient times, inasmuch as it is a more advanced age of the world, and stocked with infinite experiments and observations.[81]

In other words, the modern age could be superior to the ancient if men knew how to overthrow the myth of antiquity, shake off its influence, and follow the way of fresh experience.

Antiquity, or the childhood of the world, is something to be brought to maturity rather than a datum to be established.

Many scholars have been baffled by the apparent ambiguity in Bacon's presentation of his great reform as a 'restauration', and have been content to expose the contradiction without trying to explain it. Yet it would have been more rewarding to enquire into the problem and examine, among other things, Bacon's views on the classical fable. A notable modification took place in these views between the composition of the *Temporis partus masculus* and that of the *De sapientia veterum*; after passing through the uncertainty of the *Advancement*, Bacon reached a total acceptance of the allegorical tradition in the *De sapientia*. Though this change was motivated, in our opinion, by personal events, it drew its strength from a basic, unchanging aspect of Bacon's philosophy: for him man had renounced his original power with the Fall. This loss was perpetuated through the centuries because he trusted his fortunes to the sterility of Greek philosophy and its inheritors; but before the birth of Greek philosophy, in the remote past that precedes Hesiod and Homer, man, as yet untainted by Aristotelian intellectualism, had achieved a partial redemption of his sins and had preserved a measure of power over recalcitrant nature by the practice of true arts. Myths, for Bacon, are the expression of this long-lost past; they impart certain truths because they reflect the partial redemption of sins that must now be recovered. Adam's sin of pride was perpetuated by Greek philosophy; with it man fell a second time from power over all creation:

> We copy the sin of our first parents while we suffer for it. They wished to be like God, but their posterity wish to be even greater. For we create worlds, we direct and domineer over nature, we will have it that all things *are* as in our folly we think they should be, not as seems fittest to the Divine wisdom, or as they are found to be in fact; but we clearly impress the stamp of our own image on the creatures and works of God, instead of carefully examining and recognizing in them the stamp of the Creator himself. Wherefore our dominion over creatures is a second time forfeited, not undeservedly; and whereas after the fall of man some power over the resistance of creatures was still left to him—the power of subduing and managing them by true and solid arts—yet this too, through our insolence, and because we desire to be like God and to follow the dictates of our own reason, we in great part lose.[82]

These words from the *Historia naturalis et experimentalis ad condendam philosophiam* (1622) were written by Bacon in his maturity. Some years later, in the *New Atlantis*, he evoked the happy existence of mankind before the flood, dwelling on the art of navigation and the earliest voyages of discovery not, as Spedding has pointed out, as though he were telling a story, but with the conviction of one who believed in the authenticity of his tale.

Bacon's violent reaction against classical influence voiced in the *Temporis partus masculus*, the *Redargutio philosophiarum*, and the *New Organon*, stemmed from his desire for a radical renovation demanding a departure from tradition and also from every attempt to find inspiration for the new method and the proposed rehabilitation of mankind in past civilisations and a past glory. For what we are striving for, wrote Bacon, it is of little consequence whether or not the ancients possessed certain truths that time has engulfed; inventions must be made by the light of nature, not in the darkness of antiquity. But when he turned to the interpretation of classical myths, he saw reflected in them the exact features of his 'new' philosophy. A study of the *De sapientia veterum* exposes the unquestionable identity of its philosophical and political theories and those of Bacon's youthful unpublished works; indeed, they are often no more than an amplification of earlier theories, subsequently incorporated in the *New Organon* and the *De augumentis*: the vindication of Democritean philosophy; the necessity for a new scientific method conforming to the laws of nature yet curbing them to the service of mankind; the function of scientific co-operation in the advancement of learning; the rehabilitation of human instincts; and a political realism inspired by Machiavelli.

Thus Bacon's acknowledgement of a secret wisdom inherent in the remote origins of humanity acquires a two-fold significance and demands a double justification: on the one hand it is related to his adoption of an attitude that was common to the intelligentsia of most European countries—this was between 1607 and 1609 when Bacon's aim was to communicate his basic theories to the intellectual world of his time without alienating it. On the other hand, this belief is intrinsic to the religious character with which he invested his reform—it was to redeem man from original sin and reinstate him in his prelapsarian power over all created things. These two aspects of Bacon's attitude converge to reveal the significance of the *De sapientia veterum* and the absurdity of classing it among mere 'literary exercises'.

It may be opportune to recall here a passage from Descartes expressing a belief in the true and solid wisdom of a primitive humanity that was both rude and simple; the notion of a 'fall' from this true wisdom; the idea that this wisdom was suppressed or concealed; and respect for those who, like Francis Bacon, undertook its revival:

> . . . But I am convinced that certain primary germs of truth implanted by nature in human minds—though in our case the daily reading and hearing of innumerable diverse errors stifle them—had a very great vitality in that rude and unsophisticated age of the ancient world. Thus the same mental illumination which let them see that virtue was to be preferred to pleasure, and honour to utility, although they knew not why this was so, made them recognize true notions in Philosophy and Mathematics, although they were not yet able thoroughly to grasp these sciences. Indeed I seem to recognize certain traces of this true Mathematics in Pappus and Diophantus who though not belonging to the earliest age, yet lived many centuries before our own times. But my opinion is that these writers then with a sort of low cunning, deplorable indeed, suppressed this knowledge. Possibly they acted just as many inventors are known to have done in the case of their discoveries, i.e. they feared that their method being so easy and simple would become cheapened on being divulged, and they preferred to exhibit in its place certain barren truths, deductively demonstrated with show enough of ingenuity, as the results of their art, in order to win from us our admiration for these achievements, rather than to disclose to us that method itself which would have wholly annulled the admiration accorded. Finally there have been certain men of talent who in the present age have tried to revive this same art.[83]

It is a common practice with historians of philosophy when dealing with obsolete problems to limit their enquiry to the bare statement of this or that philosopher's attitude. Thus, after noting Bacon's allegiance to 'dark medieval superstitions', they think they have acquired the right to judge his whole philosophy. The same practice has led scholars to condemn the extravagance of his views in the *De sapientia veterum*, and has created the image of Bacon as fanciful interpreter of classical fables; as hasty—and subsequently repentant—detractor of Plato and Aristotle; and as perpetrator of magical and alchemical superstitions. In reality Bacon's semi-acceptance of the allegorical tradition (and, as we have seen, also of magic) was perfectly consistent with his religious preoccupations, and his plan of reform presented as a 'restauration'.

To end this chapter, here is a brief summary of the conclusions I have reached, without, however, by any means having exhausted the subject. They aim at breaking through the network of classifications and definitions in which scholars have entrapped Bacon's thought, and stand also as a justification for the chapter:

An examination of Bacon's attitude to the classical fable has set in evidence a hitherto little-known aspect of his thought and is invaluable for an understanding of Bacon's whole attitude to tradition. This examination has also revealed the influence on Bacon of both Democritean materialism and of Renaissance naturalism. Some of Bacon's views on the problems of matter, nature, and magic only become clear after studying his interpretations of classical myths. The *De sapientia veterum* and the *De principiis atque originibus*—both allegorical, mythological works—contain the most coherent and complete renderings of Bacon's thought in its materialistic phase. The relation between his theories of physics in these works and those he expounds in the *De augumentis* raises an interesting problem.

One of the most damaging hypotheses of Bacon scholarship is that which considers his earlier writings as mere 'precursors' of those projected in his *Distributio operis* of 1620. The editorial arrangement of his writings, planned by Bacon in his last years, has often been taken as criterion for an historical study of his work. In this way the six parts of the *Instauratio magna*—or more precisely the *New Organon* and the *De augumentis*—have come to stand almost exclusively for Bacon's entire philosophical production. To quote a distinguished historian of philosophy: 'We consider it unrewarding to study Bacon's writings in chronological order of composition. His theories underwent no real development; he thinks by aphorisms that are only diluted and supplemented in his longer works'.[84] I hold instead every attempt at singling out and following up the very real develop-

ment of Bacon's thought—even as regards individual theories— —
to be an important step towards refuting an oversimplified
interpretation of his philosophy. But the generally accepted
view that Bacon's theories knew no development and that he
thought in aphorisms possibly stems from the difficulty presented by a chronological classification of his works and the
uncertain relation of these works to each other and to the
Instauratio magna. In such circumstances, what is more natural
than to try to avoid the problems of classifying Bacon's writings
according to his intellectual preoccupations and of analysing
the inner progress of his thought?

Even the common Bacon-Vico heritage which emerges from
the works of Crocean scholars would benefit by a thorough re-
investigation. I find, for instance, Croce's brief allusions to the
cautious hesitation with which Bacon tackles, in the *De
sapientia veterum*, the problem of the philosophical allegory of
myths[85] an insufficient explanation of this attitude. And Nicolini's description of Bacon's views on hieroglyphics —'a more
or less irrelevant sally'—is far from convincing.[86] Actually,
Vico's theory that the myth precedes the allegorical significance for which it is made to stand, is clearly stated by Bacon in
the *Advancement of Learning*:

> I do rather think that the fable was first, and the exposition
> devised, than that the moral was first and thereupon the fable
> framed.[87]

Though Vico cannot have been acquainted with this particular formulation of the theory, it reappears in various guises in
the *De augumentis*:

> Now this method of teaching, used for illustration, was very
> much in use in the ancient times. For the inventions and con-
> clusions of human reason (even those that are now common and
> trite) being then new and strange, the minds of men were hardly
> subtle enough to conceive them, unless they were brought nearer
> to the sense by this kind of resemblances and examples. And hence
> the ancient times are full of all kinds of fables, parables, enigmas,
> and similitudes. Thus Menenius Agrippa among the Romans
> (a nation at that time by no means learned) quelled a sedition by a
> fable. In a word, as hieroglyphics were before letters, so parables
> were before arguments.[88]

Also in the *De augumentis*, Bacon puts the same opposition hieroglyphics-letters to another use:

> The Notes of Things then which carry a signification without the help or intervention of words, are of two kinds: one *ex congruo*, where the note has some congruity with the notion, the other *ad placitum*, where it is adopted and agreed upon at pleasure. Of the former kind are Hieroglyphics and Gestures; of the latter the Real Characters above mentioned . . . Gestures are as transitory Hieroglyphics. For as uttered words fly away, but written words stand, so Hieroglyphics expressed in gestures pass, but expressed in pictures remain . . . In the meantime it is plain that Hieroglyphics and Gestures have always some similitude to the thing signified and are a kind of emblems . . . Real characters on the other hand have nothing emblematic in them, but are merely surds, no less than the elements of letters themselves, and are only framed *ad placitum* and silently agreed on by custom.[89]

The influence on Vico of some of Bacon's fundamental theories and his frequent references to the latter's works cannot be dismissed as a mere coincidence. This problem has yet to be tackled and appreciated in all its complexity.

three means, by Illaqueation or Sophism, which pertains to Logic; by Imagination or Impression, which pertains to Rhetoric; and by Passion or Affection, which pertains to Morality. And as in negotiation with others men are wrought by cunning, by importunity, and by vehemency; so in this negotiation within ourselves men are undermined by Inconsequences, solicited and importuned by Impressions or Observations, and transported by Passions. Neither is the nature of man so unfortunately built, as that those powers and arts should have force to disturb reason, and not to establish and advance it; for the end of Logic is to teach a form of argument to secure reason, and not to entrap it; the end of Morality is to procure the affections to obey reason, and not to invade it; the end of Rhetoric is to fill the imagination to second reason, and not oppress it.[1]

But for Bacon the link between logic, rhetoric, and morality was more intricate than would appear from this passage. Thus rhetoric was a part of logic; and 'the duty and office of Rhetoric is to apply Reason to Imagination for the better moving of the Will', making it also a part of morality.[2]

What exactly Bacon meant by logic is explained in certain passages of the *Advancement of Learning* (1605) and the *Distributio Operis* (1620) (which will be the object of a more detailed study later); but we must not forget that Bacon's ideas were fundamentally the same in 1623—when he wrote the *De augmentis*—as they had been in 1605. In the *Advancement* logic is divided into four parts according to its different functions: man *finds* what he is searching for; he *judges* what he has found; he *records* what he has judged; he *communicates* what he has recorded. These four processes constitute the intellectual arts: the art of imagery or *invention*, the art of examination or *judgement*, the art of custody or *memory*, and the art of elocution or *tradition*.[3] This classification was inspired by Ramism, where, however, the term invention was restricted to the process of selecting material to convince one's audience, while Bacon, who distinguished between invention of speech and arguments and invention of arts and sciences, gave it a much broader meaning. One of the first aims of the reform of induction was precisely to supply the arts and sciences with an organon or tool for the control and mastery of nature; the most deficient of intellectual arts being, in Bacon's view, the invention of arts and sciences that was subdivided into 'literary practice' and 'interpretation of nature'.

This last was, in fact, the 'new logic' of the *New Organon*, Book II.[4]

Thus the method of scientific research of the *New Organon* is only one of the two parts that make up the art of invention, which, in turn, is one of the four subdivisions of Bacon's logic. Though the importance, for Bacon, of this method varied considerably, even in the *Distributio operis* and the *New Organon* his theory of scientific induction was inseparable from his doctrine of intellectual reform based on liberating the minds of men from their idols. If the minds of men were free, wrote Bacon, the 'new logic' would suffice to obviate the deficiencies of sensory perception. However:

> Since the minds of men are strangely possessed and beset, so that there is no true and even surface left to reflect the genuine rays of things, it is necessary to seek a remedy for this also. This doctrine then of the expurgation of the intellect to qualify it for dealing with truth, is comprised in three refutations: the refutation of the Philosophies; the refutation of the Demonstrations; and the refutation of the Natural Human Reason. The explanation of which and of the true relation between the nature of things and the nature of the mind, is as the strewing and decoration of the bridal chamber of the Mind and the Universe, the Divine Goodness assisting.[5]

So Bacon was faced with the dual problem of adapting the inductive process to scientific invention and simultaneously freeing the mind of man from the natural and historical bonds that condition and distinguish it. Hence the link between the reform of induction itself and that of its methods of diffusion. It is indeed significant that Bacon should have included rhetoric in his logic, and distinguished it as 'adornment of speech' from the art of delivery, or communication. But Bacon's 'problem' seems to have been no different from those that had preoccupied the rhetoricians and educationalists of Europe for the past century; a fact which explains the influence on his outlook of Ramistic and anti-Ramistic dissensions.

It follows that where logic is understood to signify a sequence of operations using syllogism and induction for natural research, Bacon cannot be seen as a reformer of logic.[6] In a history of science, a section dedicated to Bacon would require a minimum of pages; and histories of philosophy identifying philosophical and scientific problems have indeed—with more consistency than historical sense—catalogued Bacon's *œuvre* as a vast, unimportant 'logical machine'. Such an attitude is at fault, not in condemning the second book of the *New Organon*, but for its arbitrary reduction of Bacon's whole output to those forty-seven folio pages. We quote Spedding—whose knowledge of Bacon is of unequalled repute—on Book II of the *New Organon*:

> Of this philosophy we can make nothing. If we have not tried it, it is because we feel confident that it would not answer. We regard it as a curious piece of machinery, very subtle, elaborate, and ingenious, but not worth constructing, because all the work it could do may be done more easily another way. [7]

Bacon should certainly not be seen as the inventor of modern science on the grounds that he discovered the inductive method. Such a view, though dear to the founders of the Royal Society and to the Encyclopedists, has long been superceded. As Farrington justly observes, to see Bacon in this light is equivalent to setting him on an 'inappropriate pedestal in an inappropriate part of the gallery'. [8]

Modern science owes less to Bacon's empirical experimentalism than to Galileo's mathematical theories based on quantitative and mechanical analyses which 'instead of striving to discover *forms* by organising and purifying the world, try to discover *laws* by examining the calculable organisation of natural objects'. The anticipations of nature condemned by Bacon as arbitrary and non-conducive to experiment have proved invaluable to the evolution of science. The definitions and axioms of modern science are not, as Bacon would have wished, the fruit of inductions that gradually include wider generalisations: they are models serving to limit the field of enquiry. [9] The inductions peculiar to each science have revealed their implicit relation to axiomatic methods of a deductive nature, which puts an end both to Bacon's opposition of inductive to deductive methods, and to the logico-philosophical theory claiming to describe the process of various scientific inductive generalisations.

In this respect Bacon's uncertain views on mathematics are highly relevant. For him mathematics was never a method but only a form of calculation, and in his encyclopedia of knowledge it was included at one time in metaphysics as a 'science of quantity', and at another it was a mere supplement to natural philosophy.[10] However, only by distorting the meaning of such terms as history of science or history of philosophy, can Bacon's importance be ignored in the sphere of such histories, or indeed, in the wider sphere of the history of mankind. Bacon contributed substantially to the diffusion of ideas and convictions such as the freedom from idols, the distinction between what can be perceived by the senses and religious beliefs, metaphysics seen as a general physics based on natural history, atomic materialism, the vindication of technology, polemics against magico-alchemical ideals, co-operation in scientific research, the quest for truth as an endeavour to improve the human condition, and the importance of moral responsibility in scientific research. Is not this sufficient to entitle a man—even though he writes 'like a Lord Chancellor' [11]—to a place in the history of philosophy and of science?

By an analysis of passages from Bacon's writings we shall now attempt to prove the link between Bacon's reform of induction and his logic; to determine the varying degrees of importance the 'new logic' assumed at different times in Bacon's eyes; and to elicit the influence on his projects for the reform of logic of the rhetorical and logical discussions of his day.

At the beginning of this chapter we referred to Bacon's having already in his lecture of 1593 *In Praise of Knowledge* associated the refutation of philosophies and the state of contemporary culture with his reform of logic. Knowledge today, wrote Bacon, is entirely unproductive and given solely to discussions which throw no light whatsoever upon the still undiscovered possibilities of natural phenomena. We are content to enquire into the causes of what is already known and to reduce all things to pre-established principles. When instances occur that are in flagrant contradiction to such principles they are nonetheless retained by subtle dialectical distinctions, and not revised in any way. Ours is a knowledge made up of well-worn notions held together by a fine thread of dialectic and it throws more shade than light upon reality. We know no other natural philosophy than that of the Greeks or the alchemists. The first is distinguished by the cavilling academicism proper to Greek civilisation; the second by fraud, oral tradition, and obscurity. These two philosophies do not really differ greatly one from the other. The first is based on a handful of popular observations, the second on a handful of popular experiments; the first aims at multiplying words, the second at multiplying gold. Thus knowledge is no more than a reflection of the minds of men, with man as the measuring-rod of nature. It is time that we broke down the barriers of this culture by exterminating gullibility, impatience, vanity, uncertainties, cupidity, and verbosity, to achieve the true and happy union of nature and the mind of man.[12]

Four basic Baconian themes are already foreshadowed in this passage: the denunciation of a form of logic tending to multiply words instead of solving problems; the denunciation of empirical science based on a limited number of popular experiments that can add very little to the common store of knowledge; the call for freedom from tradition and its limitations; the vision of a new method untethered and unprejudiced, dealing directly with reality. These cornerstones of Bacon's reform of logic recur in the *Temporis partus masculus* (1603), the *Advancement of Learning* (1605), *Cogitata et visa* (1607), the *Redargutio philosophiarum* (1607), *Partis instaurationis secundae delineatio* (1607), *De interpretationis naturae sententiae XII* (1608–1620), and finally the *New Organon* (1620).

We are already familiar with the first two themes in connection with Bacon's attitude to traditional philosophy and to magic. The other two are more directly concerned with his logic, and the *Valerius Terminus*, the *Advancement*, and the *Delineatio* are the more relevant works in this respect. But as Spedding has said, Bacon's thought developed through a series of experimental variations on a vast plan of reform, rather than by following to its logical end a single project.[13] So it will be necessary to refer frequently to other works and to his plan for the reform of natural philosophy and the writing of a great encyclopedia which runs parallel to his plan for the reform of logic, linked, besides, to the refutation of philosophies, materialism, and the interpretation of classical fables.

The *Temporis partus masculus*—in fact, no more than a critique of traditional philosophy—was intended as part of a great work on the reform of logic. Thus the three books on the *Interpretation of Nature* were to have had three parts: *perpolitio et applicatio mentis, lumen naturae seu formula interpretationis,* and *natura illuminata sive veritas rerum.*[14] The first brief chapter includes some theories on the reform of logic under a title—*Tradendi modus legitimus*—clearly showing Bacon's preoccupation with problems of education and communication. Science, according to Bacon, is in the hands of men who 'whether in publishing or concealing the knowledge of nature . . . fall far short of a proper stand of honour or duty', or of men who, though well-intentioned, show a 'lack of any arts or precepts to guide them in putting their knowledge before the public.' But this failure to impart scientific knowledge correctly is not altogether the fault of such men, but rather of the futility of their objectives. Bacon's aim—the subjection of nature—requires the 'most legitimate method':

> But what, you ask, is this legitimate method? Please drop all arts and subterfuges, you say, and put the matter plainly before us, so that we may use our own judgement. Would to God, my dear boy, that your situation was such that this could be done. But do you suppose, when all the approaches and entrances to men's minds are beset and blocked by the most obscure idols—idols deeply implanted and, as it were, burned in—that any clean and polished surface remains in the mirror of the mind on which the genuine natural light of things can fall? A new method must be found for quiet entry into minds so choked and overgrown. Frenzied men are exacerbated by violent opposition but may be beguiled by art. This gives us a hint how we should proceed in this universal madness.[15]

Thus in the *Temporis partus masculus* Bacon introduces his theory of idols. There are three kinds of idols, he says, the idols of the theatre, or rostrum; the idols of the forum; and the idols of the cave. The first have been set up by traditional philosophy and Bacon attacks them mercilessly. But, he adds, attacks are not enough, the knowledge of reality alone will liberate the minds of men. A blackboard must be wiped clean of previous writings before it can be used, but the minds of men must first be written upon before old inscriptions can be erased, for otherwise, the mind is left open to the 'tortuous labyrinth of experience' and new errors replace the old.[16]

Thus a form of logic leading men to 'a chaste, holy, and legal wedlock with things themselves' must also bring light into men's minds and free them from the obstructions of prejudice. The first requirement corresponds to the new organon of science (*interpretatio naturae*) enabling man to know forms and to perform a number of natural experiments; the second to an 'amendment of the human mind' (*expurgatio intellectus*)[17] by special methods of formulation, persuasion, and communication. But the whole represents for Bacon a single problem, as there is only one method of formulating the new organon. Scientists when addressing one another should do so in aphorisms, to avoid the common fallacy of loading axioms and scientific observations with examples and ponderous sentences. For Bacon this is not a mere question of rhetoric; from this fallacy have arisen those systems of natural philosophy whose formal perfection conceals their true lack of knowledge. The aphoristic method, on the contrary, avoids rhetorical embellishments and unjustified digressions; further, its formulations are extracted, as it were, from the heart of scientific knowledge itself, so that the listener is left without the sense of false security that illusory perfection provides, and is incited to additional enquiry and experiment to supplement the deficiencies.[18]

In the *Advancement of Learning* Bacon introduces his four subdivisions of logic. It is no mere coincidence that his classification should be reminiscent of those figuring in the rhetorical texts of the period and that it should, at the same time, promote a form of logic unencumbered by long professions of faith in the value of logical sequences and dialectical laws, but providing the necessary rules and instruments for natural science as well as for ethics, politics, and pedagogy. Bacon's logic is 'divided according to the ends whereunto they [the intellectual arts] are referred'. Thus the treatment of the four intellectual arts is entirely functional and reflects a tendency to avoid hard and fast rules in favour of a method developing naturally with the development of the enquiry, because in scientific research every step forward clears the way ahead.[19]

It will be interesting to note as we go along the links that exist between Bacon's attitude and that of the logicians and rhetoricians of his time, as well as the various points where his treatment of logic coincides with the popular Ramistic doctrines of Elizabethan England.

For instance, not only Ramus but Thomas Wilson and Ralph

Lever shared Bacon's preoccupation with practical problems. They protested against Aristotelian and Scholastic logic for being no more than a technical exercise that was an end unto itself and a means for reaching foregone conclusions. Their theories became immensely popular and provoked polemics on rhetoric and methods of education, because their attitude reflected the needs of English culture and society; the demands of politics and the Court, the rapid substitution of a new class of men of law for the old aristocracy, intensive discussions on the value of sermons, and the increasing importance of Parliament contributed to a growing interest in debates, disputations, the art of persuasion, and a practical form of logic answering religious and public requirements; thus between 1650 and 1750 rhetoric became a major subject in English schools and colleges where the texts of Plato, Aristotle, Cicero, Tacitus, Quintilian, Seneca, and the *Rhetorica ad Herennium* were supplemented by those of Leonard Cox, Thomas Wilson, and later by those of Vicars and Farnaby.[20]

The following passage from Richard Hooker's *Laws of Ecclesiastical Polity* shows how a method of persuasion and a means of rooting out prejudice had become essential to religious propaganda:

> He that goeth about to persuade a multitude, that they are not so well governed as they ought to be, shall never want attentive and favourable hearers; because they know the manifold defects whereunto every kind of regimen is subject, but the secret lets and difficulties, which in public proceedings are innumerable and inevitable, they have not ordinarily the judgement to consider. And because such as openly reprove supposed disorders of state are taken for principal friends to the common benefit of all, and for men that carry singular freedom of mind; under this fair and plausible colour whatsoever they utter passeth for good and current. That which wanteth in the weight of their speech, is supplied by the aptness of men's minds to accept and believe it. Whereas on the other side, if we maintain things that are established, we have not only to strive with a number of heavy prejudices deeply rooted in the hearts of men, who think that . . . we speak in favour of the present state because thereby we either hold or seek preferment; but also to bear such exceptions as minds so averted beforehand usually take against that which they are loth should be poured into them.[21]

These words reveal a double concern, firstly for the function of speech as a means of reaching an audience, and secondly for the need to educate men by degrees as their knowledge increases, following, without rigidity or predetermination the natural curb of their evolution. For Hooker the mind of man is a blank page on which anything can be inscribed: 'We are to search by what steps and degrees it riseth unto perfection of knowledge'; hence the doctrine of 'helps to reasoning'. Our age, wrote Hooker, is famed for its culture and gives little thought to such helps; if they were put to use, those who employed them would differ from the men of today as much as men of today differ from innocents.[22] Should this, he adds, appear exaggerated, let us remember that 'no art is at first finding out so perfect as industry may after make it'. And it is at this point that he refers to Ramus' method and, while recognising its 'poverty' and inadequacy, yet 'We may define it to be an Art which teacheth the way of speedy discourse and restraineth the mind of man that it may not wax over-wise'.[23]

Hooker was certainly the most forceful and significant of those Elizabethan thinkers who represent the metaphysical and systematic tradition of medieval culture. The whole attitude of this tradition was very different from Bacon's, yet their demands for a 'functional discourse' and a doctrine of 'aids to reasoning' were identical—except that Bacon's were more energetic. But a study of Bacon's subdivision of logic will help us to discern with greater precision his affinities to Ramus and his followers, and to various sixteenth-century rhetorical writers.

This subdivision was based on the different objectives to which man tends:

(*a*) art of inquiry or *invention*;

(*b*) art of examination or *judgement*;

(*c*) art of custody or *memory*;

(*d*) art of elocution or *tradition*.[24]

These correspond almost exactly to the traditional divisions of rhetoric. For instance, Thomas Wilson in the *Arte of Rhetorique*, published in London in 1553, defines rhetoric 'as an art to set forth by utterance of words matters at large . . . that may through reason largely be discussed'. The work is divided into three books; the first on the seven divisions of an oration, the three oratorical forms, and *invention*; the second on *disputatio* (or judgement); and the third on *speech, memory*, and *delivery*.[25] Wilson's was the first complete, coherent description of the five classical divisions of rhetoric to be published in England, and the number of references to this work is evidence of its influence and popularity. On the other hand the art of memory is relatively inconspicuous in Ramus' classification of the *artes logicae*:

artes logicae

dialectica   retorica

inventio   dispositio   elocutio   pronuntiatio

It is important to note in this context that Ramus—after Quintilian and Cicero—identifies *dispositio* and *iudicium* (the second book of the *Dialectics* deals with *de iudicio et disponendis*) and discusses in the same section *dispositio*, axioms or propositions, syllogisms, and method:

> The art of logic falls into two parts; first *Topics*, which is the finding of arguments, i.e. middle terms, principles and elements (for so they are named in the *Organon*), and second, *Analytics*, which is the disposition of these arguments . . . 'Disposition' consists in the apt grouping of things . . . This is the part which is properly called 'judgement', since the rule of the syllogism is common to all questions which are to be judged . . . The art of Dialectic has two parts: discovery and disposition. Once the problem to be discussed has been expounded, let arguments and proofs be sought; then, when they have been disposed in due order, the problem itself is classified.[26]

It is quite possible that Bacon was acquainted with Wilson's rhetoric and he had certainly read Ramus, whose terminology and ideas he adopted to some extent, while criticising his works. Thus for him the words logic and dialectic were synonymous; his interpretation of the term axiom was very similar to Ramus'; after blaming Ramus for his use of dichotomy he used it himself in the *New Organon*; and, above all, he incorporated the three Ramistic rules into his new inductive method aiming at the discovery of forms.[27]

Bacon's adoption of the traditional classifications of rhetoric for his logic is of historical interest in that it shows the fundamentally 'practical' significance of works such as those of Ramus, Wilson, Agricola, and Nizolius and explains their immediate popularity and their influence on the more radical reforms of logic of a later date. In 1630, only a few years before the publication of the *Discours de la methode*, Ramism was still thriving in the French universities, and in England Milton's enthusiasm for Ramus resulted in the *Artis logicae plenior institutio ad Petri Rami methodum concinnata* in 1672. Leibniz too, intent on consolidating the link between logic and rhetoric, published Nizolius' *De principiis* with a long introduction blaming the Ramists and semi-Ramists for distinguishing rhetoric from oratory and quoting the 'incomparable Verulam' who redirected philosophy 'to serve mankind on earth':

> An alchemist had a more solid and admirable understanding of the nature of the world than any 'philosopher' imprisoned in the confines of the sun, wallowing in haecceities or hoccities.[28]

If dialectical obscurity is the language of prophets, alchemists, miracle-makers, the Delphic oracle, or even mystics and riddling poets, he added, there is nothing more alien to philosophy.

In fact, sixteenth-century philosophers were often led by their empirical tendencies to model their language on the flowery eloquence of rhetoric. Rhetoricians and philosophers or scientists shared a common aversion for a perfect, autonomous form of knowledge and opposed to theological speculations the advantages of practical arts and sciences. They frequently stressed the inadequacy of the syllogistic deductions of Aristotelian logic, with its elocutory ideals, considering it inapt for enquiries based on inventiveness and directed towards experiments performed in certain specified conditions. It was essential that logic—whether directed towards social or scientific ends—should discard such preoccupations of mere form, and take its place 'experimentally . . . in the witness box of mathematics, physics, poetry, and ethics'.[29] The revaluation of rhetoric tended naturally to detract from the compulsoriness of logical procedures, and to present them as the choice of arguments best suited for the ends in view. The anti-Aristotelianism of these new rhetoricians—mostly purely formal—was often no more than a revision of detail, setting function before truth, possibility before necessity, and exception before rule. Nizolius, for instance, writes: 'Dialecticians and metaphysicians are mainly pre-occupied with the truth and perfection of their arguments, but care very little about their utility.' This attitude stressed the practical aspects of knowledge and reduced the whole of philosophy to the social sciences. For Nizolius, Plato in the *Thaetetus* and Aristotle in the *Analytics* were the promoters of a 'completely sterile, incorruptible, and everlasting' form of knowledge proceeding by rigid demonstrations; its objectives were those universal and supposedly perfect truths that were, in fact, empirical, deriving from the practical demands of speech. Pseudo philosophers had denied the title of science to the *humanities* deeming them spurious and adulterated activities as compared to the science of universals; but ignorance alone of the subjects and aims of these arts was responsible for the elaboration of a metaphysics that was a mere verbal exercise without subject or function.

But both Nizolius, a firm supporter of rhetoric, and the scientist Fracastoro, invoked the same Aristotelian tradition— that of the *Topics* and the *Rhetoric*. Indeed Fracastoro tried to erect scientific induction on the example and the enthymeme, those Aristotelian equivalents for the dialectico-rhetorical analytical induction and the syllogism.[30] Logical processes that had been restricted to ethics by Aristotelianism were now applied to natural philosophy. And when Bacon applied the traditional syllogistic method to moral and political research he was acting on the same principle.

The demand for a form of logic capable of assisting politico-religious discussions was intimately related to that made by natural philosophers for a logic of invention, seen as art or instrument, and frequently described as a tool. Such a logic— presenting a certain roughness and simplicity compared with the discussions of late Scholasticism—would be directed, not at the subtle analyses of the terms of an argument, but at providing man with a means of controlling nature. When Ramus in his treatise reversed the Aristotelian order and placed his essay on invention before those on demonstration and judgement, he was significantly implying the vanity of writing on demonstration without previously explaining its practical applications. Further, in his theory of *places*, instead of drawing examples from physics, mathematics, or any of the 'major sciences' where dialectics have already been perfected, he took them from the poets and orators:

> I have at several points cited poets and orators as distinguished and eminent witnesses of that sagacity and human intelligence, because it was not only in the private academies of the learned, but also in law courts, in parliaments, in assemblies, in theatres, in fact in all departments of life that they exhibited the art of dialectic in a vigorous and flourishing form.[31]

We find in Peter Ramus, the image—adopted later by Bacon —of the mind as a magic mirror that must be polished anew, for it has become obscured and no longer reflects reality. A comparison of certain passages from Bacon and Ramus shows the striking similarity of themes and interpretations too often overlooked on account of their dissensions and controversies. In *La Dialectique*—after equating *inventio* to grammar (which deals with the parts of speech) and *dispositio* to syntax (which describes grammatical construction)—Ramus declares:

> Man is naturally gifted with the power to know all things: and when he will have before his eyes the art of inventing by these universal species, like a mirror reflecting the universal and general images of all things, it will be much easier for him by these, to identify individual species and thus to invent what he is looking for. But before this mirror can shine and reflect such images, it must be furbished and polished by numerous examples, many exercises, and long practice.[32]

In the *Advancement of Learning* Bacon, referring to the *doctrine of catalogues* that includes his refutation of sophistic fallacies, errors of interpretation, and idols—or false images—writes:

> For the mind of man is far from the nature of a clear and equal glass, wherin the beams of things should reflect according to their true incidence; nay, it is rather like an enchanted glass, full of superstition and imposture, if it be not delivered and reduced.[33]

This image plays an important part in Bacon's philosophy and distinguishes his attitude from that of most Elizabethan thinkers and poets. The cosmology of Spenser, Sidney, Hooker, and Digby was one of metaphysical 'order' and 'hierarchy';[34] there is a basic harmony between nature, the mind, and society;

the various spheres of reality are connected by hidden correspondences; the order of the cosmos is that of society; and the state is an organic unity whose structure corresponds to that of the human body;[35] man the microcosm reflects the order and organic unity of the universe; the divine will governs the world from angels and man down to plants and minerals. This notion of a law impressed by God upon nature is associated with that of a 'great chain of being', a cosmological unity of interdependent parts; the four elements of the universe correspond to the four humours of the human temper and physics, physiology, psychology, philosophy, and religion form an organic corpus of knowledge linked to an organic world picture.[36]

For Hooker the law of nature is intrinsically identical to that of scripture and both derive from the same Power. This Thomistic belief is the basic theme of his philosophy: the harmony of nature and the supernatural, and the gradual progression of nature to the presence of God.[37] The essence of the law for Hooker is to determine kinds and species and fix the position of every creature in relation to all others: 'that law, the performance whereof we behold in things natural, is as it were an authentical or original draught written in the bosom of God himself'. The law of nature governs all inanimate things, the motion of celestial bodies and of the elements, and makes each part of the universe aspire, not to its own perfection, but to the perfection of the whole. But the reign of angelic beings is governed by divine law; human law is the result of divine law added to the natural laws of reason that bind all rational beings. Divine and rational evidence are together infallible. All arts and sciences flow from the shining fount of divinity and are 'base' only when compared with Christian revelation.[38]

The notion of organic unity is present also in Digby's cosmology. In the *Theoria analytica* he describes the hierarchy of the different worlds—sensorial, intellectual, and divine.[39] The key that opens the first is reason, which serves science proceeding from particulars to universals, these being nothing more than the prolongation of natural objects: the intellectual world is reached by reflection of the mind, moving from universals to the discovery of the individual forms of perceptible objects; while the enlightenment of faith leads to the divine world.

The hierarchic order of this world picture fostered a 'sublime faith in the intellectual powers of man' forcefully expressed in these lines from Marlowe's *Tamburlaine*—notwithstanding the romantic tendency to stress the vanity of the world already present in this work:

> Our souls, whose faculties can comprehend
> The wondrous Architecture of the world,
> And measure every wand'ring planet's course
> Still climbing after knowledge infinite,
> And always moving as the restless Spheres,
> Will us to wear ourselves and never rest. . . .[40]

This is indeed very different from an enchanted mirror representing the mind of man. And if the truth of this image were to be accepted, Bacon knew it was necessary that 'the entire work of the understanding be commenced afresh, and the mind itself be from the very outset not left to take its own course but guided at every step; and the business be done as if by machinery'. For the constructions of the unguided mind 'I hold for suspected, and no way established, until it has submitted to a new trial, and a fresh judgement has been thereupon pronounced'. Compare the following passage from Bacon with that of Marlowe quoted above:

> But the universe to the eye of the human understanding is framed like a labyrinth; presenting as it does on every side so many ambiguities of the way, such deceitful resemblances of objects and signs; natures so irregular in their lines, and so knotted and entangled. And then the way is still to be made by the uncertain light of the senses, sometimes shining out, sometimes clouded over, through the woods, of experience and particulars. . . . In circumstances so difficult neither the natural force of man's judgement nor even any accidental felicity offers any chance of success. No excellence of wit, no repetition of chance experiment, can overcome such difficulties as these. Our steps must be guided by a clue, and the whole way from the very first perception of the senses must be laid out upon a sure plan.[41]

'Veneration of man's mind', blind faith in its innate power, are the very obstacles that must, according to Bacon, be overcome to attain true knowledge. Metaphysical constructions such as Hooker's and Digby's are to him no more than fabulous inventions aping reality; and these include the complex hierarchy of beings, and the mysterious correspondences elaborated by the versatile mind of Robert Fludd at the very time when Bacon was writing the *New Organon*. But the most relevant fact is that Bacon's favourable view of Ramistic dialectics stemmed from his refutation of these cosmologies:

> Now my method, though hard to practise, is easy to explain; and it is this. I propose to establish progressive stages of certainty. . . . I open and lay out a new and certain path for the mind to proceed in, starting directly from the simple sensuous perception. The necessity of this was felt no doubt by those who attributed so much importance to logic; showing thereby that they were in search of helps for the understanding, and had no confidence in the native and spontaneous process of the mind. But this remedy comes too late to do any good, when the mind is already, through daily intercourse and conversation of life, occupied with unsound doctrines and beset on all sides by vain imaginations. And therefore that art of Logic coming (as I said) too late to the rescue, and no way able to set matters right again, has had the effect of fixing errors rather than disclosing truth.[42]

Thus according to Bacon the supporters of dialectics had not only adapted logic to worldly ends, but they had understood that the mind as such was not a faithful mirror of reality. A gap exists between the mind and reality that must be bridged by a special method of controlling sensation and reason. This was the acknowledgement of a tendency—linked to the progress of rhetoric—to set up logic, not as arguments reflecting the organised fabric of reality, but as a delicate precision instrument patiently fashioned by man for predetermined ends.

The following chapter contains a detailed study of Bacon's treatment of the 'intellectual arts' that make up his logic. The fact that there are affinities between certain popular tendencies of European thought and Bacon's attitude should not obscure our sense of perspective nor stop us from perceiving the important discrepancies. But we must not forget that his peculiar originality is enhanced by enquiries such as this—a circumstance that has been overlooked by scholars who identify Bacon's logic with the second book of the *New Organon*, and for whom the texts that formed Bacon's intellect and inspired his philosophy were mere lucubrations of Renaissance grammatical pedantry.

V

Language and Communication

In the *Advancement of Learning* Bacon goes to some pains to explain his motives for altering traditional classifications. Firstly, he says, it should be remembered that things are classified in one of two ways according to the ends pursued: for instance, a secretary of State, sorting the papers in his office, will classify them according to their nature; while in his own private study he will classify them according to their use, taking no account of their nature. In the office of knowledge, says Bacon, it is more fitting to employ the former method, whereas, had I been dealing with a particular science, I might have used the second to greater advantage. Secondly, the desire to supplement the deficiencies of encyclopedias of science involves a modification of the traditional order: thus if the number of known sciences had been fifteen and by supplementing them we reach twenty, these cannot possibly be arranged in exactly the same order as the fifteen had been.

Bacon's extreme caution is typical of his whole attitude during the years 1603 to 1609 when he was attempting a new formula for his programme of scientific reform. In fact the alterations, far from being mere reversals of an existing order, were often—as in the case of the term *invention*—complete reinterpretations.

Invention of arts and invention of arguments

Bacon used the following diagram for his classification of the arts of invention:

I. Invention of arts and sciences
   A. *Experientia literata* or learned experience
   B. *Interpretatio naturae* or interpretation of nature

II. Invention of arguments
   A. *Promptuaria* or preparation
   B. *Topica* or suggestion
      a. General topics
      b. Special topics.

For the classical rhetoricians, as for Ramus and Wilson, invention is a way of disposing the material required to convince an audience; but Bacon gives the term a much wider significance by distinguishing the invention of arts from the invention of arguments and restricting its 'legitimate' use to the former. The invention of arguments is not properly speaking invention, says Bacon; to invent is to discover what we do not know, and not to use or recall what is known; rhetorical invention is only the skilful selection from the mind's store of knowledge of what is most apt and pertinent; it is, in fact, a remembering or suggestion adapted to the use of discourse. One can, however, use the term in this context, so long as it is remembered that its aim is to assist knowledge and not to extend it.[1]

Bacon compares the deficiency of the invention of arts and sciences to that of a dead man's estate when the inventory thereof proves 'that there is no ready money'; for as money is the means of acquiring all else, so this art is the means of purchasing all the others, and if so little progress has been made in the scientific field it is because this art has not been cultivated as it should be. As logic today, says Bacon, declines to assist the mechanical and liberal arts, science, or the axioms of science, it has become stunted and withered.[2] We have to rely for each art on the sole authority of those who practise it; the inductive method of traditional logic is vitiated and inadequate; conclusions drawn from individual instances without negative examples are not conclusions but mere conjectures; how are we to know that a negative instance invalidating the whole argument has not been omitted? The absurdity of such a method makes it difficult to see how subtle philosophers could proffer it to the public; but these men were overhasty in establishing their theories and dogmas, negligent and lax in matters of detail. And if some scientific principles and axioms have, indeed, been obtained in this way, it is none the less certain that the syllogism, in 'the subject of nature' does not allow for the deduction of middle terms from such principles. In the syllogistic method conclusions may be deduced from premises by means of middle terms. The method is useful in ethics, law, or even theology—since it has pleased God to comply with the limitations of the human intellect. The syllogism may serve to convince but the subtleties of nature elude it. Arguments are made of propositions, propositions of words, and words are the 'marks' of notions; if these notions have been improperly deduced from the particulars, the error cannot be located by an examination of the sequence of arguments, nor of the truth of the proposition; the evil must, as the doctors say, be traced back to the first digestion, and further organic functions will not cure it. For this reason many philosophers turn to scepticism: truth, they say, cannot be known, for the field of human knowledge is restricted to the probable and the apparent. But their main error is to refer the cause of failure to the senses. These, on the contrary, though quibbling, are 'sufficient to certify and report truth', if not directly, at least by the aid of instruments producing perceptible effects where objects are too minute for these effects to be otherwise perceived. As the hand of man must rely upon ruler and compass to draw a straight line or a circle, so the mind of man must rely on intellectual aids and instruments.[3]

In both the *Advancement of Learning* and the *De augmentis* Bacon refers the reader to another work (the already published *New Organon* in the *De augmentis*) for a discussion of the interpretation of nature. Though learned experience is not dealt with in the *Advancement* it occupies a number of pages in the *De augmentis*[4] and we shall therefore refer to this work in attempting to elucidate Bacon's interpretation of the term. Learned experience is neither an art nor a part of philosophy but rather a form of wisdom. It leads from one experiment to another, whereas the new logic leads from experiments, through axioms, to a selection of new experiments. The way of learned experience (also known as Pan's chase) is not lit, like that of the interpretation of nature, by the bright star of the new induction. But Pan's chase is not a mere groping in the dark, for the mind is guided as it were by an invisible hand. The method known as Pan's chase proceeds by varying, exchanging, extending, inverting, constraining, joining, connecting, and selecting experiments. Let us examine the process of exchanging experiments to try and get a clear idea of Bacon's meaning. There are three forms of exchange: from nature or natural phenomena to art; from an art or method to another art or method; from a particular section of a given art to another section of the same art. Most mechanical arts originate from observations of nature or natural phenomena—for nature is indeed 'art's mirror'—so that there are many examples of the first form: reproductions of the spectrum, distillation, artificial thunder and lightning, etc. The second form is less common because though nature is at the disposal of all men, the different arts are usually known only to those who practise them. But as lenses have been produced to assist sight, could not a similar device be invented to assist hearing? A drawing of an object will recall it to memory; could not the same principle be translated into the art known as artificial memory? Such exchanges from one art to another could be exploited in many ways if those who are learned in the different arts were to unite their endeavours and communicate their ideas. The third form is not very different from the second, and certain arts are so extensive that this method of exchange would assuredly give good results if carried out from one section to another. For instance, in medicine certain remedies that are only applied in specific cases might be used with advantage to preserve health and prolong life.

Thus for Bacon, to say that an argument is 'invented' means 'out of the knowledge whereof the mind is already possessed, to draw forth or call before us that which may be pertinent to the purpose which we take into our consideration'.[5] This, Bacon says in the De augumentis, is so much the case that 'places' of invention are entirely useless for those who are ignorant of the subject under discussion, whereas those who are well informed can produce arguments without the help of this art.

The 'drawing forth' from a store of knowledge is made possible either by the method of 'preparation' (or prompting), that is, by storing as much information as possible on every imaginable subject, or by that of 'suggestion' (or 'topics') which provides a guide or reference for future research. The first method, common to logic and rhetoric, hardly deserves the name of science as it has more of shrewdness and diligence than real learning.

In thus describing the method of preparation as depending on shrewdness and diligence Bacon has no intention of detracting from its validity. Aristotle, he says, by scorning and disdaining this sphere of the art of invention bartered a rich wardrobe for a pair of shears. And when, in the doctrine of adornment of speech, or rhetoric, Bacon discussed this method it was to add three supplements to it—the colours of good and evil, the *antitheta* and the *formulae minores*—all connected with his own rhetorical literary productions *Promus*, *Colours*, and *Essays*. However, if the importance of 'preparation' is considerable where purely rhetorical problems are concerned, 'topics' are directly related to the scientific method of natural research. Their use is not so much to provide arguments in a discussion as to exercise the intimate development of thought. They do not concern our assertions only, but provide a guide for our enquiries. For Bacon the term 'general topics' designates those enquiries of places that are to be found in the texts of Aristotle and all subsequent logicians. Already in the *Advancement* and the *De augumentis* Bacon, discussing primal philosophy, had criticised the stressing of argumentation rather than the reality of the thing itself, in enquiries on littleness and greatness, similarity and disparity, possibility and impossibility. To counteract such a propensity he desired that primal philosophy should be 'a receptacle for all such profitable observations and axioms as fall not within the compass of any of the special parts of philosophy or science, but are more common and of a higher stage'.[6] By refusing to see the general topic as a weapon to be used against an opponent in an argument, it would seem that Bacon considered it as a catalogue of the logical places common to all sciences, thus consolidating the links between general topics and primal philosophy. But owing to his ambiguous treatment of this first part of the topics, such an interpretation must remain hypothetical.

The problem of 'special topics' offers some interesting clues which will be discussed in the context of Bacon's 'method'. If he insisted so much on this aspect of the topics, it is probably because he had realised that a single method of research could not be applied indifferently in all spheres of knowledge. There is a definite association or 'mixture' between logic of discourse in a special field and the 'matter' of this field. A special topic, as such, takes this association into consideration providing rules of procedure for each particular field. This explains how Bacon came to conceive the topic as a basic element for natural scientific research. In the *De augumentis* he goes so far as to plan a whole book on topics of natural research, and though it was never written, the many existing fragments give some idea of the type of work Bacon had in mind.[7]

The art of judgement and the refutation of idols

The 'art of examination or judgement' includes:

I. Judgement by induction

II. Judgement by syllogism

first division:

A. Reduction direct
B. Reduction inverse

second division:

A. Analytics
B. Elenches or doctrine concerning the detection of fallacies
   a. Detection of sophistical fallacies
   b. Detection of fallacies of interpretation
   c. Detection of fallacies of false appearances or idols.

Bacon scholars have ignored this diagram as they have all Bacon's diagrams concerning the classifications of the logical arts. I believe, for my part, that Bacon's interpretation of the term 'analytics' and his reason for separating analytics and refutations will provide a clue to the significance of his reform of logic; but to understand Bacon's thought fully we must return to the rhetorical tradition which moulded it.

It should be remembered that for Ramus—as for Cicero and Quintilian—*iudicium* (judgement) and *dispositio* (arrangement) are one, and indicate the regular disposition of invented matter in speech. The formula 'according to Ramus' division' signified an interpretation of *dispositio* including syllogisms.[8] But for the classical rhetoricians a demonstrative or laudatory kind of oratory already constituted the main section of *dispositio*, being, in fact the practical realisation of invention for oratorical ends.[9] For Bacon the art of judgement is 'to judge that which is invented',[10] and it deals with the proof, exposition, and refutation of fallacious sophistic arguments. We have seen that although Bacon adopted the diagrams of rhetoric for his classifications, these were modified by his distinction of invention of arts and sciences and invention of arguments; a distinction which also explains his division of the art of judgement.

Indeed, for Bacon the relation of invention to judgement alters with the type of invention. In the case of invention of arts and sciences Bacon substitutes his new logic of the interpretation of nature—based on the new induction—for the syllogistic method which had, according to him, proved fruitless here. Thus, in the last analysis, the relation: invention of arts-judgement becomes induction-judgement, and finally the two elements of this relation are identified, and thus the logic of scientific knowledge eliminates the distinction indicated in the diagram between invention and judgement:

> With regard however to judgement by induction there is nothing to detain us: for here the same action of the mind which discovers the thing in question judges it; and the operation is not performed by help of any middle term, but directly almost in the same manner as by the sense. For the sense in its primary objects at once apprehends the appearance of the object, and consents to the truth thereof. In the syllogism it is otherwise; for there the proof is not immediate, but by mean. And therefore the invention of the mean is one thing, and the judgement of the consequence is another; for the mind ranges first, and rests afterwards.[11]

But the relation invention of arguments-judgement depends on the syllogistic method 'which procures assent but can do no work' and is restricted to the moral and humane sciences. Exposition, proof, and refutation are here equivalent to argument, persuasion, and rhetoric.

Thus Bacon's definition of analytics—which 'sets down true forms of consequences in argument; from which if there be any variation or defection the conclusion is detected to be faulty'— is clear. It regulates the progress of discourse, fixing certain laws wherein a refutation is implicit for 'the straight indicates what is not straight as well as what is'. However, it is better to append a doctrine of refutations to the analytics so that the fallacies which tend to obscure judgement may more readily be detected. Bacon prefers not to dwell at too great a length upon analytics as it has already been the subject of too much talk. But it is evident that his interpretation of the term is typically Ramistic.[12] In his preface to the *Animadversiones*, Books IX–XX, Ramus had in fact explicitly distinguished two parts of logic:

> The art of logic falls into two parts; first *Topics*, which is the finding of arguments, i.e. middle terms, principles and elements, and second *Analytics*, which is the disposition of these arguments.[13]

It is noteworthy, however, that for Bacon analytics is one of the two parts of judgement. His classification of logic completely reversed the Aristotelian order by placing analytics or *dispositio* after invention, and by attributing to the former the task of 'judging that which has been invented'. Aristotelian logic discusses exposition independently from its function; but for Bacon, as for Ramus, there is little point in discussing the rules that govern discourse without previously discussing invention, that is, without collecting subject-matter for the exercise of judgement. Even Ramus' detractors had to admit the originality of this reversal:

> Ramus attacks Aristotle and the Schoolmen, on the ground that they treat topics according to presupposed, traditionally received rules of ratiocination, whereas he asserts that on the contrary a discussion of rules may take place only after the topics have been explained and all that relates to their invention communicated. Ramus holds that we ought to amass our material before we deliberate upon its proper disposition.[14]

Thus Bacon's analytics is only the art of arguing consistently or, in other words, establishing a sequence of points along which discourse must travel to reach an authentic conclusion. And authentic here does not imply that the conclusion has been deduced from authentic premises containing, as Aristotle stipulated 'the principle of their own credibility in themselves alone', but simply conclusions that can stand up to the attacks launched by the doctrine of refutations. Indeed, the relation Bacon establishes between analytics and refutations recalls the common distinction of classical rhetoric where *demonstratio* (or exposition) was included in *confirmatio* and *reprehensio* (confirmation and refutation). In fact, the term *redargutio* so dear to Bacon is to be found in Cicero.[15]

In the *Advancement of Learning* the division of the 'doctrine of refutations' into refutation of sophistry, of interpretations, and of idols, is not explicitly stated, but in the *De augmentis* it is discussed at great length. Logical sophisms must be distinguished from rhetorical sophisms with which Bacon deals in that appendix of rhetoric, *The Colours of Good and Evil*. The first derives from 'subtlety of illaqueation' and perplexes the reason, the second derives from 'the strength of the impression' and overwhelms reason with the power of the imagination.[16] Thus the first or 'the more subtle sort of them doth not only put man beside his answer, but doth many times abuse his judgement'. There is nothing to add to this doctrine, says Bacon, after the texts of Aristotle, Plato's polemic against the Sophists, and Socrates' comments. But the refutation of interpretations which is really a subdivision of the former, needs going into. Interpretations, or the 'Sophistry of Sophistry', derives from the ambiguity of language 'specially of such words as are most general and intervene in every inquiry', such as more, less, first, next, identity, act, totality, part, existence, lack, etc. According to Bacon, Aristotle wrongly attributed to analytics the task of examining general terms, for it is not a question of logical judgement but of revising predictable usages to avoid any chance of ambiguity. It is not categories that should be examined but the linguistic usage of certain general terms.[17] On the other hand Bacon's 'primal philosophy' deals with these terms from the standpoint of 'physics'. But Bacon's refutation of interpretations is so intricately connected to his refutation of idols that one cannot fully understand the one without having examined the other.

The doctrine of idols[18] is, for Bacon, an integral part of his new logic of science, which deals with the invention of arts, where traditional logic deals with the invention of arguments.

It does not try to show the way for success in discussion, but in the control of nature. 'The doctrine of idols is to the interpretation of nature what the doctrine of the refutation of sophisms is to common logic.'[19] The concept of idols was already explicitly expressed in the *Temporis partus masculus*, where Bacon, after enumerating the three types of idol (of the theatre, of the market-place, of the cave) attacked traditional philosophies in an attempt to liberate men's minds from the first. Of all Bacon's works the *Valerius Terminus* (1603) is the one where he is least given to historical polemics; here idols are a consequence of human nature and are divided into four groups: 'of the nation or tribe, of the palace, of the cave, of the theatre' though he mentions the possibility of 'numerous subdivisions'.[20] The two points where this formulation of the doctrine of idols differs from that of the *New Organon* and the *De augumentis*[21] are that the idols of the theatre are not imposed from outside, but are integral to the nature of the human mind; and 'idols of the market-place' are replaced here by 'idols of the palace', though it is not impossible that the substitution of 'palace' for 'place' was due to an error of transcription.[22] In the *Advancement of Learning* (1605) Bacon refers generically to three 'profound kinds of fallacies in the mind of man' and discusses three types of idol corresponding to those of the tribe, the cave, and the market-place.[23] The idols of the theatre are here omitted and the distinction between 'adventitious' and 'innate' idols is only referred to in the title. But Bacon probably included the idols derived from language in the second group. In the *Partis instaurationis secundae delineatio et argumentum* (1607) the idols are divided into three groups corresponding to three refutations: of philosophies, of interpretations, and of the nature of human reason.[24] In the *New Organon* and the *De augumentis* the first two refutations come under the heading of idols of the theatre, but here, as we have seen, there are four groups: the idols of the tribe, which derive from the general nature of the human reason; the idols of the cave, which are peculiar to each individual; the idols of the forum (or market place) which derive from society and language; and the idols of the theatre deriving from the influence of philosophers and false interpretations. The distinction between adventitious and innate idols is made in the *Distributio operis* where the former are said to penetrate the mind 'from the doctrines and sects of philosophers or from perverse rules of demonstration'.[25] These can, with difficulty, be eliminated, but it is impossible to be rid of the others; all that one can hope is, by warnings and signals, to make men aware of the presence of these powerful forces in their minds. In the *New Organon* the distinction is not explicitly indicated, but it recurs later in the *De augumentis*—which seems to confirm Levi's theory that for Bacon the idols of the market place were also innate. The idols deriving from language are 'intrinsic to human existence . . . for man cannot live outside society and must therefore of necessity use language', thus partaking of the nature of innate idols that cannot be eliminated.[26]

The idols of the theatre have been amply discussed in the chapter on the refutation of philosophies, and those of the market place will be dealt with in the context of Bacon's doctrine of language. Here we shall examine Bacon's description of the phenomonology of error, in other words, his theory of the idols of the tribe and of the cave. This theory has its most comprehensive exposition in the *New Organon* and the *De augumentis*, and it is to these works we shall refer throughout.

Bacon's theory of the idols is based on the assumption that the existing relation of man's mind to nature is not what it should rightfully be. This assumption is consistent with his religious beliefs, his conception of Christianity, and his ideal of the reform of knowledge. Truth of being and truth of knowledge are one, wrote Bacon in *Praise of Knowledge* (1593): they differ only as a beam differs from its reflexion. When the human mind issued forth from the hands of the Creator it was as a glass that could reflect the whole world; man was endowed with the pure and original knowledge of nature and the universe, so that he was able to name the animals in the Garden of Eden, according to their true natures. It is not this pure and chaste knowledge, but the human presumption to know good and evil, which occasioned the Fall. When man knew evil he lost simultaneously his freedom and this chaste intellectual enlightenment. Heaven and earth also, that had been made for man's use, were subjected to corruption, and a chasm opened out between the spirit of man and the spirit of the world; thus the mind of man became an 'enchanted glass' distorting the beams of things. And from the very nature of man, independently of learning and education, was born that power of seduction, that familiar spirit which obsesses the mind of man with vain and varied phantoms.

But the Word of promise had been spoken: by religion and faith man could have regained the state of justice which had been his; by his arts and works he might still have curbed it to his needs, for man had preserved a certain degree of domination over nature. But once again he committed the sin of pride and perpetuated it through the centuries, aspiring to be like God Himself. He created fabulous worlds, aping reality, and believed he could substitute a drop of elixir for the sweat of his brow. With sinful arrogance he tried to make reality correspond to his assumptions rather than to the stamp set upon it by God. It is these worlds and assumptions that must be destroyed before the mind of man can again reflect reality, and the chaste and holy wedlock of Mind and Universe can be renewed. Thus the claim to precede experience rather than understand it will be eradicated, as will the arrogant pride that inhabits the intellect and leaves no place for the reverence and humility which are required for the perusal of the Great Book of Creation.[27]

For Bacon the freeing of minds depends upon a revision of man's attitude to the world, and is part of the reform of knowledge, but also of a more vital reform bearing on ethics and religious faith. The struggle against the false images in the mind of man has become a means of redemption. Man must be purified to receive again the true images of things and the New Logic is the way of purification:

> God forbid that we should give out a dream of our own imagination for a pattern of the world; rather may he graciously grant to us to write an apocalypse or true vision of the footsteps of the Creator imprinted on his creatures.
>
> Therefore do thou, O Father, who gavest the visible light as the first fruits of creation, and didst breathe into the face of man the intellectual light as the crown and consummation therof, guard and protect this work, which coming from thy goodness returneth to thy glory. Thou when thou turnedst to look upon the works which thy hands had made, sawest that all was very good, and didst rest from thy labours. But man, when he turned to look upon the work which his hands had made, saw that all was vanity and vexation of spirit, and could find no rest therein. Wherefore

if we labour in thy works with the sweat of our brows thou wilt make us partakers of thy vision and thy sabbath. Humbly we pray that this mind may be steadfast in us, and that through these our hands, and the hands of others to whom thou shalt give the same spirit, thou wilt vouchsafe to endow the human family with new mercies.[28]

This prayer concluded the *Distributio operis* in 1620, and was, significantly enough, included in the *Instauratio magna* upon which all Bacon's hopes were staked and which summed up all the work of his life. One can now see how the functional aspect of science and the importance of achievements and arts came to be associated with this form of religious inspiration and stemmed from an Anglicanism that was strongly reminiscent of Calvin.[29]

The idols of the tribe, or first group of idols, are innate, deriving from the inadequacy of our senses, the limitations of our intellect, the effects of our passions, our reactions to the impact of reality, and our attitude to preconceived ideas. The fallacy and obtuseness of our naturally unreliable senses proves the greatest obstacle. For instance, when observations are restricted to what is directly visible, they can but ignore the activity of the spirits residing in tangible bodies, the alterations in the disposition of particles in the denser parts of bodies, and the qualities of air and of bodies lighter than air. Instruments capable of extending and sharpening the senses are not much help either. However, there are some conclusive experiments, as when sense controls the experiment and the experiment evaluates nature and reality. As for reason, sustained by the will and the passions, it tends to believe what it would like to be true, and is in great danger of being wholly dominated by the passions. Thus from impatience it dismisses what is difficult, from unfounded hope it disdains what is simple, from superstition it refuses to admit the most secret aspects of nature, from pride, arrogance, and a misplaced aversion for what seems common and base it neglects experiment, and its reverence for man makes it loth to accept apparent paradox. That which awakens the intellect by chance is swollen out of all proportion by fantasy so that the mind establishes as law for all else the little it has perceived. Once reason is satisfied with a given theory it applies it to everything, whether it fits or not, dismissing negative instances—even when these exceed those that corroborate the theory—by subtle distinctions, for its sole aim is to confirm the previously accepted theory. Thus for astrology, dreams, prophecies and other superstitions men only consider positive cases, never giving a thought to the negative. The man who was confronted with a painting offered as a vow by men who afterwards escaped shipwreck, pertinently enquired: 'Yes, but where are they painted that were drowned after paying their vows?' The error of continuously believing positive rather than negative examples is typical of the human intellect and is harmful in that the negative examples carry most weight in establishing axioms for scientific enquiry. But it is a natural tendency of the mind to suppose that things are more orderly and regular than they are in fact, to see what fluctuates as fixed. The mind elaborates arbitrary parallels, correspondences, and relations: thus the perfect circles traced by celestial bodies or the addition of fire and its attributes to the three elements to make a total of four. The intellect is finally given to abstractions, prefers to distinguish rather than to dissect nature, knows no restraint and can conceive the extreme limits neither of space nor of time. A lack of restraint is particularly noxious for the enquiry into causes, for when aiming at what is furthest one should start with what is nearest and examine the final causes first that are more consistent with human, rather than with universal nature. Indeed it is characteristic of inexperienced and superficial philosophers to enquire into the cause of universal principles without realising the necessity of enquiring first into the cause of subordinate and secondary principles.

The idols of the cave derive from the nature peculiar to each individual, his constitution, education, habits, and the accidental circumstances of his life. In the *De augumentis* Bacon illustrates his theory with Plato's myth of the cave, using Aristotle's interpretation later adopted by Cicero in the *De natura deorum*. If a man who has spent his life in a deep, dark cave were suddenly to emerge, he would conceive the most fantastic notions of the world with which he was confronted. We are free, but our souls are imprisoned in our bodies as in caves and the natural light of things is refracted according to our constitution, our reading, our changes of temper. There are four different forms of these idols: predilections for a special form of research; propensities either to analyse or to synthesize; preferences for special periods of history; tendencies to consider exclusively either the primal elements or the totality of nature. Typical of the first form are men who have grown accustomed to the particular interests which they have taken up. When they turn to other matters they distort them, adapting them to the requirements of their habitual enquiries; thus Aristotle subjected natural philosophy to his logic so that it became nothing but words; the alchemists built their whole philosophy on a few experiments; and Gilbert constructed a complete system of natural philosophy on the few principles that absorbed him. Types of the second form can be found among one or other of the two great subdivisions of philosophers: those with an aptitude for differences and those with an aptitude for similarities. Exact, diligent minds check their observations and carefully record the minutest distinctions, while the quick and proud perceive and connect the slightest resemblances. But both tend to exaggeration resulting in over-subtle analyses or over-broad syntheses. The third form is seen in those philosophers who would prove that truth is to be found in the happy condition of a given historical age. Thus there are men for whom the olden days alone were sublime, and others who are solely interested in what is new; and there are not many who strike the happy medium and judge both old and new impartially. The last form is no better than the others, for an exclusive preoccupation with primal elements narrows the mind, while an exclusive consideration of the whole stupefies and may, indeed, destroy the intellect. Ideally the two forms of preoccupation should be combined so that the mind becomes simultaneously penetrating and comprehensive.[30]

Signs, language, and the idols of the market-place

The art of 'tradition or delivery'[31] 'concerning the expressing or transferring of knowledge to others' includes the doctrine of the 'organ of tradition or discourse' (notes of things, speech, writing); the doctrine of the 'method of tradition or discourse'; and the doctrine of the 'illustration of tradition or discourse'.

Bacon's long essay on the art of tradition—later expanded and included in the *De augumentis*—presents three points of particular interest: observations on the 'notes of things' or signs; the distinction between the doctrine of method and rhetoric; the anti-sophistic role given to rhetoric that, in its own sphere and by its own means, must restore the activities of reason, disturbed by verbal acrobatics. The relation between rhetoric and ethics depends on the first having to apply reason to the imagination to stir the will. We shall endeavour to show how these three points link up with some of Bacon's basic theories.

Bacon starts his essay on the doctrine of the organ of tradition by recalling Aristotle's words in the *De interpretatione*: 'Words are the images of cogitations, and letters are the images of words'. Thus writing is made up of a series of symbols symbolising other symbols, referring indirectly to reality by way of notions. Bacon is unwilling to identify 'language' and 'communication by word or writing', for language is an 'instrument of transmission' and as such it makes use of other means besides words and letters:

> We are handling here the currency (so to speak) of things intellec- tual, and it is not amiss to know that as moneys may be made of other material besides gold and silver, so other Notes of Things may be coined besides words and letters.[32]

Language is therefore not only composed of words but more generically of 'signs', that Bacon defines:

> This then may be laid down as a rule; that whatever can be devided into differences sufficiently numerous to explain the variety of notions (provided those differences be perceptible to the sense) may be made a vehicle to convey the thoughts of one man to another.[33]

In other words, for a sign (or series of signs) to act as a symbol it must be made of components that are perceptible to the human senses, and sufficiently numerous to represent the various distinct elements that constitute an idea. These require- ments are answered by gesture, hieroglyphics, 'real characters' or ideograms, which are therefore as much a part of language as words and letters.

Bacon goes on to explain the difference between a language expressed by words and a language expressed by signs other than words. He calls the non-verbal signs 'notes', but whereas in the *Advancement* they are 'notes of cogitations', in the *De augumentis* they are 'notes of things'—and the distinction has, as we shall see, its significance. In both cases, however, their peculiarity is to signify without using the medium of words. Gestures, hieroglyphics, and ideograms are the direct symbols of notions and things. It is well known, says Bacon, that in China and the Far East real letters are used, representing 'neither letters nor words . . . but things and notions'.

Yet even these non-verbal representations are of two kinds: those that signify 'by analogy', and those that signify 'by convention' or 'having force only by contract or acceptation'. Gestures and hieroglyphics are of the first kind 'having some similitude or congruity with the notion' or as in the *De augumentis* 'having similitude to the thing signified'. In his essay on the art of memory Bacon defined the 'emblem' as an image that has a certain analogy to the place and thus stimulates the memory, providing the means of recalling what is to be found. The emblem's function was therefore to lead intellectual concepts onto a sensory level where memory is more easily impressed.[34] Thus the function of gestures and hieroglyphics is similar to that of the emblem which is not restricted to the use of memory, and is simply another means of communication. Gestures are transitory emblems while hieroglyphics are emblems fixed by writing, so that the relation between the two is similar to that between spoken and written words. This explains Bacon's theory—reminiscent of Vico—that hieroglyphics precede letters, implying the natural, sensory origin of language in gestures (or 'dumb acts' as Vico calls them) and hieroglyphics that, like emblems, are 'similar to the thing signified'.[35]

For Bacon, however, real characters or ideograms, are distinct from emblems; their meaning depends on convention and habit, like letters of the alphabet, from which they differ only in that they refer directly to the thing signified. Thus, says Bacon, men who do not understand one another's language can nevertheless read one another's writings if the characters are accepted conventions, and books using such characters could be understood in many different provinces.[36] However, this type of communication has the disadvantage of requiring an almost unlimited variety of characters, as many, indeed, 'as radical words'.

Bacon's observations on grammar are brief but not without interest. It is a sphere of knowledge that lacks greatness but is useful and necessary for the study of foreign tongues. Indeed, by the art of grammar man has sought to redeem the curse of the confusion of tongues. But philosophical grammar is a more worthy form, for it studies 'not the analogy of words with one another, but the analogy between words and things or reasons'. It should not, however, be confused with logic, for it aims primarily at extracting from linguistic data a knowledge of the customs and history of a given people. Neither has it anything in common with that form of enquiry invented by Plato whose object was to give names to things and study etymologies on the assumption that languages were not arbitrary or conventional, but sprang from the rational naming of things. On such assumptions, says Bacon, we can reach whatever conclusions we choose, for the subject matter is like wax in our hands. Bacon considered it more rewarding to trace the mental structure of a given society from linguistic data:

> And how came it that the Greeks used such liberty in composition of words, the Romans on the contrary were so strict and sparing in it? One may plainly collect from this fact that the Greeks were fitter for arts, the Romans for business; for the distinctions of arts are hardly expressed without composition of words; whereas for the transaction of business simpler words are wanted. Then again the Hebrews have such a dislike to these compositions that they had rather abuse a metaphor than introduce a compound word: and the words they use are so few and so little mixed that one may plainly perceive from their very language that they were a Nazarite nation, separated from the rest of the nations. . . . There are numberless observations of this kind, enough to fill a good volume.[37]

Such passages make one regret that Bacon did no more than mention the subject. There are others of no less interest where he refers to the different pronunciations of languages, to phonetics, to the fact that different populations have different reactions to similar sounds, to the relation of metrical forms to linguistic structure, to cyphered languages. But in a general study such as this it is impossible to follow up this particular aspect of Bacon's thought.

But Bacon's various attitudes to language are more relevant

to our enquiry. His Latin translation of the *Advancement* repeatedly gives *res* (thing) for 'notion' or 'cogitation'. In the *De
augumentis* language is not only a representation of the ideas or
images of objects—of the substance of knowledge—but reflects
a material reality foreign to and independent from itself. This
is particularly so for 'descriptive' language; when Bacon deals
with the persuasive aspect of language, its pliability to the
various needs of man, or its functionality as means of communication, this notion is less obtrusive. The material reality which
language describes is not identical—from a scientific point of
view—with the so-called reality of common sense. It consists in
a series of geometrico-mechanical structures and is, for Bacon,
the only possible criterion for proving the truth of any linguistic
enunciation. Bacon's theory of language and of its function in
the sphere of scientific research depends on this attitude, and the
limitations of a great many studies on his doctrine of the idols
of the market-place are due to this fact having been ignored.
R. F. Jones, in a very important essay, describes Bacon's
attitude as 'a certain antipathy to language'.[38] It is in fact more
and other than an antipathy: Bacon's attitude stems from his
mistrust of language—as of all the products of the human mind
—because, though it is indispensable to humanity as such, it
tends to hinder the true understanding of reality by coming
between man and the world he inhabits:

> It seems to me that men look down and study nature as from
> some remote and lofty tower. Nature presents to their gaze a
> certain picture of herself, or a cloudy semblance of a picture, in
> which all the minute differences of things on which the practise
> and prosperity of men rest, are blurred by distance. So men toil
> and strive, straining the eyes of the mind, fixing their gaze in
> prolonged meditation, or shifting it about to get things into better
> focus. Finally they construct the arts of disputation, like ingenious
> perspective glasses, in order to seize and master the subtle differ-
> ences of nature. A ridiculous kind of ingenuity, is it not, and mis-
> directed energy for a man to climb his tower, arrange his lenses,
> and screw up his eyes to get a closer view, when he might avoid
> all that laborious contrivance and tedious industry and achieve
> his end by a way not only easy but far superior in its benefits and
> utility, namely by getting down from his tower and coming close
> to things?[39]

In order to come close to things one must discard the names that do not correspond to their reality and learn instead to make up names that fit them exactly:

> The idols imposed by words on the understanding are of two kinds. They are either names of things which do not exist . . . , or they are names of things which exist but yet confused and ill-defined, and hastily and irregularly derived from realities. Of the first kind are Fortune, the Prime Mover, Planetary Orbits, Element of Fire, and like fictions which owe their origin to false and idle theories. And this class of idols is more easily expelled, because to get rid of them it is only necessary that all theories should be steadily rejected and dismissed as obsolete. . . . But the other class, which springs out of faulty and unskilful abstraction, is intricate and deeply rooted.[40]

This passage gives the clue to Bacon's attitude: notions should be correctly derived from things and correspond to them, since names are the symbols of notions and where a notion is faulty so also is the name. But conversely, the names given to things, or words, influence the mind: 'those faulty meanings of words cast their rays or stamp their impression on the mind itself, and they do not only make discourse tedious, but they impair judgement and understanding'. If by careful observation we try to correct vulgar notions derived from superficial distinctions, so that they become better suited to reality 'words rebel' and endless controversies arise respecting, not reality, but names and words. And 'that which is the remedy for this evil (namely definitions) is in most cases unable to cure it, for definitions themselves consist of words, and words beget words'.

Bacon objects unambiguously to the theory according to which the truth of a proposition resides in the logical coherence of its component terms. This attitude is perfectly consistent with his theory of language as convention. 'Ad placitum are the characters real before mentioned and words',[41] he says in the *Advancement*; and in the *De augmentis* the idols of the market-place are said to derive from the tacit agreement between men to impose words and names on reality.[42] For these conventions refer only to the signs used for communicating notions and never to the notions themselves that should mirror the reality from which they are rigorously derived. In the *New Organon*, for instance, Bacon criticises the ambiguity of the term 'humid', deriving from the ambiguity of a notion applied indiscriminately to a variety of states and effects, and 'taken by abstraction only from water and common and ordinary liquids, without any due verification'. The remedy lies not in limiting its possible uses and its meaning by predetermination, but in examining individual cases to extract a completely new and comprehensive notion of humidity that will serve as a criterion and explain its diversity; the validity of such a criterion would depend on the greater or lesser 'correspondence to reality' of the new notion. This example shows how Bacon could identify 'notion' and 'word' yet propound his theory of the conventionality of language. Thus in paragraph XLIII of the *New Organon* he says that 'the ill and unfit choice of words wonderfully obstructs the understanding', and in paragraph LX he talks of 'names . . . hastily and irregularly derived from realities'.

The basic materialism of Bacon's conception of language is most striking where he imagines a scale for the various 'degrees of distortion and error'. At the bottom of the scale are the names of some common substances such as chalk or mud; then come the names of actions: to generate, to corrupt, etc; but the most distorted of all are the names of qualities which the senses do not perceive such as heaviness, lightness, density. According to Bacon scientific language must reach a degree of precision similar to that of vulgar language describing common notions. A scientific method should endeavour to establish the various points of congruity and incongruity in 'kindred natures'; but such relations will always be seen as actually existing, so that the figures of scientific speech will continue to be taken for authentic representations of reality. The enquiry would not aim at determining abstract relations to be used as models; but would concentrate on the substance's perceptible natures and effects. The empiricism of Locke and Newton likewise stressed the inadequacy of natural scientific methods for distinguishing and abstracting, and claimed that it was only by referring to experimental data that 'a physicist was entitled to invent and accordingly define names'.[43] But here the problems pertaining to Bacon's theory of language merge with those of his new inductive method for the discovery of forms.

The method of tradition

Bacon's reform of logic hinged on the problems of penetrating and liberating the mind. For nearly two centuries these inter-dependent problems had been discussed by European intellectuals; but when Bacon, in the *Advancement of Learning*, mentions the abundance of words and few conclusions attached to them he was probably referring specifically to the controversies between Jacques Charpentier and Peter Ramus[44] and between Digby and Temple. Bacon, who considered such controversies fruitless, decided to segregate his method of tradition from logic and rhetoric, though this did not imply a total break: logic was connected by the doctrine of judgement—the syllogism includes rules for judging that which has been found, the method, rules for judging that which must be communicated, for the art of examining or judging 'follows that of invention and precedes that of tradition'. The connection with rhetoric is obvious: the doctrine of the method of tradition is concerned with formulating discourses to suit the speaker's intentions, the audience he is addressing, and the circumstances in which the speech is made. According to Bacon scientific discourse is not exempt from such preoccupations; its form can be varied and reflects upon the content; certain forms of discourse and methods of communication are incompatible with the advancement of learning, but the doctrine of the method of tradition is based on an ideal of unerring scientific progress. As the life and toil of one man, says Bacon, do not suffice for the achievement of perfect knowledge, it is the 'wisdom of tradition' that ensures the continuity and progression of science.

Bacon's treatment of the various methods of communication is particularly relevant, firstly in that it proves his awareness of the diversity of human discourse and special modes of communication, that are irreducible to a single pattern; secondly in that he opposes here certain aspects of traditional culture. His very awareness of a plurality of methods is a refutation of Ramus, who maintained the existence of a 'one and only method', unvarying in its diverse functions, though he distinguishes the *methode de prudence* that changes with the time, the place, and the person, from the *methode de doctrine ou de nature* that proceeds from less to more evident principles, and from general and universal to particular terms:

> So since there exists a single power and nature of reason, by which all things are explained—for all that reason's subject-matter may be cut up into diverse parts, one part being comprehended under mathematics, another under physical nature, another under morals, and others under other designations—nevertheless all dialectics are contained and treated within common principles of invention and disposition.[45]

For Ramus 'the virtue and the nature of reason are one'. In his preface to the *Scholae in liberales artes* he stresses this theory declaring that there is no such thing as a Ramistic method opposed to the Platonic or Aristotelian; there is only one method common to Ramus, Plato, Aristotle, Galen, Virgil, Cicero, and Demosthenes; the same method that governs mathematics and philosophy, and the judgement and conduct of every man.[46] There is a 'natural logic' in the mind of man, and dialectics operates on three levels: nature, art, and action. The first is the faculty of reason, the second fixes rules for the best use of this faculty, the third acts according to these rules, turning them into habits. But art and action only restore and consolidate the natural faculty of reason:

> Dialectics is the art of arguing well, and in this sense is also called logic for the two words derive from *logos*, that is reason, and *dialegestha* like *logizestha* means precisely to argue or reason, namely (as Plato teaches in the first Alcibiade) to use reason, the true and natural use of which must be exposed and trained in this art.[47]

Bacon opposed Ramus's theory of a single method and also his exclusive use of dichotomy. In Ramus as in Plato the latter took the form of classifications in decreasing order of comprehension; any word can be included in one of the two classifications A or B according to whether it possesses a quality *a* belonging to A and not to B.[48]

> And first, for the 'one and only method' with its distribution of everything into two members, it is needless to speak of it; for it was a kind of cloud that overshadowed knowledge for a while and blew over: a thing no doubt both very weak in itself and very injurious to the sciences. For while these men press matters by the

laws of their method, and when a thing does not aptly fall into those dichotomies, either pass it by or force it out of its natural shape, the effects of their proceeding is this, the kernels and grains of sciences leap out, and they are left with nothing in their grasp but the dry and barren husks.[49]

There is a method of communication suited to each subject, according to Bacon. Thus it is not possible to use the same method for mathematics—the most abstract and simple science—and for politics—the most positive and complex; and it is impossible, in particular, to employ the same method when addressing a knowledgeable audience or one that is wholly ignorant of the subject. When trying to present new ideas to an unprepared audience metaphors and similitudes are required or the ideas will be dismissed as paradoxes; yet this does not excuse the artifices of esotericism veiling the secrets of science, especially as this method—once handled with great caution— has fallen into the hands of men who use it to get across their counterfeit ware.

Bacon's distinction of 'magistral' and 'initiative' methods brings us back once again to the polemics over the singleness or duality of the Ramistic method. In 1580 Digby published *De duplici methode libri duo, unicam Petri Ramo methodum refutantes*. This was, in fact, an assertion of Aristotle's rights against Ramus, but Digby also recognised the method's dual function of discovering new truths and co-ordinating previously acquired knowledge, which implied two methods, one of instruction and one of discovery. Temple, in his *Admonitio de unica P. Rami methodo*— published the same year in London—denounced Digby and affirmed the singleness of the method whose sole function was to co-ordinate the confusion of knowledge. Truth cannot be discovered by any special method or instrument but only by a proposition's clear enunciation, or by a logical syllogistic sequence:

> To be sure knowledge either shines forth instantaneously as a result of the clear disposition of elements in the enunciation of the proposition, or else springs from the rational sequence of the syllogism. But indeed by 'collocation' according to the method one acquires no knowledge of nature; rather light is thrown on the elegance of that order by which things already known and judged are linked together . . . The method has bestowed its

proper reward most generously, if it has reduced confusion to simplicity and has imposed on anarchy the clear divisions and categories of knowledge . . . Ramus argues that there is one method which applies both to that art which is already invented and separately expounded and to that art which is yet to be assigned, after syllogistic appraisal, its place in the order. You say, in opposition to Ramus, that the method is double, one part being applicable to the art which is yet to be assigned a place, the other to the invention of the same.[50]

Not only was Digby lecturing at Cambridge when Bacon was there, but he was, according even to his worst enemy, one of the most popular dons of his time; so that Bacon most probably attended his lectures. Be that as it may, Freudenthal has proved that Bacon borrowed, without acknowledgement, some of Digby's ideas.[51] Thus his unambiguous distinction between methods of co-ordination (for an informed audience) and methods of discovery (for the uninitiated) is strongly reminiscent of Digby, though it assumes, with Bacon, a more revolutionary aspect. Indeed, besides its relatively limited significance in the context of the doctrine of the method of tradition, it is operative in Bacon's separation of the invention of arts (the only true 'invention') from the invention of arguments, where he opposes a logic of discovery to a logic of instruction, and stresses the difference between acquiring knowledge and drawing from 'the knowledge whereof the mind is already possessed'. The magistral method is no other than the logic of instruction; it must inspire confidence to novices in the study of science, and tries to make the best use of science at its present stage of development. The initiative method corresponds to the new logic of invention and incites the audience to examine the speaker's assertions, is addressed to the 'sons of science', and aims at the progress of science, the advancement of learning. The term 'initiative'—borrowed from the vocabulary of religion—refers to the method's ability to reveal the mysteries of science and not to its imparting the first or 'initial' elements of scientific knowledge. Yet the ways of this method are as yet arid and full of obstruction. Those who teach prefer enforcing their beliefs to encouraging a serious critical examination of their assertions, and those who learn prefer a ready-made answer to their queries to being urged on to draw their own conclusions: 'doubt not' is their motto, and errors can take care of themselves. Thus from ambition the master hides his deficiencies, while the pupil, to avoid exertion, fails to try his own strength. In fact, where possible, science should be instilled into the pupil's mind by the method that served for its invention; scientists of the new induction would have no difficulty in following this precept, but with scientific research at its present level who can explain how he has come by a given conclusion? Yet it should not be impossible to retrace the scientist's steps, checking affirmations, and thus transplant science to the mind of the disciple exactly as it developed in the master's. If you want to make use of a plant the roots may be discarded, but if you want to transplant it to a different soil it is better to preserve the roots. Actual methods of communication make use of a section of the tree's trunk—beautiful to see, no doubt, and perhaps useful to a carpenter, but hardly fit for planting. Roots with a little earth attached are what is needed for the growth of science. The method used by mathematicians is not dissimilar, for in both cases a job must be started and a gap must be bridged; the 'passing of lighted torches or hereditary method' is among the desiderata.[52]

Bacon's distinction between aphoristic and expository methods is, in the last analysis, motivated by the same demands as his other distinctions. The latter method achieves a false air of competence by verbal artefact and linguistic contortions. Examples, similitudes, and rhetorical gambits fill the gaps in discourse, but do not serve the purpose of scientific progress. On the other hand the poverty of nearly all current scientific discourse would be immediately apparent if it were expressed in aphorisms, for aphorisms do not create illusions of security but are an incentive to further enquiry, and the fulfilment and stability of the scientific edifice rests on such enquiries.

Thus from discussing methods of communication Bacon came back full circle to the solution of problems that, to him, were vital. Which in fact confirms our theory that, for Bacon, the discovery of new scientific methods and the problems of penetrating the minds of men and organising scientific research are only three facets of a single, constant preoccupation: the reform of knowledge.

The function of rhetoric

To appreciate fully the originality of Bacon's views on rhetoric they must be compared to those of the sixteenth- and early seventeenth-century treatises on rhetorical art. According to a plan suggested by W. S. Howell and later enlarged by K. R. Wallace[53] English rhetoric of this period followed two main trends. The 'classical' trend includes such works as *The Art of Rhetoryke* by Leonard Cox (1524), the *Arte of Rhetorique* by Thomas Wilson (1553), and the *Manductio ad artem rhetoricam* by Thomas Vicars (1619), where rhetoric is seen as the art of speaking and writing in prose. It is completely autonomous, comprising the five classical divisions: invention, disposition, speech, memory, and tradition; and its function is to provide instant practical assistance to scholars who wish to achieve brilliant effects in the forensic and demonstrative manners. Thus the links between rhetoric and logic or ethics take second place: formal laws for inference are drawn from logic; generalisations on 'passions' and 'character' from ethics; and both logic and ethics are considered in connection with 'persuasive discourse'. What Wallace has called the 'stylistic' trend identifies rhetoric with style and delivery; such are the *Rhetorica* of Talaeus (1577), the *Treatise of Schemes and Tropes* by Richard Sherry (1550), the *Artes of Logicke and Rhetoricke* by Dudley Fenner (1584), the *Arte of English Poesie* by George Puttenham (1589). Everything concerning *inventio* and *dispositio* pertains to logic, the study of passion and character to ethics. Rhetoric is 'an arte of speaking finely'; its function is to 'garnish' speech and make delivery pleasant.

By describing rhetoric as 'the illustration of tradition'[54] Bacon would seem to have classed himself in this second category; but his attitude is, in fact, quite different from that of Puttenham or Fenner. For them the 'adorning' aspect of rhetoric stemmed from its separation from logic and from the fact that it was an art that came after logic, presupposing it and the rules of *inventio* and *dispositio*; whereas for Bacon rhetoric is one of the four intellectual arts that constitute logic and like logic, its function is to extend the empire of reason and defend it against every onslaught, even if in a different field and with different tools. Besides, Bacon's polemics against a form of knowledge favouring verbosity rather than serious enquiry are radically opposed to an interpretation of rhetoric as mere ornament. In the *Valerius Terminus* Bacon had already hinted at the existence of two distinct methods, one to instruct and fix the rules of procedure, the other to encourage an incessant examination of statements to further scientific progress. The latter must adopt and impart the exact methods employed in the invention, while the former requires to be 'most compendious and ready', being a method for prompt and immediate use.[55] This foreshadows Bacon's definition of the function of rhetoric in the *Advancement* and the *De augumentis*: parallel to a 'scientific logic' serving intellectual purposes, there exists a 'common logic' which is to the imagination what the former is to the intellect. This method, dictating rules of behaviour, is rhetoric: its function is to instil reason into the free actions of men.

Rhetoric has thus a rational function, being one of the tools employed by reason to consolidate its powers:

> For we see Reason is disturbed in the administration thereof by three means: by Illaqueation or Sophism, which pertains to Logic; by Imagination or Impression, which pertains to Rhetoric; and by Passion or Affection, which pertains to Morality . . . the end of Rhetoric is to fill imagination to second reason, and not to oppress it.[56]

Yet the function of rhetoric is not to create superstitions, but to determine attitudes, and is thus akin to ethics. Before examining this relation, however, let us define Bacon's interpretation of the term 'imagination'. Bacon's encyclopedia opens with the first basic tripartition of knowledge corresponding to the three faculties proper to all rational beings: history corresponding to memory; poetry corresponding to imagination or fancy; and philosophy or science corresponding to reason. The object of history is man situated in time and space. The object of poetry (or history invented at will), like that of history, is man, but considered here from a purely arbitrary point of view: imaginary man instead of real man. It also resembles philosophy in that it puts together and takes apart images; but these compositions and divisions are made as it were in play, and poetry does not deal with abstract ideas like philosophy, but with subjective images.[57] Thus for Bacon poetry is the fruit of a creative but capricious fancy, completely uninhibited and therefore beyond control. But fancy has other functions besides poetry, and acquires a singular importance in the pages of Bacon's encyclopedia. Indeed, the role of 'messenger between the provinces of ethics and reason' devolves upon fancy.[58] Logic has the mind or reason for its object; ethics deals with the will, desires, and passions. The former inspires decisions, the latter actions. Between the two imagination comes and goes without pause like a messenger, for the images of the senses are entrusted to fancy who transmits them to reason to be judged; reason then returns the selected images to fancy so that they may become actions. Thus the actions of the will are always preceded and motivated by the imagination which is the common instrument of reason and of will; like a two-faced Janus it bears the double mask of truth and of virtue; hence the importance of its function. Its authority is above that of a mere messenger for in matters of faith and religion imagination rises to greater heights even than reason to penetrate the minds of men by means of parables and visions. Imagination is no less useful for persuasion when an opinion must be insinuated into the minds of others by the use of eloquence; and here, indeed, lies the danger, when fancy overcomes reason and the minds of men are thrown, as it were, from one side to another by the speaker's images.

This long digression has at least served the purpose of elucidating Bacon's definition: 'the duty and office of rhetoric is to apply reason to imagination for the better moving of the will'. Rhetorical images insinuate themselves into the mind by striking the imagination so that the messages of reason result in positive actions. Thus rhetoric can 'make virtue visible' and, by elaborating appropriate images, set her for ever before the eyes of man. Cicero, says Bacon, rightly mocked the Stoics' claim to introduce virtue into the souls of men by concise sentences; if men's passions were amenable to reason, there would be little use for methods of persuasion or other ways of penetrating the mind: the naked truth would suffice; but passion is hostile to reason's government, and reason, left to its own devices, would be reduced to impotence. The duty of rhetorical persuasion is to stop imagination from siding with the affections and 'contracting a confederacy between Reason and Imagination against the affections'. The passions know only present gains, while reason sees further and knows future gains as well. What is present strikes the imagination more forcibly, so that rhetoric must endeavour to make future gains as lifelike and visible as the present, thus drawing imagination onto the side of reason. For this end rhetorical discourse must adapt itself to the demands of the audience: Aristotle justly placed rhetoric between dialectics on one side and ethics and politics on the other, for while dialectics may be used as proof and demonstration in all occasions and for all men, rhetorical proofs and persuasions should vary according to the audience.

Rhetoric had thus for Bacon the dual function of reinstating reason by freeing the mind from the 'juggling of words' and false images, and of creating 'visible' images of moral concepts. For the first, rhetoric must be able to refute rhetorical sophisms which derive, not like those of logic from 'subtle wiles', but from the 'impact of impression' by which imagination overpowers reason. Bacon calls such rhetorical sophisms 'colours of good and evil',[59] each colour comprising two parts: an assertion, having the appearance of truth, concerning the nature of good and evil; and a negation. The first of the twelve colours in the *De augumentis* declares 'What men praise and honour is good, what they dispraise and condemn is evil', a statement which is accepted, not for its truth, but for its impact on the imagination. It is, in fact, misleading for four reasons:

> By reason of ignorance, of bad faith, of party spirit and factions, of natural dispositions of those who praise and blame. By reason of ignorance; for what is popular judgement worth as a test of good and evil? Better was Phocion's inference, who when the people applauded him more than usual, asked whether he had done wrong. By reason of bad faith, because in praising and blaming, men are commonly thinking of their own business, and not speaking what they think. The merchant praises what he wants to sell. And again 'It is naught, it is naught' says the buyer; but when he is gone his way he will vaunt his acquisition. By reason of factions; for any man may see that men are wont to exalt those of their own party with immoderate praises, and depress below their desert those of the contrary. By reason of natural disposition; for some men are by nature formed and composed for servile adulation, while others on the contrary are crabbed and captious; so that in praising and blaming they do but gratify their own dispositions, with little regard to truth.[60]

The first three colours were inspired by Aristotle's *Rhetoric*; though, according to Bacon, this work did not provide enough examples: Aristotle had partly overlooked the true use of colours, and his assertions were not followed by negations. Both Bacon and Aristotle saw rhetoric as a practical art capable of controlling men's actions by swaying their will, but for Bacon it had besides the specific moral function[61] of liberating their minds from sophisms; when the imagination is impressed by statements or 'common places', reason may be rendered useless and uncritical; such tyrannical images must therefore be replaced by others 'to second reason'; this substitution is accomplished by negations.

The other two additions to rhetoric mentioned in the *Advancement* and expanded in the *De augumentis* are the *antitheta* and the *formulae minores*. The first, a collection of forty-seven instances designed to assist the invention of arguments, are composed, in most cases, of statements for and against a given subject. Thus the sixteenth, on envy, runs:

For	*Against*
It is natural for a man to hate that which reproaches him his fortunes.	Envy keeps no holiday. Nothing but death can reconcile envy and virtue.
Envy in commonwealth is a wholesome kind of ostracism.	Envy puts virtue to laborious tasks, as Juno did Hercules.

A. E. Abbott has noted the extensive use to which Bacon put the *antitheta* in the second and third editions of his *Essays*.[62] Thus in the essay *Of Envy* the following paragraph was added in the third edition:

A man that hath no virtue in himself, ever envieth virtue in others . . . and whoso is out of hope to attain to another's virtue, will seek to come at even hand by depressing another's fortune . . . Now, to speak of public envy. There is yet some good in public envy, whereas in private there is none. For public envy is as an ostracism, that eclipseth men when they grow too great. And therefore it is a bridle also to great ones, to keep them within bounds.[63]

Such examples are numerous. However, our intention is to prove Bacon's constant preoccupation with this form of discussion. Thus his first edition of the *Essays* (1597) includes fragments of the *Colours of Good and Evil*;[64] the *Promus or Formularies and Elegancies*—one of his first works, but not published till 1883 —is a kind of short fragmentary manual of hints for juridical and parliamentary debates;[65] such were also the *formulae minores* of the *De augumentis* described by Bacon as 'antechambers of speech'. They are in fact preambles, conclusions, digressions, and premisses suitable for all arguments; here, for instance, is a conclusion: 'so may we redeem the faults passed and prevent the inconveniences future'.[66]

During the whole of his life Bacon continued to collect material for his *promptuaria*. From 1593, or thereabouts, when he wrote the *Promus*, till a few years before his death (the *De augumentis* was written in 1623, the third edition of the *Essays* appeared in 1625) his interest in these popular literary and philosophical problems of his time never flagged. Such an attitude is totally incomprehensible if one ignores Bacon's five hundred or so pages of juridical writings and the place of rhetoric in Elizabethan culture. There are a number of notable works giving social, political, and intellectual reasons for the status of rhetoric in sixteenth- and seventeenth-century England, and a problem of such proportions has no place in this study; but at no time have words been valued so highly. The whole of Elizabethan poetry, philosophic, pastoral, lyric, and elegiac was dominated by rhetoric. Indeed, the aim of poetry was held to be none other than to influence human actions, and George Puttenham, one of the greatest rhetoricians of poetry, says that by the music and imagery of poetry man's judgement can be swayed. In a society where university teaching was based on rhetoric, and where it was taught even in the grammar schools, where words were considered the best means of influencing the actions of mankind, descriptions such as this of the Lord Chancellor by Ben Jonson, were not uncommon:[67]

> Yet there happened in my time one noble speaker, who was full of gravity in his speaking. No man ever spake more neatly, more precisely, more weightily or suffered less emptiness, less idleness, in what he uttered. His hearers could not cough, or look aside from him, without loss. He commanded where he spoke; and had his judges angry and pleased at his devotion. No man had their affections more in his power. The fear of every man that heard him, was lest he should make an end.[68]

It was these qualities of oratorical gravity and strictness that Bacon had so often stressed and opposed to the vain subleties of style and to the acrobatic contortions and juggling dexterity that only serve to show off the speaker's ability. Thus Bacon attacked 'the great injustice of Plato' who considered rhetoric 'as a voluptuary art', like the art of cooking,[69] and opposed to the grand phrases and elegant style of public speakers the ability to adapt a speech to one's audience and to one's ends. In fact Bacon's doctrine of rhetoric was based on his distinction between invention and elocution, between convincing by the logic of ideas, and persuading by awakening the passions. Enquiry into nature *as such* has no use for this kind of persuasion; it requires a strictness and a rigour that exclude emotion, and must work in the 'bare light of logic' bowing before reality, not before words. Thomas Sprat, outlining the programme of the Royal Society, said that their aim was to free the present age from errors of the past:

> This is the compass of their Design. And to accomplish this, they have indeavor'd to separate the knowledge of Nature from the colours of Rhetoric, the devices of Fancy, or the delightful deceit of Fables.[70]

Such an ideal is unmistakably Baconian. Indeed Bacon's distinction between emotional persuasion and rational conviction implied that between rhetoric—as a section of the art of tradition—and the 'doctrine of the method of tradition' or *prudentia traditivae*, to which he had given the status of an autonomous science. Already in the *Temporis partus masculus* when dealing with the problem of penetrating the minds of men and freeing them from 'dark conceits' he refers to the 'legitimate method of communication'. Thus for Bacon the problem of purifying the intellect and the connected problem of a new organon of science could not be solved by what he calls 'rhetoric' but by the 'doctrine of the method of tradition'. Logic and ethics alone cannot guide humanity on the path of righteousness but require the assistance of rhetoric which governs the passions by images contrived to turn fancy from the side of passion. It should not be forgotten that the main section of Bacon's ethics, the 'Georgics of the Soul', is directed towards indicating the way in which some passions can overcome others:

are not jurisdiction and politics, says Bacon, based on the art of controlling 'dangerous' passions by means of such passions as hope and fear?[71]

Thus for Bacon the art of rhetoric pertains to the sphere of reason and ethics, because it governs moral actions. By 'moral' Bacon means stable and unimpassioned. In this sense rhetoric cannot be reduced to 'style' and 'ornament': the form and the 'illustration of speech' have a specific function which is not to 'delight' but to attain certain predetermined ends. As J. N. D. Bush[72] has rightly noted, even Bacon's *Essays* are not recreative literature, but are part of the *Instauratio magna*—a supplement, in fact, to the *Advancement of Learning*, and an enquiry into methods for subjecting the imagination to practical reason. In a letter to Casaubon, written in 1609, Bacon says:

> To write at leisure what is to be read at leisure does not interest me. My concern is with life and human affairs and all their troubles and difficulties.

And the *Essays* were intended as another contribution to that science of man to which Bacon dedicated for many years the best part of his inexhaustible energies.

VI

Rhetorical Tradition and the Method
of Science

The birth of time

Bacon's refutation of the philosophical tradition involved a complete revaluation of the very concept of philosophy and philosophical discourse. By changing man's attitude to reality Bacon wished to redirect the whole course of philosophical research, its aims, methods, duties, and function. Thus his *œuvre* cannot be seen as a simple reform of Scholastic Aristotelian logic, or an empirical solution to the problem of knowledge. Even the less perceptive Bacon scholars have seen that his work assumed the proportions of a total reform based on his faith in an imminent change in the destinies of mankind—a change that rested with man himself, and that was not to be identified with the reform of philosophy on which it was only partly dependent. Bacon's work was not 'a product of the mind but a parturition of Time', and his language has the religious solemnity of a summons to mankind, a summons inspired by historical facts of such overwhelming significance to Bacon that they become the basis of his attempted reform. We saw, in the section on Bacon's history of philosophy, how his refutation of tradition differed from Descartes'. Bacon has no intention of dismissing the whole past, but he advocates a thorough examination of the causes of its philosophical failure: Greek philosophy and Aristotle's historiographical outline must be revised, and above all the relation of a given philosophy to the civilisation that fostered it must be studied to reveal their interdependence. For Bacon the failure of traditional philosophy was mainly determined by specific historical factors: Greek philosophy flourished in an age of fables and historical and geographical ignorance; Roman philosophy was diverted from the study of nature by the claims of a vast empire; Scholasticism was vitiated by the idleness and isolation of men who had no other food for their vivacious wits than the texts of Aristotle.

Even the positive side of Bacon's reform has intricate connections with history. The reform of knowledge cannot be the work of a single intellect, the choice of one mind; for it is the outcome of a vast upheaval and a common cause. The advancement of learning is not limited to propounding theories and perfecting their logical structure, but depends equally on the state of civilisation and culture. The invention of the printing press, of gun-powder and of the magnet have changed the face of the world and the human condition; indeed, there is not an empire, a planet, or a school of philosophy whose influence on mankind has been so great, or that has served the cause of humanity as much as these mechanical inventions.[1] More than philosophers and politicians, the 'mechanicists' have contributed to the evolution of mankind. Yet:

> It would be a disgrace for mankind if the expanse of the material globe, the lands, the seas, the stars, was opened up and brought to light, while, in contrast with this enormous expansion, the bounds of the intellectual globe should be restricted to what was known to the ancients.[2]

And elsewhere Bacon says:

> And surely, when I set forth before me the condition of these times, in which learning seems to have now made her third visitation to men; and when at the same time I attentively behold with what helps and assistances she is provided; as the vivacity and sublimity of the many wits of this age; the noble monuments of ancient writers, which shine like so many lights before us; the art of printing, which brings books within reach of men of all fortunes; the opened bosom of the ocean, and the world travelled over in every part, whereby multitudes of experiments unknown to the ancients have been disclosed, and an immense mass added to Natural History . . . the peace which Britain, Spain, Italy,

France too at last, and many other countries now enjoy . . . and lastly, the inseparable property of time, ever more and more to disclose Truth; I cannot, I say, when I reflect on these things but be raised to this hope, that this third period will far surpass the Greek and Roman learning.[3]

In the *Cogitata et visa* Bacon states his belief in a single law governing the material and the intellectual progress of humanity,[4] and if we overlook this fundamental notion of his philosophy we run the risk of taking him for what he never wanted to be and never was: a constructor of systems or the founder of a philosophical school. Even in those works that were never intended for publication, Bacon always disclaimed such a role. Though in this respect the *De interpretatione naturae proemium* has some relevant passages, his dismissal of all claims to figure as a builder of speculative philosophical systems is clearest in the preface to the *Instauratio magna* and the *Distributio operis*. Bacon's whole work is based on the indissolubility of the destinies of mankind and the success of the new philosophy. In their own interest and free from all prejudice, wrote Bacon in the *Preface*, men must strive together with all their might to achieve the restoration of science. Such a reform should not be deemed limitless or beyond human power; but it will put an end to a long period of error. However, Bacon does not forget that he is mortal and that such an enterprise cannot be accomplished by a single man in a single life span; he lays therefore his trust in posterity, doing no more than to enunciate a truth upon which others may experiment. And this is not a matter of mere contemplative felicity, says Bacon in the *Distributio operis*, but of the future success of mankind. But he has no hope of completing his task, and in the sixth part of the *Instauratio*—which represents the completion of the entire reform—he is content to have given the signal of departure.[5]

All this should help us understand—besides some of the views Bacon held on logic—the inclusion of certain theories in his philosophy. According to Bacon the ancients had developed a given type of philosophical discourse based on the pre-eminence of contemplation over action, of theories of nature over the conquest of nature, and of introspection over the quest for reality; and this attitude had conditioned their philosophical logic. This logic was an adequate tool in the contemplative or theoretical field, for discussions rather than experiments on nature; but it was fruitless and inefficient where the principal aims of humanity were to transform reality, invent new arts and sciences, and dominate nature. As I have tried to prove throughout this book, traditional philosophy was not for Bacon a fallacious philosophy, but its aims were limited and insufficient, and such shortcomings reflected a mentality for which the excursions into the countryside of Plato and Democritus assumed the proportions of 'great expeditions'.[6]

Traditional logic and new logic

Bacon's views naturally led to the concept of two different types of philosophy and of logic: one for use in discourse, disputes, controversies, conversations, and other social and professional activities; the other, or 'new logic', to help man in his progressive conquest of nature. The first 'actually exists', having been invented by the Greeks and developed through the centuries; the second is only a 'project' and 'enterprise', a 'voyage of discovery'. The realisation of such a project requires a total change in the attitude of man to reality and in the very conception of philosophy and science. It is no mere coincidence that Bacon's reform of logic was to be part of the *Instauratio magna*. The new logic must fill a gap in present-day knowledge by responding to the demands of a changed historico-social situation and it must become an organ or instrument for the new aims of philosophy and science.

But on one point Bacon is quite emphatic: traditional philosophy has not failed in what it attempted. Though it may require integrating, revising and perfecting it is quite capable of preserving and transmitting sciences and teaching man to follow and exploit known truths or the art of inventing arguments to outwit others in a discussion. We are not interested, says Bacon, in popular controversial arts, and the new logic has not the pretention of serving the ends of traditional logic: anticipations and dialectic, he says in the *New Organon*, are good for sciences based on probabilities, that is, where the aim is to control opinions not nature.[7] In the *Preface* to the *Instauratio magna* he declares that actual dialectic ' is not nearly subtle enough to deal with nature' though it be 'very properly applied to civil

business and to those arts which rest on discourse and opinion.'
But when instead we wish to overcome not opponents but
nature, and to achieve not well-turned, convincing theories, but
sure, demonstrable instances, not to invent probabilities, but
arts and accomplishments, then we must resort to the 'interpretation of nature'.

> The art which I introduce is a knowledge, though the difference
> between it and ordinary logic is great: indeed immense.[8]

All these two logics have in common is that both try to find
a means of assisting and sustaining the mind; they differ in
their aims, the sequence of their demonstrations, and the point
of departure of their enquiries. The new logic is 'the doctrine
concerning the better and more perfect use of human reason
in the inquisition of things'. The main object of discourse in
traditional logic is the syllogism, for dialecticians, intent on
finding formulae for arguments in a discussion, are not interested
in induction. But if syllogisms are used for natural research
'nature slips through the hands'; the middle terms of syllogisms
are 'barren of works, remote from practice, and altogether un-
available for the active deportment of sciences', whereas induction proves to be a much more useful instrument because it
sticks to reality, following action so closely that it is almost
identified with it. Thus the traditional sequence of demonstrations is reversed; formerly one passed directly from particulars to the most general principles that were as 'fixed poles'
in the unravelling of discourse, and all other principles were
then drawn from these by means of middle terms. Such hasty
methods are most apt for discussion but are quite incapable of
leading us along the narrow paths of nature. Dialectical induction must be completely revised and adapted to the precept
that axioms be reached by degrees and almost imperceptibly;
for as it stands, it proceeds by simple enumeration, concludes
precariously, always exposed to the dangers of contradictory
instances, and 'is a puerile thing'. Science requires instead 'a
form of induction which shall analyse experience and take it to
pieces, and by a due process of exclusion and rejection lead to
an inevitable conclusion'. It follows that the point of departure
of the new logic must be different from that of traditional logic,
'nearer the source than men have done heretofore', and that

the principles that the old logic had taken for granted must be re-examined. The dialecticians 'borrow the principles of each science from the science itself', they hold in reverence 'the first notions of the mind', receive as conclusive 'the immediate information of the senses'; but the new logic will penetrate into the province of each science 'with higher authority than belongs to the principles of those sciences themselves' and will call them to account for their own validity; it is suspicious of all first notions of the mind and doubts the information of the sense that lets slip a great deal of reality and 'has reference always to man, not to the universe'.[9]

The distinctions between old and new logic were lucidly described in the *Distributio operis* of 1620 and in the *New Organon*, I; but in the *Advancement of Learning* (1605) and the *Partis instaurationis secundae delineatio et argumentum* (1607)[10] they were less clearly outlined. In the *Advancement* Bacon made ample use of the traditional classifications of rhetoric for his treatment of the four intellectual arts, one of which included his reform of scientific methods. Thus he borrowed from rhetoric his quartering of logic, his doctrine of the relation between invention and judgement, his doctrine of memory, and even the discussion of the diverse functions of the various forms of discourse and modes of communication. However, he departed from this tradition on a point of basic interest: when he distinguished invention of arguments from invention of arts and saw that traditional logic could only be applied to the first he opened the way to a new form of enquiry. According to Bacon the invention of arts was totally deficient and devoid of rules and methods, for traditional logic refused to assist the mechanical and liberal arts and to serve as an instrument of invention. The basic distinction between invention and judgement disappears where the interpretation of nature—depending on induction—is concerned: 'the same action of the mind which inventeth, judgeth'.[11]

In the *Advancement of Learning* the section of the invention of arts and sciences ends with these words:

This of invention, concerning the invention of sciences, I propose (if God give me leave) hereafter to propound; having digested it into two parts, whereof the one I term *Experientia literata*, and the other *Interpretatio Naturae*: the former being but a degree and rudiment of the latter. But I will not dwell too long, nor speak too great upon a promise.[12]

This passage is significant in that it expresses Bacon's attitude in 1605 to the problem of a new logic of science. It is evident that this logic was already clearly formulated in Bacon's mind and one has the impression that he is referring to a work in progress. The *Valerius Terminus of the Interpretation of Nature* was, indeed, written in 1603 and it contains a rough outline of the new scientific method later expanded in the *Novum Organum sive interpretatione naturae*. The latter includes the theory of interpretation of nature from the *Valerius Terminus*; the diagnosis of the state of science and the refutation of tradition contained in the *Cogitata et visa*, the *Redargutio philosophiarum*, and, earlier still, in the *Temporis partus masculus*; and the doctrine of aids to memory and the mind expounded in the *Delineatio* of 1607.

Adoption of rhetorical patterns for the logic of scientific knowledge

In chapter IV, referring to Fracastoro's inductive theory, we noted that it was an attempt to apply to natural research logical methods that the Aristotelians had considered valid only for rhetoric. The same could be said of Bacon's concept of topics when—making use of a typically rhetorical terminology —he applies to scientific and natural enquiries certain instruments elaborated by this tradition for the invention of arguments or for rules of discourse aiming at 'persuasion'. My intention is to show how much Bacon's scientific knowledge owed to this dialectico-rhetorical tradition of the Renaissance, and how a number of his scientific theories were transplanted from the field of rhetoric.

Bacon's earliest formulation of the interpretation of nature— in the *Valerius Terminus*—includes quotations from Ramus and borrowings from his texts. Thus, not only were Bacon's classifications of logic taken from sixteenth-century rhetoric, but it invaded even his method for the discovery of forms; and this was not a mere coincidence, since the Ramistic rules recur again in the *New Organon*, II. Again, Bacon's doctrine of aids to memory expounded in the *Delineatio* and the *New Organon* is an adaptation to the uses of science of sixteenth-century rhetorical rules for the invention of arguments and the art of memory. Lastly, for Bacon, the topics, or logical places, is a basic element of scientific research; he deals with problems concerning the understanding of nature in the typically rhetorical terms of a discussion of the invention of arguments; and the art of questioning in a discussion serves Bacon as an illustration for the art of questioning nature.

The interpretation of nature in the 'Valerius Terminus' and the adoption of the Ramistic rules

In the *Valerius Terminus* of 1603—which, like the *Temporis partus masculus* is a fragment of a larger, projected work on the interpretation of nature—Bacon is not so much preoccupied with eliminating the errors of past philosophies as with outlining the new method of science referred to in the autobiographical fragment of the same period: *De interpretatione naturae proemium*:

> . . . if one succeeded, not only in making a particular discovery, however useful, but in setting a light upon nature that would illuminate regions beyond our present knowledge, and that, rising ever higher, would reveal and uncover the remotest secrets, he would I believe be the instigator of man's domination of the universe, the champion of freedom, and the conqueror of need.[13]

The absence of historical polemics such as we find in most of Bacon's other works is notable in the *Valerius Terminus* where, for instance, the idols are all derived from the particular nature of the human mind;[14] but he is just as antagonistic to tradition as in the *Cogitata et visa* and the *Redargutio*. However, his reflections on the aims, nature, and characteristics of knowledge are more particularly relevant to our enquiry. The true end and duty of knowledge, says Bacon, is not to produce plausible, delightful, admirable, or precise discourse, or arguments to satisfy the mind, but 'effecting and working', discovering hitherto unknown particulars for the improvement of the human condition. 'In determining of the truth of knowledge' men have always relied on unsatisfactory evidence, such as the authority of the ancients, common knowledge and public opinion, the internal coherence of discourse and the reducibility of its various terms to established principles, the absence of negative instances, and the response of the senses, none of which is a sufficient guarantee either of truth or efficiency. 'The discovery of new works and active directions not known before, is the only trial to be accepted.' On the other hand, one should not go in search of 'things concrete' which are infinite in number and transitory, but of 'abstract natures' which are rare and lasting, and are as the alphabet of nature or the colours on a painter's palette that combine to produce the variety of faces and figures. The 'effective' ends for which scientific knowledge must strive should not, therefore, be confused with the sort of efficiency involved with the 'errors and conjectures of art, or the length or difficulties of experiences'. Art and direct experience can only lead to a knowledge of the causes of particulars, whereas the scientific method establishes a contact with abstract natures that, when combined, produce reality.[15]

Bacon's opposition of abstract natures and concrete things and his exclusion of the latter from the objectives of scientific research stresses the reduction of natural phenomena to the combination of a finite number of primal elements, as well as the radical difference between common and scientific experience. Abstract natures—which, in Bacon's later works became 'simple natures'—are the 'primal irreducible qualities' that are present in every sensually perceived substance, and from whose mixture and combination each substance is made.[16] The reduction of 'concrete' to 'abstract' is precisely what produces a given effect: 'every particular that worketh any effect is a thing compounded (more or less) of diverse simple natures (more manifest or more obscure) and it appeareth not to which of the natures the effect is to be ascribed'. The method requires, therefore, a process of 'analysis' and of 'breaking' (*secare naturam*) of particulars so that they be finally reduced—by a series of inclusions and exclusions—'to a definite point'. According to Bacon this was not understood by the followers of the traditional method who, discarding analysis and breaking, employed a rudimentary form of induction and concentrated on producing immediate effects for direct use, without a thought for scientific axioms.[17]

The reduction to a definite point of abstract natures resulting from the analysis of particulars, amounts to exposing the ratio of correspondence between the 'nature' and the required effect—the latter necessarily coinciding with the presence of a given nature whose absence coincides with the failure to obtain the effect. The criteria used for the realisation of this correspondence is what Bacon is seeking to define. To this end he advocates a method proceeding by 'inclusions' and 'exclusions', that is, a method which does not only take into consideration positive instances—leading to merely probable conclusions—but also negative instances, thus eliminating all chances of error. To produce authentic effects a 'direction' must be followed which, according to Bacon, must answer two basic requirements: 'certainty', that is 'when the direction is not only true for the most part but infallible' and 'liberty', that is 'when the direction is not restrained to some definite means but comprehendeth all the means and ways possible'. A merely 'conjectural direction maketh a casual effect' and 'for want of certainty you are frustrated in success'. A 'particular and re-strained' direction—besides such casualness—tends to be un-certain because 'for want of variety in direction you are stopped in attempt'.[18]

The affinities of Bacon's theory to the Ramistic doctrine are evident. The theory of which I speak, says Bacon, was per-ceived by Aristotle who did not, however, put it into practice; the Ramists neatly called his two rules for the 'convertibility' of scientific propositions, the rule of truth (because it preventeth error) and the rule of wisdom (because it freeth election). These two rules, adds Bacon, 'are the same thing in speculation and affirmation which we now observe'. In the *Temporis partus masculus* Bacon had called Ramus 'a hide-out of ignorance, a pestilent bookworm, a begetter of handy manuals'.[19] In the *Advancement* he adopted the Ramistic diagram of logical clas-sifications. In the *Valerius Terminus* he accepts two out of the three Ramistic rules and uses them as the basis for his reform of the method of science, precisely in that section of his logic which, more than any other, was to have broken with tradi-tional doctrines.

The following interpretation of an Aristotelian text by Ramus will help us to understand what Bacon meant by the two rules. Ramus, like Bacon, believed that Aristotle had an inkling of these rules, though he usually disregarded them, and he would have us return, beyond the Scholastic betrayal, to the letter of true Aristotelian teaching:

> By this method natural philosophy and medicine—which two arts are especially embarrassed with a quantity of extraneous matter—by this same method any discipline can be made easy and brief, if just the following precepts, generally, essentially, primarily, in this order as Aristotle tells us, were taught . . . Let us return to the letter of Aristotle's teaching . . . we have wandered for too long and must go back to the fairest rule of logic, neglected and despised in our schools.[20]

Ramus is referring to chapter IV of the *Posterior Analytics*, Book II. Here Aristotle, discussing the premisses from which demonstrations derive, explains the meaning of the three expressions 'general', 'essential', and 'primal'. A general predicate is one that is not only true for certain subjects or instances, but is the definition of the quantitative universality of judgements or 'extension' of the notion; where, that is, the 'logical subject designates a class of things, that which is predicated of it must be valid for each of the things included in that class'. Essential predicates are those that co-inhere with the essence of the thing. Thus a line is of the essence of a triangle and a point is of the essence of a line because it is impossible to define a triangle without referring to the notion of a line, or a line without referring to the notion of a point. This definition 'refers to the so-called understanding of the notion designating those attributes that are part of the essence of the thing or that co-inhere to it not by accident'. Primal predicates are those which co-inhere to the subject: in every instance; particularly; and in so far as the subject is what it is. Thus primal definitions necessarily co-inhere with things. To say of a figure that its angles are equal to two right angles is not a primal definition (though it is an attribute) of the isosceles triangle, for the isosceles is not the first specification to which this definition co-inheres, as the triangle precedes it. A primal predicate requires of the subject that it represent the definition in its widest sense—in this case, the triangle as such and precisely in its quality of triangle. Such predicates also make propositions convertible: a figure whose angles equal two right angles is a triangle and a triangle is a figure, etc.[21]

Scientific discourse, says Ramus echoing Aristotle, must be made of the general, the essential, and the primal:

> As for the General, I say that cannot be general which inheres in one instance but does not inhere in another, nor can that be general which is sometimes present and sometimes absent . . . those things are essential which are in the definition of a given thing; as the line is in the triangle and the point in the line. For the essence of the things themselves both derives its existence from these things and inheres in the definition which says what the thing is . . . but I call something primal when it inheres both generally and essentially—and is coextensive with the thing itself. It is therefore evident that the primal must necessarily inhere in things.[22]

For Ramus the three rules derived from these characteristics of scientific knowledge are: first the rule of truth and certainty, according to which every scientific notion must be true always and in all cases (necessarily true) and present itself as universally evident—this rule aims at excluding error from scientific knowledge; second, the rule of justice, according to which every scientific notion must be homogeneous and incorporated into the objectives and the sphere of a particular art—this rule aims at establishing the sphere of each different science and insuring its homogeneity; third the rule of wisdom, according to which scientific propositions must be not only true and homogeneous, but also convertible, and this convertibility is linked, as we have seen, to the predicate's primality:

> The first rule is the rule of truth. This excludes from the art any thesis which is not entirely and necessarily true. By the second rule care is taken that any decision within an art be not only entirely and necessarily true, but also homogeneous and like a limb from the same body . . . This is the rule of justice, and its justice is exercised in controlling the boundaries of the arts and assigning each item to its proper place. By the third and last rule it is laid down that the teaching of an art be not only entirely and necessarily true, not only homogeneous, but in addition compounded of reciprocally convertible elements . . . this third rule is the rule of wisdom.[23]

Ramus and the Ramists insisted indefatigably on these three rules, making all their theories concerning each separate method of the various arts dependent upon them, and elaborating around them their concept of a single tree of knowledge which was divided into separate branches. Bacon ignored the second rule, but adopted the first and third, translating them into a more adequate language for the demands of practical operative science. His rule of certainty corresponds to the Ramistic rule of truth: a rule to be certain must be infallible, or, to use Bacon's own terms, a way that is certain must lead to 'something' which, when present, inevitably produces the desired effect. Thus the certainty of the rule involves not only —as for Ramus—a guarantee that no error exists, but also the efficiency of the enquiry. Without such a certainty, writes Bacon, 'may you perform but not obtain'. This 'something' is the abstract nature whose discovery and definition is the aim of knowledge. Bacon's rule of liberty corresponds to the Ramistic rule of wisdom: to be free a rule must depend on the reciprocal implicitness and convertibility of effect and rule. Each time the effect occurs the rule has been realised; each time a given type of rule occurs a given effect necessarily follows. In other words every instance where a given nature occurs may be taken as a rule for its artificial reproduction.[24] When air and water are combined—as in snow and foam—whiteness results; this is not only an instance of a given nature occurring, but also, simultaneously, of a rule for obtaining such a nature; thus whiteness is obtained by combining air and water.

Hence Bacon's assertion that the only valid proof of a notion's truth is the production of new results, and that this proof 'is not only upon the point whether the knowledge be true or no'.[25] For Bacon's theory of the convertibility of effect and rule led inevitably to the theory that productivity and truth were identical. Nature—as abstract nature—and effect are reciprocally conditioned: the occurrence of an effect alone guarantees the validity of the theoretical definition of an abstract nature; conversely only the definition of an abstract nature makes possible the occurrence of a corresponding effect.

However, Bacon's rule of liberty differs considerably from the Ramistic rule of wisdom. Indeed, from this rule Bacon derives a method of exclusion similar to the method for the detection of forms in the *New Organon*, as we shall see if we examine the rather involved examples in the *Valerius Ter-*

minus. There are other ways of producing whiteness, says Bacon, besides the combination of air and water;[26] thus the first rule is not free, since it is particular and there are other rules besides. The rule may be 'freed' from water and a second rule followed, whiteness occurring, for instance, by a combination of air with a transparent substance such as powdered glass, or the white of an egg to which air has been incorporated by beating or cooking. Or a third rule may be pursued to remove the 'restraint' of a colourless substance, for powdered amber produces whiteness, and also the foam of beer. A fourth rule removing the restraint of transparency is that of the flame, etc. However all four rules indicated are 'restrained' by the presence of air; but this restraint too can be removed by following a fifth rule and combining two transparent substances in unequal proportion, for instance, water and oil in an ointment; but the rule now freed from air is still restrained by transparency. Here Bacon declares that he will go no further for his intention was to give an example of the rule of liberty and not to describe the whole process. He mentions, nonetheless, a sixth rule or direction: 'we admit the sixth direction to be that all bodies or parts of bodies which are unequal equally, that is in a simple proportion, do represent whiteness'. This statement is only seemingly ambiguous, for absolute equality— or an identical refraction of light beams—produces transparency; a simple or proportionate degree of inequality—or a different refraction of light beams—produces whiteness; a combined degree of inequality produces all the other colours, and total inequality produces black. 'If so gross a demonstration be needful,' says Bacon, 'here are four images, a blank, a chequer, a fret, and a medly.' The sixth rule, according to Bacon, accounts for the inherent whiteness of things and not for whiteness as perceived by the senses. Any further enquiry would force him to refer to that which he does not, at present, intend to reveal.[27]

Thus the method for the detection of forms and, in the last analysis, the theory of new induction, were based on the notion of free direction or rule of liberty. Here are the premisses and conclusions of this theory of induction as they are presented in the *Valerius Terminus*:

There is a marked distinction between 'whiteness fantastical or appearing' and 'whiteness fixed and inherent'. The first can be distinguished by a 'physical' examination—Bacon later called it 'metaphysical'—tending to establish by a sequence of exclusions and 'freeings' what is inevitably present each time the colour white (to stick to the former instance) is present, independently of the substance in which white occurs or of the particular action or cause which produced it. Aptly enough, Bacon describes the traditional distinction of 'physics'—or the study of the active causes of concrete things—and 'metaphysics' —or the knowledge of the forms of primal natures—as 'a good and fit division of knowledge'.[28]

In the *Valerius Terminus* Bacon does not say explicitly that 'whiteness fixed and inherent' is 'form', though he says that free direction is something very similar to what philosophers call the search for form or formal cause.[29] It is clear from what precedes that 'whiteness fixed and inherent' depends—if we consider the sixth rule—on a certain structure of the parts of bodies and their fixed geometrico-mechanical condition. The 'gross demonstration' given by Bacon is significant in this respect and recalls the passage in the *Regulae* where Descartes declares that colour is inevitably diffuse and therefore figured, the difference between white, blue, red, etc., being comparable to the difference between the following figures or others of the same kind:

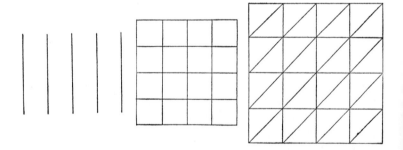

Though Bacon here makes the distinction between physical and metaphysical enquiries, he does not, as in his later works, stress the distinction between primal nature and form, as objects of two different types of enquiry.

One of the basic theories of Bacon's reform of the method

of science is practically non-existent in the *Valerius Terminus*. This is the theory that experiment requires a technical means of control for the human faculties of sense, memory, and reason. In this work the notion of 'governing' these faculties is completely irrelevant, for the structure of abstract natures does not depend upon a method dictating the laws of such a 'government'. It is, of course, imperative to go beyond the sphere of sensation, appearance, and phenomenological immediacy if we wish to 'attain a reality composed of the mechanical processes of elements having geometrical properties'.[30] In the *Valerius Terminus* Bacon gives no indication of the method by which to effectuate the passage from common to scientific experience, and his reticence concerning the thorough treatment of the rule of liberty may be connected with this omission. As Bacon had written in the *Advancement*, the new method of science for the detection of forms was, indeed, only a promise and though he dedicated twenty years of his life to the study of these problems, it was never to be anything else. Instead of trying to complete the unfinished *New Organon*, Bacon chose, under the impulse of new interests to adopt a new programme, and natural history became his main preoccupation during his last years.

The doctrine of tables or the classification of natural data

Two theories that were basic to Bacon's philosophy and from which he never departed are already contained in the 1603 fragment on the *Interpretation of Nature*: the properties of bodies are not objectively perceived by the senses; and the mechanical processes of particles gifted with geometrical properties that form the basis of objective, material reality may be perceived by means of appropriate instruments and logical techniques. It has been correctly observed that these theories are the premises or 'working hypotheses' of Bacon's induction.[31]

As we know, the purpose of Bacon's new scientific method was the discovery of forms, that is, the investigation of the forms of 'simple natures'—or irreducible qualities of all perceptible substances. The material and effective causes of a simple nature are the 'latent configuration' or organisation of material particles, and the 'latent process' or sequence of infinitesimal movements that constitute perceptible motion. The investigation of such causes for a given substance where a particular nature is present constitutes physics, and the knowledge thus acquired enables man to arrive at new discoveries in similar substances only. But the knowledge of forms—that constitutes metaphysics—will enable him to embrace the unity of nature in dissimilar substances 'and detect and bring to light things never yet done'.[32] Thus metaphysics, for Bacon, is a generalised natural science based on natural history leading to the discovery of forms by determining—quite apart from particular substances—the relation between the latent configuration and the latent process that constitute a given nature. Form is thus a relation between simple natures. It has been rightly said that, from the point of view of man, form is a definition enabling him to discover every organisation and movement from which a given simple nature can result, and from the point of view of nature it is the relation between organisation and movement.[33]

Though a recent theory propounds the absence of affinities between Bacon and Aristotle in this context, the former's mechanistic interpretation of nature clearly coincides at this point with typically Aristotelian attitudes.[34] For Bacon, indeed, natural research does not consist in determining quantitative relations for the solution of 'phenomena' in a system of correspondences, but in an enquiry into essences and absolute natures. However, our intention here is not so much to discuss Bacon's complex, confused theory of forms, as to examine that 'intellectual instrument' to which he entrusted the task of discovering the objective and essential structure of reality.

To this end it would be well to consider the workings of Bacon's 'tables', to which he assigned a definite role—'. . . Natural and experimental history is so various and diffuse that it confounds and distracts the understanding,' says Bacon; therefore the tables must order and classify instances so that we may master and control them. In this sense the tables can be assimilated to the aids to memory, and Bacon defines their function in typical juridical terms as a 'summonings to mind'.[35] In the *New Organon*, II, investigating the form of heat, Bacon compiles a 'Table of Essence and Presence' to collect 'Instances agreeing in the Nature of Heat'. There are twenty-seven of these including:

the rays of the sun, especially in summer and at noon; the rays of the sun reflected and condensed, as between mountains or on walls, and most of all in burning glasses and mirrors; eruptions of flame from the cavities of mountains; liquids boiling or heated; sparks struck from flint and steel by strong percussion; animals, especially and at all times, internally; strong vinegar, and all acids, on all parts of the body where there is no epidermis. . . .

Then a 'Table of Deviation or Absence in Proximity' to collect 'Instances in Proximity where the Nature of Heat is Absent'. As here the list would be endless, the table only includes those instances which occur in substances that resemble those where the nature is present. Thus we find 'the rays of the moon and of stars and comets; the reflection of the rays of the sun near the polar circle; liquids in their natural state. . . .' For Bacon form is thus necessarily present when the nature is present, absent when it is absent, and since the form of a thing is the thing itself, it will inevitably increase or decrease with that thing. So the third table is the 'Table of Degrees or Comparison' where Bacon lists, among other instances, the increase of heat in animals by 'motion and exercise, wine, feasting, venus, burning fevers, and pain'; variations of heat 'in different parts and limbs of the same animal . . . brain, stomach, heart, etc.'; the different temperatures of the heavenly bodies; the varying degrees of heat at different points of a single flame; and variations depending on circumstances and subjective conditions.[36]

Now that everything is classified and ordered and 'confusion and distraction' are dispelled, 'induction itself must be set at work'. This true induction—unlike that of traditional philosophy proceeding by simple enumeration and lacking any kind of evidence—leads to universal, inevitable conclusions and eliminates wrong solutions and unfounded theories. The affirmative cannot be reached till rejection and exclusion have been duly achieved. Given the premiss that the form is present when the nature is present, absent when the nature is absent, increasing or decreasing with the increase or decrease of the nature,[37] the natures to be excluded are: those that are not present in the instances when the nature of heat is present; those that are present in the instances when the nature of heat is absent; those that increase when the nature of heat decreases; and those that decrease when the nature of heat increases. On the basis of the classification of his three tables Bacon outlines an 'Example of Exclusion, or Rejection of Natures from the Form of Heat'. The rays of the sun are both luminous and hot, those of the other heavenly bodies are only luminous. Boiling water and air, and metals heated not to ignition, are hot but not luminous. Thus light can be excluded from the form of the nature of heat; the nature of heavenly bodies can also be excluded because 'common fire, and chiefly subterraneous fires' are hot independently of these; rarity can be excluded because gold and other metals 'of the greatest density' can acquire heat. In the same manner are rejected 'the subtle texture of bodies', the elements, expansion, the 'violent communication of any new nature', contraction, etc. These rejections make possible an 'Essay of Interpretation of Nature in the Affirmative way' or 'Indulgence of Understanding' or 'First Vintage', the result of which is that heat is a species of the genus of motion '. . . not that heat generates motion or that motion generates heat . . . but that heat itself, its essence and quiddity, is motion and nothing else'. Given that the relation of heat to motion is that of species to genus there are a number of specific 'differences' limiting motion so that it takes the form of heat. The first difference is that 'heat is an expansive motion whereby a body strives to dilate . . . itself'; the second, that it is a motion that tends to rise; the third, that it is motion not of the whole body, but of its parts; the fourth that the motion is rapid. The resulting definition of heat is both speculative and operative, for if in a natural body one produces a form of motion possessing the requisite qualities—expansion, levitation, partiality, and speed—he will inevitably generate heat.[38]

The rules Bacon used in the *New Organon* are the same he had employed in the *Valerius Terminus*, and an expression which has puzzled a number of scholars can only be clearly understood with reference to the earlier text. 'For a true and perfect rule of operation, then,' says Bacon writing of the discovery of form, 'the direction will be *that it be certain, free, and disposing or leading to action*'.[39] The fact that the presence of the form naturally entails that of the nature is proof of the certainty of the direction, and the freedom of the direction derives from that rejection of inessentials described in the doctrine of exclusion.

The whole inductive method expounded by Bacon in the *New Organon* is based on the doctrine of tables. To grasp the meaning of this doctrine we must discard the common concept of the *New Organon* as representing Bacon's philosophy to the exclusion of all his other works; we should, indeed, pursue through his entire *oeuvre* the development of his theory of natural classifications for the organisation and ordering of instances to enable the intellect to find its way through nature's chaos and profusion. In this respect the tables are similar to the 'invention of natural places' which occupied so much of Bacon's time. His first systematic attempt at outlining an invention of natural places and a method of tables was in 1607–8 when, significantly enough, he uses the terms topics and tables (or charts) synonymously. In the *Cogitata et visa* of 1607 he gives a detailed account of the tables' purpose:

> So after long and anxious thought, he decided that the first thing necessary was to set forth Tables of Discovery or, as it were, formulae of a legitimate mode of research, in certain fields, to serve as an example and to be a sort of visible embodiment of the work to be done.[40]

The following year in the *Commentarius solutus* he wrote 'the finishing the three tables, de motu, de calore et frigore, de sono'. Further notes include a list of what were nothing less than 'natural places' divided into tables:

> Three imperceptible kinds of motion—by reason of slowness, as with the hand of a clock; through minuteness, as liquid or water becomes impure or freezes etc.; because of tenuity, as all the various things of air, of wind, of breath, which are invisible— their too subtle motions are comprehended by no sense; we feel only their weight, their effects.
>
> The nodes and spheres of motions, and how they concur and how they succeed and interchange in things most frequent. The times and moments wherein motions work, and which is the more swift and which is the more slow. . . .[41]

Three short works of this period *Inquisitio legitima de motu, Sequela cartarum sive inquisitio legitima de calore et frigore*, and *Historia et inquisitio prima de sono et auditu*[42] follow the same pattern. Here for the first time Bacon applied the principles outlined in the *Cogitata et visa* and the *Commentarius solutus*. The ordering of natural diversity imagined as a thread leading man from the labyrinth of nature is expressed in a number of chapter headings, but it is in the preface to the *Inquisitio legitima motu* that the theory of topics and tables is first introduced in detail. The traditional method, writes Bacon, skips from a smattering of sensually perceived particulars to the most generalised conclusions and then ingeniously fits all particular instances to the demands of typically speculative constructions; but we should not be misled by the odd example or the particular instance quoted by these philosophers, for they are proofs after the fact and have no part in the acquisition of their knowledge: 'but my account is the contrary of this: for the tables place it beyond dispute'.[43]

The invention of natural places and the compiling of tables, says Bacon, opens the way that leads to things themselves. The tables will, besides, be as weights and as brakes on the excessive precipitation of human thought that is fatal to knowledge; for by means of the tables 'intelligences are made equal', and a common level of sense is established.[44] Bacon distinguished two kinds of tables in the *Inquisitio legitima motu*: those for collecting the more obvious instances connected with a given object of research (or *machina intellectus inferior*) and those with the higher function of assisting the mind in the discovery of 'hidden' things and finally forms themselves (or *machina intellectus superior*). The nineteen tables listed include findings on species, causes, means, and effects of movement. They were to be 'temporary organisations' or topics, enabling one to pass to the second group of tables which are, in fact, the tables of presence, absence, and degree of the *New Organon*. These serve to complete the task and lead from the 'construction of the instrument' to the 'use of the instrument'.

Bacon's doctrine of scientific knowledge is entirely conditioned by his conception of the universe as a labyrinth and forest filled with 'so many ambiguities of way', 'deceitful resemblances of objects and signs', 'natures irregular in their lines and so knotted and entangled'.[45] One of the method's first objectives is to set order in the variety and confusion of nature so that the mind may reflect the natural world. In the *Partis instaurationis secundae delineatio et argumentum* of 1607 Bacon admits that truth emerges more readily from error than from confusion, and reason finds less difficulty in modifying incorrect classifications than in delving into disorder and confusion.[46] The all-important function of dispelling confusion is included here among those of the aids to memory. We find, in embryo, the thought developed later in the *New Organon* of a 'method of control over sense, memory and reason' as a means of achieving knowledge by a transition from the sphere of common experience to that of scientific experience. Sense and reason tend to judge reality in relation to man instead of in relation to the universe, but by controlling the three human faculties a freeing from prejudice becomes possible on the one hand, and on the other, a perception of reality that will be detached from 'subjectivity'.

Indeed the art of memory assumes, in the theory of the interpretation of nature, a singular importance against the background of Bacon's 'labyrinthine' universe where the main function of his method is 'ordering' natural data. Inventing natural 'places' and compiling tables are, in fact, part of this art, but of what exactly it consists and what is its function are questions that can only be answered after examining Bacon's observations on memory in the *Advancement of Learning* (1605) and in the *Delineatio* (1607)—reprinted respectively in the *De augumentis* (1623) and the *New Organon*. Such an examination will further provide a means of elucidating that transposition of rhetorical concepts to the sphere of science mentioned at the beginning of this chapter.

Mnemonics and the art of memory, rhetorical places and natural places

Bacon's treatment of memory in the *Advancement* and the *De augumentis* has a great deal in common with the Renaissance conception of this problem. Indeed, Bacon held very definite views on sixteenth- and seventeenth-century mnemonic texts. It was not until between 400 and 100 B.C. that memory became a part of rhetoric, the earliest exhaustive works on the subject being those of Cicero and Quintilian and the *Rhetorica ad Herennium*.[47] Quintilian, in fact, makes use of a proper topological system, and the same method was employed by Martianus Capella and some of the major fifteenth-century theoreticians. Jacopo Publicio, Pietro da Ravenna, Conrad Celtis, and Cosimo

Rosselli were among the more famous fifteenth- and sixteenth-century writers of a type of treatise which assumed the proportions of a veritable literary genre,[48] where the classical rhetorical tradition—the *Rhetorica ad Herennium* ran to about twenty editions between 1470 and 1569—intermingled curiously with emblems and allegory, Lullism, and attempts to construct a 'tree' or encyclopedia of knowledge. The three themes recurring in these writings which present the greatest interest are the notion of an encyclopedia of knowledge, the idea of an artificial memory making possible the creation of a 'perfect science', and most relevant for the present study—the concept of an art of memory as a means of dispelling 'confusion' and establishing 'order and coherence' in arguments and discourse.

Ludovico Dolce's *Dialogue on the way to increase and preserve memory* is one example among many of the first theme. Here the tree of scientific classifications responds precisely to 'mnemonical' demands:

> Though different writers have written different treatises on the divisions of the sciences, I shall here, nonetheless, give only one of the many examples that may be cast to memory.[49]

Dolce's division presents certain aspects of singular interest and is not without affinities to the tradition of Lull. Indeed, the influence of this tradition can be traced in all those texts where memory is represented as the section of rhetoric by which may be realised Lull's dream of a perfect science capable of overcoming every obstacle at once. For instance, the Frenchman Jean Bellot in the seventeenth century compares Lull's art to artificial memory and sees him as unsurpassed master of the art of memory:

> Artificial memory is no more than the art of supplementing natural memory, for the one cannot subsist without the other. The artificial would be of little use without what is natural; but natural memory, if directed towards some art or science, may be greatly improved and assisted by this artifice which can abridge considerably the acquisition of knowledge that otherwise would be long and tedious; in this way Raymond Lull, a man of exquisite culture, worked very hard to discover the perfection of this short art and artificial memory.[50]

In Lull this art was disguised in enigmas and ambiguities but Bellot's intention was to make it clear and comprehensible to all. Memory 'assisted by artifice' is the means of achieving 'perfect science'. This art is precisely that which:

> . . . ancients and moderns have endeavoured to learn, as R. Lull and many others who spent much time and energy—their own and others' too—but discovered some worthy means of abridging the study of sciences, yet not perfection such as here I give it to you.[51]

Bellot's conclusions tend to unite the arts of memory, dreams, face-reading, and astrology, but his references to Ramus—whom he never names, however—and to Agrippa and Giordano Bruno are most significant.[52]

Bellot thus brings us to the third theme, or the art of memory as an instrument for 'introducing order' into knowledge and discourse. Ramus' identification of the art of memory with the doctrine of judgement acquires here a peculiar significance if we remember that judgement for him is the same thing as the ability to place or dispose objects of invention in an exact and rational sequence. Though Ramus expresses some doubt as to the possibilities of the art of memory as an autonomous science, his views seem to include this notion:

> Let us define judgement . . . the technique of grouping dis-coveries, and with the help of that grouping forming a judgement concerning the question before one: this technique is without doubt identical with the most true and sure technique of memory (if any scientific discipline of memory can be), so that the primary constitution of the two principle powers of the mind is one and the same—that is, of memory and judgement . . . Reason may be divided into two parts: the finding of plans and arguments; and then the judging of these as they are disposed in order . . . memory is a sort of shadow of disposition. . . . Let these three, discovery, disposition, memory be the three parts of the art of dialectic.[53]

The image of the method as a means of 'organising and ordering ideas' was common to all sixteenth-century dialec-ticians. Melanchthon, for instance, is quite clear on this point: the method is

> . . . a temper, or really a science or art, making a way by sure

reason, that is to say, an art which as it were through trackless regions, through places choked with brambles, through utter confusion, finds a road and opens it up, and tears out all that is relevant and sets it out in order.[54]

Bacon's discussion in the *Advancement* evolves around typically rhetorical problems. Arguments, says Bacon, are not invented in the true sense of the word; when we speak of inventing an argument we mean 'out of the knowledge whereof our mind is already possessed to draw or call forth before us that which may be pertinent to the purpose we take into our consideration'. The art of inventing arguments enables one to recall more easily and readily the statements required for a given end. This work of recalling or retracing is accomplished by means of two basic instruments: one, preparation or promptuary, to collect ready prepared arguments on as many subjects as possible for use when required; the other, suggestion or topic, to serve as guide for research or to recall prediscovered ideas. Aristotle, says Bacon, unjustly scoffed at the promptuaries, comparing the Sophists to cobblers who could not make shoes but only exhibited them in a great variety of shapes and sizes. We might reply to Aristotle, adds Bacon, that a cobbler with no wares in his shop and who only works to order will have very few customers: Aristotle 'would have us change a rich wardrobe for a pair of shears'. Such a 'wardrobe' was essential to Bacon who had been brought up on Cicero's rhetorical texts, appreciated the works of Ramus, cultivated the art of oratory himself, and had elaborated theories and methods of peroration and 'personal success'. Yet it is in the suggestion or topic that his major interest lies. For the purpose of the topic is not only to provide arguments in a discussion; it has a very definite function in all forms of research, since it serves as a 'guide to research and enquiry', and a question well posed, says Bacon, is the best part of knowledge.[55]

Bacon takes up this notion of a catalogue of places in the pages on the art of memory. We are in the habit of saying, he writes, that catalogues of places are detrimental to knowledge, whereas, on the contrary, the work that goes into compiling them is ever rewarding because nothing can be achieved in the sphere of knowledge without a solid foundation of learning. Such work 'supplies matter to invention and contracts the sight of judgement to a point'. The two main instruments of the art of memory are 'prenotation' and emblems. The first sets a limit to research which would otherwise be boundless, restricts the sphere of knowledge, and creates a frame in which memory can operate with ease; for first and foremost memory requires boundaries; they are provided by the ordering and arranging of recollections, by places of artificial memory 'digested and prepared beforehand', and by verse. A recollection must fit into a pre-established order, it must have a specific relation to the places, and it must rhyme with another word or words, in the verse. Thus places establish order and sequence in the formulation of images, which, however, can be more easily evoked by means of emblems. An emblem, says Bacon, 'reduces intellectual conceptions to sensible images; for an object of sense always strikes the memory more forcibly and is more easily impressed upon it'.[56]

But Bacon's views on Renaissance mnemonic texts are really more relevant to our enquiry than his theories of emblems. Not one of the methods or 'systems of places' that we have encountered, says Bacon, is of the slightest value. If we judge by their titles these texts have more to do with the school than with the world, and they make use of 'pedantical divisions' that cannot penetrate the mysteries of nature. Bacon was, however, more lenient in his estimation of works on the art of memory proper. Much has been done here, he writes, though there is still room for amplification and consolidation as regards both theory and practice:

It is a barren thing (as now applied) for human use. . . . And for my own part (owing perhaps to the life of business I have led) I am ever disposed to make small account of things which make parade of art but are of no use. For the being able to repeat at once and in the same order a great number of names or words upon a single hearing, or to make a number of verses extempore on any subject, or to make a satirical simile of everything that happens, or to turn any serious matter into a jest, or to carry off anything with a contradiction or cavil, or the like, (whereof in the faculties of the mind there is great store, and such as by device and practice may be exalted to an extreme degree of wonder,) all such things I esteem no more than I do the tricks and antics of clowns and rope-dancers.[57]

This important passage is notable, not so much because it condemns an exploitation of the art of memory for mere effect and criticises the attitude of rhetorical humanism[58] (though this is remarkable enough), as for the belief that the art of memory can be put to other than traditional uses. The point is not to exhibit the marvels that can be achieved by mnemonics, nor to work 'miracles' with it, but to apply it to concrete, serious, human uses. This seems to Bacon both legitimate and possible if people realise that the art of memory operates on two different levels: that of 'old popular sciences' and that of a 'completely new' scientific method of natural enquiry. In the *De augumentis* Bacon explicitly states this belief:

> This is particularly the case in inductive philosophy and the interpretation of nature; for a man might as well attempt to go through the calculations of an Ephemeris in his head without the aid of writing, as to master the interpretation of nature by the natural and naked force of thought and memory, without the help of tables duly arranged. But not to speak of the interpretation of nature, which is a new doctrine, there can hardly be anything more useful even for the old and popular sciences, than a sound help for the memory.[59]

We have seen that Bacon's bent for clear-cut oppositions did not allow him to perceive the ambiguity of his own attitude to traditional and 'new' logic. When dealing with 'old and popular sciences' he tried to explain the function of memory in persuasive discourse,[60] that is, in a form of logic that aims, not at the invention of arts and sciences, but only at the invention of arguments. And by including the art of memory in his new logic certain concepts pertaining to traditional rhetoric became incorporated in the 'interpretation of nature'.

In the *Delineatio* Bacon stresses the total discrepancy between the aims and methods of ordinary logic and of scientific logic. But where that section of the new logic—the aids to memory—is concerned, this does not stop him from adopting a mode of reasoning almost identical to that he had employed for the 'art of discourse', or 'ordinary logic'. In the case of discourse, a multitude of terms and arguments has to be recollected and organised; in the case of the scientific method this applies to the multitude of instances. . . . Bacon's doctrine of aids to memory outlined in the *Delineatio*—and later in the *New Organon*—is an adaptation to a different sphere of the rules governing the invention of arguments or the art of recollecting and arranging arguments.

According to Bacon, if we wish to utter coherent persuasive discourse and invent arguments we must: dispose of an extensive collection of arguments (promptuary); and possess the rules for restricting a boundless field, reducing it to the proportions of a specific, limited discourse (topic). The art of memory consists precisely in the elaboration of a method permitting the realisation of both these requirements.

For Bacon this procedure undergoes very little change when applied to the scientific sphere:

> The aids to memory (*Ministratio ad Memoriam*) fulfil the following mission: from the confusion of particular instances and the bulk of natural history a given history is selected, and its elements are disposed in an order such as to enable the mind, according to its own capacity, to work thereon.[61]

He is no less explicit in the *New Organon*, II, X:

> Now my directions of the interpretation of nature embrace two generic divisions; the one how to educe and form axioms from experience; the other how to deduce and derive new experiments from axioms. The former again is divided into three ministrations; a ministration to the sense, a ministration to the memory, and a ministration to the mind or reason. For first of all we must prepare a *Natural and Experimental History* sufficient and good; and this is the foundation of all; for we are not to imagine or suppose, but to discover, what nature does or may be made to do. But natural and experimental history is so various and diffuse, that it confounds and distracts the understanding, unless it be ranged and presented to view in a suitable order. We must therefore form *Tables and Arrangements of Instances*, in such a method and order that the understanding may be able to deal with them.

Memory when left to itself, says Bacon in the *Delineatio*, is not only unfit to embrace the multitude of instances but cannot even specify the particular instances required for a given enquiry. Alongside the general natural history—corresponding to the rhetorical promptuary—we must dispose of certain rules for limiting the field of research and classifying the material.

In order to supplement 'natural' memory so that it may serve as an instrument for scientific research we must resort to topics (or catalogues of places of invention) indicating the relevant instances for a given object of research and to tables classifying the instances so that the mind, instead of being confronted with natural confusion, finds an ordered sequence of data. From Ramus to Melanchthon, from Rosselli to Romberch and Gratarolo scientists investigating the problem of topics and artificial memory had always stressed the importance of places as a means of restricting an otherwise boundless field and of classifying its material. *Loci* for Melanchthon—to pick an example at random:

> . . . advise us when material is to be sought or generally as to what should be selected from the great heap available and in what order it should be classified. For the places of invention both in the writings of dialecticians and in the orators do not lead us so much to the discovery of material as to the solution of the problem of choice once a means . . . has presented itself.[62]

To sum up, Bacon's interpretation of nature adapts fifteenth-century rhetorical and philosophical mnemonics to its own ends. In this way certain typically rhetorical concepts and doctrines were transplanted by Bacon into the scientific field of natural research and the new inductive method. For Bacon this vision of a form of logic assisting in the classification of instances collected in a 'great encyclopedia' was particularly seductive.

Topics and natural histories

Bacon was the first to perceive the inadequacy and inconclusiveness of his arrangement of instances in the tables of the *New Organon*. There are, he says, infinite possibilities open to men of only average intelligence, if they set themselves to this rewarding and eminently useful task of compiling tables of research and classifying particular instances and natural observations; for natural history in its present state is not sufficiently reliable for a 'legitimate' interpretation of nature.[63] At the conclusion of the 'Tables of Degrees' he adds:

> How poor we are in history any one may see from the foregoing tables; where I not only insert sometimes mere traditions and

reports (though never without a note of doubtful credit and authority) in place of history proved and instances certain.[64]

For Bacon one of the first—if not the first—of scientific duties would be to supplement this lack so as to make the collecting of 'instances certain' possible. Thus his tables are really no more than samples of the great task ahead.[65] Indeed, after the tables and 'first vintage' Bacon's method was to have included nine 'intellectual aids' to perfect the results obtained. However, only one of these—*the prerogativae instantiarum*—was ever completed, the remaining eight being no more than names on a list.[66] But Bacon's work on scientific logic—which he had been meditating since the *Valerius Terminus*—was abandoned in favour of compiling these tables, because he was so firmly convinced of their incomparable value for scientific progress.

> The strongest means of inspiring hope will be to bring men to particulars, especially to particulars digested and arranged in my Tables of Discovery (the subject partly of the second, but much more of the fourth part of my Instauration) since this is not merely the promise of the thing but the thing itself.[67]

In this way the fourth part of the *Instauratio* which was to have been a classification of materials for natural history took first place for Bacon even over his 'logic'. Farrington has pertinently stressed the significance from this angle of the last paragraph of the *New Organon*, I, written probably after the completion of Book II. Here Bacon sees his method of the interpretation of nature as lacking absolute value, necessity, or perfection and as not indispensable for the reform of science. If we disposed of a reliable natural history and diligently perused it without paying heed to traditional beliefs and theories and refraining from hasty generalisations we could attain also, by the genuine and spontaneous powers of our own minds, this new method of interpretation of nature. In the *De historia naturali et experimentali monitum* Bacon writes:

> It comes therefore to this: that my Organum, even if it were completed, would not without the Natural History, much advance the Instauration of the Sciences, whereas the Natural History without the Organum would advance it not a little.[68]

When discussing Bacon's views on the mechanical arts we mentioned the increasing importance he attributed to natural history during his last years.[69] In the *Parasceve* he stresses this importance with particular effect, giving to a certain extent the clue to his change of attitude. Even if the best intellects of all times were to unite, the entire human race to take up the study of philosophy, and the whole world to be filled with academies and colleges, if there were still no natural and experimental history like the one he was intent on compiling no progress would be possible; but once such a history has been completed and increased by the many auxiliary and 'light-bringing' experiments that inevitably arise in the course of research, it will be only a matter of a few years before the enquiry of nature and of all sciences is concluded; in this way and in no other can the foundations be laid for a true and active philosophy.[70] Thus Bacon considered the collecting of material for scientific research far more important than any effort to perfect the theoretical apparatus of science.

We all know what Bacon's projected—and partially completed —natural history was to have been, so there is no point in dwelling on it in detail. However, it is interesting to note that each of the particular histories at which he worked so anxiously after 1620 had a twofold purpose: to eliminate traditional theories and doctrines 'by means of certain instances'; and to arrange the instances in given fields so as to form a 'systematic catalogue' serving as a basis for the new philosophy. There is little doubt that Bacon failed to carry out the first of his objectives; besides, the second—connected as it is with some of his most typical attitudes—is more relevant to our enquiry. Neither should we overlook the fact that, for Bacon, the *Parasceve* was a 'direction of natural and experimental history that sufficeth for the basis and foundation of a true philosophy'. Indeed, a direct study of these 'histories' shows them to be a collection of places arranged in order, and an endeavour to complete the compilations begun in the *Inquisitio legitima de motu*, the *Inquisitio de calore et frigore*, and the *Historia et inquisitio prima de sono et auditu* where the topics play an equally important part. Bacon uses the topics to restrict the multiplicity of natural instances by successive classifications, and to question nature as, for example, the *Topica particularia sive articuli inquisitionis* inserted in the *Historia ventorum* and the *Historia vitae et mortis*, or those—included as illustrations in the *De augumentis*—referring to the *Historia gravis et levis*. Among the nineteen places for heaviness and lightness we find the following: which substances are subjected to the movements of heaviness, which to those of lightness and are there any intermediary substances of an indifferent nature? After the 'simple enquiry' we proceed to the 'compound enquiry': which substances of equal dimensions weigh more and which less? Which light substances rise more quickly and which more slowly? Does the quantity of matter and the surrounding resistance influence the movements of weights? Does the shape of a falling body determine its movement? Does the nature of the substance through which a weight moves have any influence on the movement? Is the movement through soft, porous substances equal to that through hard, solid ones? Does the commingling of a light and a heavy substance alter the movement of the fall? What is the line and direction followed by heavy bodies falling?[71]. There is an undeniable affinity between the first three of these places and the 'tables of presence, absence, and degree'. But they are all remarkable for their tendency to list and classify; thus the nature of falling results from the classification of falling bodies, an observation of their differences, and a singling-out of the nature common to all. As Cassirer has pointed out[72] this was the very method Galileo's Aristotelian opponents employed when they attacked —in favour of an analysis of particulars—'the reduction of nature to a system of abstractions and general mathematical relations'.

Bacon uses exactly the same method for the history of winds and that of life and death: he enquires whether there are constant winds and whence they blow; how the various 'vapours' and 'exhalations' influence the wind; which of these generates wind; how far the nature of wind is dependent on such matters. It was during this time, while Bacon was compiling the different histories, that he expounded his theory—in the *De augumentis* (later expanded in the *Advancement*)—on the function of 'particular topics' as 'places or directions of invention and inquiry in every particular knowledge'. As we have seen, Bacon includes 'promptuaries' and topics in his subdivisions of the 'invention of arguments', where topics are in turn divided into 'general' and 'particular'. The first, says Bacon, were fully appreciated by traditional dialecticians, but particular topics, on the other hand, have been totally neglected; yet their purpose, like that of the former, is to indicate the direction of an enquiry. Such directions cannot be signified once and for all, because in this field there is no method that is perfect from the start: the arts of invention are perfected by the progress of the inventions themselves; that is why particular topics are required. There is not one way, valid for all sciences, of consulting and ordering material in the 'store' or promptuary; so the particular topic is a compound of 'logic'—or the four intellectual arts—and the matter of each individual science: there is a topic for rhetorical discourse and argument, one for moral discourse, and different topics for each particular history. For Bacon catalogues of places do not serve, therefore, only to supply arguments for discussion; they are directly linked to the scientific method of natural research.

The list of projected 'particular histories' published by Bacon after the *Parasceve*[73] is, indeed, impressive. There are 130 in all: 40 are concerned with nature, 18 with the study of man, and 72 with man's accomplishments in the field of nature. The size of this last section is not a mere coincidence, for here, in this 'history of technology' or of man's relation to nature, Bacon saw the realisation of that 'intellectual revolution' that was basic to his philosophy; and it is in this sphere that his attitude departs significantly from tradition. In this *Catalogue of Particular Histories* a considerable place is given to the mechanical arts. The history of arts 'takes off the mask and veil from natural objects' and upon this history 'mechanical and illiberal as it may seem—all fineness and daintiness set aside—the greatest diligence must be bestowed'.[74] Such a plan—describing the alterations made on nature by the hand of man—implies both a refutation of rhetorical culture and a new appreciation of the significance of the mechanical arts in intellectual spheres. Descartes, Leibniz and Boyle acknowledged this aspect of Bacon's thought, and it found its total fulfilment in the achievements of the Royal Society and the great Encyclopedia of the Enlightenment.

But as to the amount of material accumulated, even the numerous particular histories at which he laboured for so many years must have appeared quite inadequate to the Lord Chancellor; for in his last years he began an unsystematic collection of natural data or 'general history' to provide new material for the particular histories. The *Sylva silvarum*—hurriedly concluded shortly before his death—is really a promptuary for scientific research. Because he believed that an enormous collection of data was indispensable for the progress of scientific research, while knowing that his time was running out, Bacon's history became more and more 'literary' as he was reduced to making uncritical and indiscriminate use of an increasing number of traditional sources. In the *Historia ventorum* and the *Historia vitae et mortis* he had already borrowed extensively from Pliny, Acosta, and Ficino; in the *Sylva silvarum* Della Porta and Cardano, whom he had once so violently attacked, provide material for Bacon's proposed 'instances certain' that were to have been rigorously and scientifically proved.

Conclusions

Bacon's programme of scientific reform for man's mastery of nature was thus concluded—at least chronologically—in one of the most literary and unscientific books produced in the first half of the seventeenth century. The *Sylva silvarum* is no different from the magical texts of Della Porta and Cardano or those of the seventeenth-century English hermetics and magicians John Dee and Robert Fludd. This is probably why Bacon's logic has been seen by so many scholars as a failure; such a judgement, however, is based almost exclusively on arbitrary analogies rather than on an analysis of the historical and cultural environment in which Bacon's philosophy developed and eventually failed.

But this is precisely the task we undertook when stressing the connections between Bacon's new logic and the tradition of Renaissance rhetoric. In his 'new' scientific logic, Bacon incorporated some typical concepts of traditional rhetoric. He substituted the collection of natural places for that of rhetorical places. He adapted the art of memory to other than traditional ends. He devised the tables or instruments of classification to organise reality and thus enable the memory to assist intellectual operations. And he used the Ramistic rules for defining forms. In this respect his logic was much closer than he believed to the dialectic of Ramus or Melanchthon, who saw it as the necessary means for disposing in orderly fashion a chaotic reality. Indeed, Bacon's definition of his method as a 'thread' guiding mankind through the 'chaotic forest' and 'complex labyrinth' of nature is very similar to theirs, though the actual method included a number of significant innovations. Its limitations may be attributed in part to Bacon's total neglect of mathematics as a scientific instrument; but this failing—though it led to his greater appreciation of the 'practical' Agricola than of theorists such as Copernicus and Galileo—is consistent with his vision of logic as a means of establishing order in the forest and labyrinth of nature; a vision certainly not shared by Galileo:

> Philosophy is written in this grandest of all books forever open before our eyes (I mean the universe), but which cannot be understood if we do not learn first to understand the language and interpret the characters in which it is written. It is written in mathematical language, the characters are triangles, circles and other geometrical figures, without which it is quite impossible to understand a single word: without these there is only aimless wandering in a dark labyrinth. [75]

This typically Platonic image of a mathematical, rational world composed by a geometrician God in number, weight, and measure will certainly be more fruitful in the development of modern science than Bacon's image. The vision—almost completely discarded by Bacon—of a 'simple', 'spare', 'inexorable' nature was basic to Galileo, and even to Newton, despite the affinities of some of his views with Bacon's.

For a new method for questioning nature had been discovered. It was very different from Bacon's method modelled on rhetoric, and it was better attuned to the current Platonic interpretations and belief in nature's simplicity. Galileo's questionings did not probe the essential forms and common properties of different phenomena; he sought to specify 'the phenomenon's structural elements, considered absolutely valid and such as to constitute a law for all similar phenomena'. The function of the hypothesis, or theoretical model, was here explicitly acknowledged: scientific data could only be obtained by criteria of a strictly theoretical nature. Thus it was considered legitimate to interpret data based on pre-established propositions, the non-conclusive results of certain experiments being simply dismissed as 'disturbing circumstances'—all of which was in complete opposition to Bacon's principles.[76] Galileo writes:

> I argue *ex suppositione*, imagining a movement towards a given point, starting from immobility, gathering speed, and increasing in velocity proportionately with the passage of time; and from this movement I demonstrate conclusively a number of phenomena. I then add that if experience reveals similar phenomena occurring in the movements of weights naturally falling we can truly assert that the movement is the same as that which I had defined and foretold. If this should not be, my demonstrations, based on suppositions, will have lost nothing of their force and conclusiveness; as the conclusions demonstrated by Archemides on the spiral were in no way invalidated by the fact that no spiral can be found in nature to move in such a way.[77]

And Torricelli:

> I imagine or suppose that a certain body moves up and down according to the given law, and with similar motion horizontally. When this is done I say that all Galileo and I myself have said will follow. If balls of lead, iron, and stone do not then follow the supposed direction, it is their loss: we shall say that we are not concerned with them.

Though passages such as these may not serve for an anti-empirical interpretation of Galileo's method, they played an important part in the seventeenth-century revolution of scientific thought; and their theories were certainly foreign to Bacon's methodology. Indeed the following passage from the *Redargutio philosophiarum*—reprinted in the *New Organon*—seems explicitly to refute them:

> When a controversy arose over any example or instance, as being in contradiction to their views, they did not take steps to revise their theories. No; they retained the theory . . . either by some dialectical distinction or (since they were not such bad fellows after all) they let it stand as an exception . . . The whole of this enterprise and effort I regard as baseless.[78]

Bacon refuted the deductive method, asserting that notions were no more than the 'marks of things' and declaring that they should be subtly extracted from particulars. Thus he ignored the use of the hypothesis for scientific purposes and considered it, in fact, an arbitrary and illegitimate anticipation of nature. The refutation of hypothesis, together with his opposition to deduction, has been rightly considered one of the greatest weaknesses of his method. He had certainly no conception of sciences 'where a choice and concatenation of propositions, proved and accepted in advance, constitute a sounder and more efficient method of research than direct experiment, however accurate; sciences where, in fact, only deductive methods are used for verification and, especially, for discovering new laws and new combinations'.[79] And, significantly enough, the deductive method's use was limited for him to the moral sciences, where consequences may be deduced from unquestionably sound principles of conduct.

Indeed, Bacon's protest against deduction and against syllogism should be set in its historical context, but neither should its significance in the perspective of modern culture be forgotten. He wrote:

> For the other judgement by Syllogism, what need to speak; seeing it has been beaten over and over by the subtlest labours of men's wits and reduced to many niceties? And no wonder, for it is a thing most agreeable to the mind of man. For the mind of man is strangely eager to be relieved from suspense, and to have something fixed and immovable upon which in its wanderings and disquisitions it may securely rest. And assuredly as Aristotle endeavours to prove that in all motion there is some point quiescent; and as he very elegantly interprets the ancient fable of Atlas, who stood fixed and supported the heavens on his shoulders, to be meant of the poles or axletree of heaven, whereupon the conversion is accomplished; so do men earnestly desire to have within them an Atlas or axletree of thoughts, by which the fluctuations and dizziness of the understanding may be to some extent controlled; fearing belike that their heaven should fall. And hence it is that they have been in too great a hurry to establish some principles of knowledge, round which all the variety of disputations might turn without peril of falling and overthrow.[80]

It is obvious that Bacon is not attacking here the use of hypothesis in scientific research; he is opposing to a logic directed towards the indoctrination of man a logic of discovery and invention, unrestricted by sacred principles and tending to re-examine principles formerly considered too holy for examination. For Bacon the logic of evidence—solely preoccupied with sustaining an intellectual heaven—is a mere instrument of cultural conservatism, beside which the summons to experience, and particularly the summons to a suspended judgement on the value of accepted principles, sounds a revolutionary note.[81]

Nineteenth-century historians were fond of an historical outline where the birth of modern science is made to coincide with the substitution of inductive, experimental methods for traditional deduction and *a priori* assertions. But the artificiality of such an antithesis soon became evident where scientific methodology was concerned; and in the sphere of scientific history it is now possible to trace the influence of Scholastic tradition, seen for four centuries as no more than an incidental aberration in human culture. However, opposition to the exclusive use of deductive methods in favour of induction was not as trivial as some scholars make out who trace the continuity of certain formal procedures and try thereafter to weld Socratic and Modern philosophy together and to identify the method of Robert Grosseteste with that of Galileo and Newton.

The passages from Bacon quoted here show conclusively that he was bent on attacking the implicit relation between deductive methods and a tendency to accept blindly traditional principles and theories.[82] His modernity does not lie in his championing induction against deduction, but in his courageous rejection of pre-established limitations to scientific enquiry, and in his disdain for an 'Atlas of thoughts' to hold up his heaven.

Bacon's logic was, indeed, an instrument made by man for the domination of a resisting, recalcitrant nature; he stressed the inadequacy of abstract, theoretical methods in natural research, and the necessity of referring to experimental data to prove the authority of definitions and theories; he denied the correlation of elegantly constructed theories and practical scientific results; and he saw theoretical methods only as means of directing and encouraging experiments. Thus Bacon, for all that he was influenced by rhetorical culture and incapable of appreciating the works of Copernicus, Galileo, and Gilbert, raised a number of fundamental problems for the development of scientific knowledge.

List of Abbreviations used in the Notes

Sp. (followed by the number of the volume and of the page) indicates R. L. Ellis, J. Spedding, and D. D. Heath's edition of *The Works of Francis Bacon*, London, 1887–92, VII vols.

Sp.L. indicates J. Spedding's edition of *The Letters and Life of F. Bacon, including all his occasional works*, London, 1890 seq., VII vols.

B.F. indicates the English translation of *Temporis Partus Masculus, Redargutio Philosophiarum*, and *Cogitat et Visa* contained in B. Farrington, *The Philosophy of Fr. Bacon, an essay on its development from 1603 to 1609, with new translation of fundamental texts*, Liverpool, 1964. For all other English translations the texts of Spedding, vols. IV, V, VI, have been used. If the original is in Latin, the first reference is to the Latin, the second (in brackets) to the translation.

The titles of Bacon's works most frequently referred to are indicated by the following abbreviations:

Adv.—*Of proficience and advancement of learning.*
Aph. C.—*Aphorismi et consilia de auxiliis mentis et accensione luminis naturalis.*
C.S.—*Commentarius solutus.*
C.V.—*Cogitata et visa.*
Cog. hum.—*Cogitationes de scientia humana.*
Cog. nat.—*Cogitationes de natura rerum.*
Conf.—*A Confession of Faith.*
D.A.—*De dignitate et augmentis scientarum.*
D.G.I.—*Descriptio globi intellectualis.*
D.I.S.—*De interpretatione naturae sententiae XII.*
D.O.—*Distributio operis.*

D.S.V.—*De sapientia veterum.*
De Princ.—*De principiis atque originibus.*
Filum Lab.—*Filum labyrinthi sive formula inquisitionis.*
H.D.R.—*Historia densi et rari.*
H.G.L.—*Historia gravis et levis.*
H.S.—*Historia sympathiae et antipathiae rerum.*
H.S.A.—*Historia de sono et auditu.*
H.S.M.S.—*Historia sulphuris, mercurii et salis.*
H.V.—*Historia ventroum*
H.V.M.—*Historia vitae et mortis.*
Hist. nat.—*Historia naturalis et experimentalis ad condendam philosophiam sive phaenomena universi.*
I.N.P.—*De interpretationie naturae proemium.*
Inq. Leg.—*Filum labyrinthi sive inquisitio legitima de motu.*
M.N.—*Magnalia naturae praecipue quoad usus humanos.*
Med. S.—*Meditationes sacrae.*
N.A.—*New Atlantis.*
N.O.—*Novum Organum.*
P.I.D.—*Partis instaurationis secundae delineatio et argumentum.*
Parasceve—*Parasceve ad historiam naturalem et experimentalem.*
Phaen. Un.—*Phaenomena universi sive historia naturalis et experimentalis ad condendam philosophiam.*
Praef.—*Praefatio generalis.*
R.Ph.—*Redargutio philosophiarum.*
Scala Int.—*Scala intellectus sive filum labyrinthi.*
Sylva—*Sylva silvarum or a Natural History in Ten Centuries.*
T.P.M.—*Temporis partus masculus sive de interpretatione naturae libri tres.*
Val. Term.—*Valerius Terminus. Of the Interpretation of Nature with the annotations of Hermes Stella.*

References to the *Novum Organum* give the volume and page, e.g. N.O. 11, 4.

The following works are referred to by the author's surname and the specific page number:

Agrippa, H. C. *Opera*, Lyons, 1600.
Allmayer, V. Fazio. *F. Bacone*, Palermo, 1928.
Anderson, F. *The Philosophy of F. Bacon*, Chicago, 1948.
Bellot, J. *L'Oeuvre des oeuvres ou le plus parfaict des sciences steganographiques, paulines, armadelles et lullistes*, Paris, 1622.
Berthelot, M. *Les Origines de l'alchimie*, Paris, 1885.
Bush, D. *English Literature in the Earlier Seventeenth Century*, Oxford, 1945.

Caspari, F. *Humanism and the Social Order in Tudor England*, Chicago, 1954.

Cassirer, E. *Individual and Cosmos in the Philosophy of the Renaissance*, trans. M. Domandi, New York and Oxford, 1963.

Farrington, B. F. *Bacon: Philosopher of Industrial Science*, New York, 1949.

Fowler, T. (ed.), *Bacon's Novum Organum*, Oxford, 1889.

Hall, A. R. *The Scientific Revolution (1500–1800)*, London and New York, 1954.

Lemmi, C. *The Classical Deities in Bacon, a study in Mythological Symbolism*, Baltimore, 1933.

Levi, A. *Il pensiero di F. Bacone considerato in relazione con le filosofie della natura del Rinascimento e col razionalismo cartesiano*, Torino, 1925.

Liebig, J. von. *Ueber F. Bacon von Verulam und die Methode der Naturforschung*, Munich, 1863.

Ramus, Peter, *Animadversionum aristotelicarum libri XX*, Paris, 1556.

Rossi, M. M., *Saggio su F. Bacone*, Naples, 1935.

Schuhl, P. M. *La Pensee de Bacon*, Paris, 1949.

The Seventeenth Century: Studies in the History of English Thought and Literature from Bacon to Pope, Stanford, 1951.

Seznec, J. *La survivance des dieux antiques*, Warburg Institute, London, 1940.

Sortais, G. *La Philosophie moderne depius Bacon jusqu'à Leibniz*, Paris, 1920.

Thorndike, L. *History of Magic and Experimental Science*, New York, 1923–4.

Vives, Juan Luis, *De disciplinis libri XX*, Cologne, 1536.

Willey, B. *The Seventeenth Century Background*, London, 1949.

Yates, F. A. *The French Academies of the Sixteenth Century*, London, 1947.

The following shortened forms refer to the works below:

Clavis Universalis—Rossi, Paolo, *Clavis Universalis: arti mnemoniche e logica combinatoria da Lullo a Leibniz*, Milan-Naples, 1960.

I filosofi—Rossi, Paolo, *I filosofi e le machine, 1400–1700* Milan, 1962.

La cultura—Garin, Eugenio *La cultura filosofica del Rinascimento italiano*, Florence, 1961.

MR—Garin, Eugenio *Medioevo e Rinascimento*, Bari, 1954.

Abbreviations for Journals:

JHI—Journal of the History of Ideas.

JWI—Journal of the Warburg and Courtauld Institutes.

RF—Rivista di filosofia.

SP—Studies in Philology.

Notes

INTRODUCTION

1. Bush, 1.
2. Willey, 42.
3. 'Dr Wallis' Account of Some Passages of his Own Life', *Peter Langfot's Chronicle*, Oxford, 1725, pp. 161–4.

INTRODUCTION TO THE ENGLISH EDITION

1. P. H. Kocher, 'Bacon on the Science of Jurisprudence', *JHI*, 1957, 1, pp. 3–26; C. J. Ducasse, 'F. Bacon's Philosophy of Science', *Theories of Scientific Method* by R. M. Blake, C. J. Ducasse, and E. H. Madden, Seattle, 1960; R. Hooykaas, 'De Baconiaanse traditie in de natuurwetenschap', *Alg. Nederk. Tijdschr. Wijsb. Psycol.*, 1960–1, pp. 181–201; R. F. McRae, *The Problem of the Unity of Science, Bacon to Kant*, Toronto, 1961; R. E. Larsen, 'Aristotelianism of Bacon's N.O.', *JHI*, 1962, 4, pp. 435–50. I have published the following studies on Bacon's philosophy in *Rivista critica di storia della filosofia*, 1957: 'Per una bibliografia degli scritti su F. Bacone' (pp. 75–89) and 'Sul carattere non utilitaristico della filosofia di F. Bacone' (pp. 22–40). I have analysed Bacon's attitude to the mechanical arts in *I filosofi* and the relation of his induction to the *artes memorativae* in *Clavis Universalis*. Two articles have just gone to press: 'Bacone e Galilei' will appear in the second book of *Saggi su Galileo Galilei*, a cura del Comitato Nazionale per le celebrazioni nel IV centenario della nascita, Consiglio Nazionale delle Ricerche, Rome and 'Bacone e la Bibbia' will appear in *Reformation and Philosophy*, Polska Akademia Nauk, Warsaw.

NOTES TO CHAPTER I

1. Trans. J. M. Cohen, Penguin Books, 1955, p. 92.
2. See Hall, 45–51, 129 seq., 217–43; E. Callot, *La Renaissance des Sciences de la vie au XVIe siècle*, Paris, 1951.
3. For the importance of experiments and the influence of technology on philosophy and scientific research see A. C. Crombie,

Augustine to Galileo, London, 1952, pp. 274-7. The cultural significance of these technical writings is not stressed in A. Wolf's important
study, *A History of Science, Technology, and Philosophy in the Sixteenth and
Seventeenth Centuries*, London, 1950, or in *History and Technology*, ed.
C. Singer, E. J. Holmyard, A. R. Hall, and T. I. Williams, Oxford,
1957, III. H. Butterfield, *The Origins of Modern Science*, London,
1949, gives an historical study of the 'internal expansion' of science
and more or less ignores the link between technology and science and
the 'external expansion' of science. In this respect the chapter on the
development of experimentalism in the seventeenth century is
particularly disappointing. E. A. Burtt, *The Metaphysical Foundations
of Modern Physical Science*, London, 1950, suffers from the same limitations.

4. For the situation in England see J. U. Nef, *Industry and Com-
merce in France and England 1540-1640*, Ithaca (N.Y.), 1957. In the
following works (which are all invaluable for an understanding of
English economy in the sixteenth and seventeenth centuries) the
author comes to the same conclusion: *The Rise of the British Coal
Industry*. London, 1932, and 'The Progress of Technology and the
Growth of Large Scale Industry in Great Britain 1540-1640',
Economic History Review, V, 1934-5, pp. 3-24. Also G. N. Clark,
Science and Social Welfare in the Age of Newton, Oxford, 1937, of which
the chapter 'The Economic Incentives to Inventions' is more
especially relevant. For the relation of the new scientific attitude to
English society see the article by one of the best authorities on the
subject: R. K. Merton, 'Science, Technology and Society in
Seventeenth Century England', *Osiris*, IV, 1938, pp. 360 seq., and
the review of this article by R. F. Jones in *Isis*, XXI, 1940, pp. 438-
41; *idem*, 'Science and Criticism in the Neo-Classical Age of English
Literature', *The Seventeenth Century* and 'Puritanism, Science and
Christ Church', *Isis*, XXXI, 1939, pp. 65-7, where the author
discusses among other things the relation between the new scientific
attitude and religion and literature. On the organization of scientific
research see Yates, 95-104; H. Brown, *Scientific Organizations in
Seventeenth-Century France*, Baltimore, 1934; M. Ornstein, *The Role of
Scientific Societies in the Seventeenth Century*, New York, 1938; Hall's
chapter referring to this question is particularly enlightening. H.
Brown, 'The Utilitarian Motive in the Age of Descartes', *Annals of
Science*, London, I, 1936, pp. 182 seq.; P. M. Schuhl, *Machinisme et
philosophie*, Paris, 1947, makes a brief but interesting contribution to
the problem, especially pp. 23-42. Some relevant texts in *British
Scientific Literature in the Seventeenth Century*, ed. N. Davy, London,
1953.

5. For Agricola see n. 7. Vanoccio Biringuccio, *De la pirotechnia*,

Venice, 1540. Besson, *Théâtre des instrumens mathématiques*, Lyons, 1579. Fausto Veranzio, *Machine novae*, Venice c. 1595. Vittorio Zonca, *Novo teatro di machine et edificii*, Padua, 1621. Giacomo Strada de Rosberg, *Dessins artificiaux*, Frankfurt-am-Main, 1617–18. Benedetto Castelli, *Delle misure dell'acque correnti*, published posthumously in Rome in 1628. Apart from the studies on these works already quoted see: A. P. Usher, *A History of Mechanical Inventions*, New York, 1929; R. J. Forbes, *Man the Maker, A History of Technology and Engineering*, London, 1950; R. Dugas, *Histoire de la mécanique*, Neuchatel, 1950.

6. Agricola's real name was George Bauer (1494–1555).

7. Agricola, *De ortu et causis subterraneorum*, Italian trans., Venice, 1550, p. 519v.

8. *ibid.*, p. 520.

9. *idem, De re metallica*, Italian trans., Basel, 1563, preface, p. 6.

10. *ibid.* On this subject see Thorndike, I-V; Hall, 31. Also F. A. Pouchet, *Histoire des sciences naturelles au moyen âge*, Paris, 1853; C. H. Haskins, *Studies in the History of Medieval Science*, Cambridge, 1927; L. White, Jr., 'Technology and Invention in the Middle Ages', *Speculum*, IV, 1940, pp. 141 seq.

11. G. M. Bonardo, *La Minera del Mondo*, Venice, 1589.

12. *ibid.*, p. 10, 57v.

13. See C. T. Onions, 'Natural History', *Shakespeare's England*, Oxford, 1950, I, p. 477.

14. See n. 9 above.

15. p. 4.

16. p. 5.

17. *ibid.*

18. p. 4.

19. p. 1.

20. p. 22.

21. For the influence of technical research on art and culture see A. Banfi, *Galileo Galilei*, Milan, 1949, pp. 31 seq. For a more general view of the historical situation mentioned here see *I filosofi*.

22. Sir Humphrey Gilbert, (1539?–83), *Queen Elizabethes Academy*, ed. F. J. Furnivall, Early English Text Society, 1869. Cf. *The Voyages and Colonising Enterprises of Sir Humphrey Gilbert*, Hakluyt Society, 1940, II. For Gilbert's pedagogical work see W. H. Woodward; *Studies in Education during the Age of the Renaissance 1400–1600*, Cambridge, 1906, pp. 295–306.

23. Gilbert, p. 11.

24. See Caspari, 1–27. P. N. Siegel, 'English Humanism and the New Tudor Aristocracy', *JHI*, 1952, 4, pp. 450–68.

25. Thomas Starkey, *A Dialogue between Reginald Pole and Thomas Lupset*, ed. K. M. Burton, London, 1948, p. 26. (cit. Caspari, 118)

26. Antony a'Wood, *Historia et antiquitates universitatis oxoniensis*, Oxford, 1647, I, 62; II, 108.

27. For Bernard Palissy (1510–98) see L. Audiat, *Bernard Palissy*, Paris, 1864; E. Dupuy, *Bernard Palissy*, Paris, 1894; for Palissy's works: *Discours admirables*, Paris, 1580; *Recepte véritable*, La Rochelle, 1553. Both have been reprinted in A. France, *Les Œuvres de Bernard Palissy*, Paris, 1880.

28. Sir T. Clifford Allbutt, 'Palissy, Bacon and the Revival of Natural Science', *Proceedings of the British Academy*, 1913–14, VI, 223 seq. (Palissy's influence had already been noted by A. B. Hanschmann, *B. Palissy und F. Bacon*, Leipzig, 1903). For Farrington's views see pp. 13–14, and for a more detailed discussion, his article 'On Misunderstanding the Philosophy of Francis Bacon', *Science, Medicine and History, Essays . . . in Honour of Charles Singer*, Oxford, 1953, I, 439–50. Bacon quotes Agricola in D.A., Sp. I, 572.

29. N.O., I, 81 (Sp. IV, 79).

30. See France, *op. cit.* n. 27 above; P. Duhem, *Etudes sur Leonardo da Vinci*, Paris 1906, I, 223–53, shows that although Palissy expressed some irony for Cardano's works he was nonetheless influenced by the French translation of *De subtilitate*, (*Les livres de Hiérome Cardanus traduits par Richard Le Blanc*, Paris, 1556).

31. B. Palissy, *Discours admirables. Advertissement aux lecteurs* in France, *op. cit.*, n. 27 above, p. 166.

32. Farrington, art. cit., n. 28 above, p. 445, rightly refutes Sir Clifford Allbutt's theory that Bacon's philosophy resembled Palissy's and declares that it is a mistake to compare them.

33. For Bacon's views on the importance of collections see n. 90 below.

34. See Val. Term., Sp. III, 226; Adv., Sp. III, 289–90; C.V., Sp. III, 616; Parasceve, Sp. I, 398–99; Praef., Sp. I, 126 seq.; N.O., I, 74; D.A., Sp. I, 457–8, 572.

35. D.S.V., Sp. VI, 675–6, 753.

36. J. von Liebig, *Lord Bacon*, Paris, 1866, pp. 24–5, 29–31.

37. For instance Farrington's interpretation of Bacon's plan to 'introduce new qualities into a given substance' (p. 119), and his a-historical treatment of Bacon's attitude to the 'mechanical' aspects of the new method (p. 115) which deprives it of all significance. But these are only minor limitations that do not detract from the basic value of Farrington's book.

38. For Bacon's opinion of natural magic see Val. Term., Sp. III, 223; Adv., Sp. III, 361–2; C. V., Sp. III, 591 seq.; Filum Lab., Sp.

III, 496–7; H.S., Sp. II, 81; N.O., I, 5, 73, 85; II, 27, 29, 50; D.A., Sp. I, 456–7, 573–4.

39. The editor of Benedetto Varchi's *Questione sull' alchimia* (Florence, 1827) appended a 'Notice to the learned reader' in which he described the nefarious influence of 'astrological and hermetic speculations' in the sixteenth century; but a number of famous historians from De Wulf to Gilson and to De Ruggiero (not to mention earlier and later ones) have reached substantially similar conclusions. Garin, *MR*, 172, justly observes the difficulty of understanding western philosophy' if we refuse to consider certain all-pervading topics, concerned as much with the whole conception of man and his relation to reality as with methods of exorcism and invocation of spirits'. See also pp. 150–91 and the notes collected in *La cultura*, 143–65.

40. An outline of Bacon's plan is to be found in Parasceve (Sp. I, 391–403). The *Catalogus historiarum particularium secundum capita* (Sp. I, 405–10) is a list of the enquiries that should be made. In the *Aphorismi de conficienda historia prima* (Sp. I, 403) Bacon announces his decision to carry out these enquiries himself. The 'vow' was made in the dedication to the Prince of Wales of the *H.V.*, London, 1622 (Sp. II, 9). A list of the six particular histories is in *Tituli historiarum et inquisitionum in primos sex menses destinatarum* (Sp. II, 11). The *D.R.* was published by Rawley in 1658. Bacon wrote no more than the *Aditus* (Sp. II, 80–3) to the remaining histories.

41. Farrington, pp. 132 seq., explains the motives for this interruption. For the connection between *logica* and *historiae* see Ch. VI of this book.

42. von Liebig, *op. cit.*, 36 above, p. 46.

43. See M. Munsterberg, 'Bacon's Sylva silvarum', *Public Library Quarterly*, Boston, III, pp. 86–7; Anderson, p. 277. The main sources of the Sylva have been traced by Ellis (Sp. II, 438l seq.) George Sandys, *A Relation of a Journey*, London, 1615, ran to seven editions before 1673. Ellis points out that paragraphs 701–83 of the Sylva are based on Sandys' work to the extent that in reading them we can follow his journey from Lemmo to Vesuvius. Cardano, *De subtilitate*, Nürnberg, 1550, G. C. Scaliger, *Exotericarum exercitationum libri XV de subtilitate ad Hieronymum Cardanum*, Paris, 1554. Cardano's reply, *Actio prima in calumniatorem*, in *De subtilitate*, Basel, 1560, and a new ed. of *De subtilitate*, Basel, 1561. For this controversy see Bayle, 'Cardan', *Dictionnaire historique et critique*, Rotterdam, 1697.

44. Thomas Browne, *Pseudoxia Epidemica*, London, 1664 (1650, 1658, 1669, 1672, 1688); now in *Works*, ed. Keynes, London, 1928–31, 6 vols. For Bacon's influence on Descartes see A. C.

Howell, 'Thomas Browne and Seventeenth-Century Scientific Thought', *SP*, XXII, 1925, pp. 61–80; for contrasting Baconian and metaphysical influences on Browne see Willey, 41–56. Comprehensive studies by W. P. Dunn, *Sir Thomas Browne, a Study in Religious Philosophy*, Minneapolis, 1950, and F. L. Huntley, *Sir Thomas Browne*, Michigan, 1962.

45. See Sylva, Sp. II, 602 seq. For motion as an active virtue in matter see N.O., II, 48. For Bacon's views on the imagination see H. Marion in *Revue philosophique de la France et de l'étranger*, XI, 1881, pp. 91–101, and G. Bachelard, *La Formation de l'esprit scientifique*, Paris, 1939, pp. 146–7. The best known Renaissance text on the occult powers of the imagination is the *De incantationibus* by Pomponazzi, Basel, 1546.

46. See the interpretation of the Cupid fable in D.S.V. and all Ch. IV of D.A. Book III.

47. For this tradition see Thorndike, VI; C. Singer, *From Magic to Science, Essays in the Scientific Twilight*, New York, 1928. With particular reference to alchemy see H. S. Redgrove, *Alchemy Ancient and Modern*, London, 1911; R. J. Forbes, *Short History of the Art of Distillation*, Leiden, 1948; F. S. Taylor, *The Alchemists, Founders of Modern Chemistry*, New York, 1949; E. J. Holmyard, *Alchemy*, London, 1957. For the English tradition see R. Steele, 'Witchcraft and Alchemy', *Social England*, IV, London, 1901–4, pp. 323–67 and 'The Sciences: Alchemy', *op. cit.*, n. 13 above, I, 462 seq. For the influence of alchemical writings on Bacon see P. Janet, *Baco Verulamius alchemicis philosophis quid debuerit*, Angers, 1889; D. Brinkmann, *Mensch und Technik*, Bern, 1947, pp. 120 seq.

48. Spedding (Sp. II, 94) has a most unsatisfactory interpretation of this belief which he attributes to a generic 'primitive mentality'. On very similar lines see Fowler, *Bacon's N.O.*, Oxford, 1889, p. 227.

49. See H.D.R., Sp. II, 256. For the vital spirit as a compound of air and fire see H.V.M., Sp. II, 215.

50. See for instance Basileus Valentinus quoted by Redgrove, *op. cit.*, n. 47 above, p. 25, and Benedictus Figulus, *A Golden and Blessed Casket of Nature's Marvels*, trans. A. E. Waite, London, 1893.

51. For Aristotelian sources of this notion see *Meteorologica*, III, 6, 378 c. For the concept of spirit in Bacon see Phaen. Un., Sp. III, 690; N.O., II, 40; H.V.M., Sp. II, 213 seq.; H.D.R., Sp. II, 254 seq.

52. Numerous examples of this terminology in the various *Historiae* and in the Sylva, also in N.O., II, 40. On the use of the term 'fixation' see Lemmi, 78 seq.

53. For the theory of Vapours see Artistotle, *op. cit.*, n. 51 above, and the study by Taylor, *op. cit.*, 47 above, pp. 12 seq.

54. *ibid.*, p. 204; and more exactly relevant Berthelot, 263. By the same author, *Introduction à l'étude de la chimie des anciens et du moyen âge*, Paris, 1889, 2 vols., is a basic work on this subject.

55. Cog. nat., Sp. III, 17–18.

56. *ibid.*, 20.

57. N.O., II, 8; I, 121; for superinducing various natures on one substance see N.O., II, 3, 5; D.A. Sp. I, 574.

58. N.O., II, 1, 4. Schuhl (54–5), notes with great lucidity Bacon's link with alchemical traditions on this point. For Bacon's belief in the possibility of manufacturing gold the following significant contradictions are worthy of note: in N.O., II, 3, 5, and D.A. Sp. I, 574, he appears to be in favour of the possibility: in *H.D.R.*, Sp. II, 250, he seems doubtful where gold is concerned but not so for mercury and the transmutation of lead to silver; in Sylva., Sp. II, 448 seq. he has completely forgotten or overcome his doubts to the extent of giving a recipe for the manufacture of gold.

59. Berthelot, 242; Taylor, *op. cit.*, n 46 above, p. 31. The term 'dye' is common to a number of titles, for instance, Basilius Valentinus, *Révélation des mystères des teintures essentielles des sept métaux.*, Paris, 1668; Gabrielis Clauderi, *Academici curiosi dissertatio de tincture universali (volgo lapis philosophorum dicta)*, Altenburg, 1678.

60. Berthelot, 281.

61. N.O., II, 7.

62. For sulphur and mercury: T.P.M., Sp. III, 532–3; C.V., Sp. III, 505; H.S.M.S., Sp. II, 82; Sylva, Sp. II, 459. For the convertibility of air into water: N.O., II, 48; H.V.M., Sp. II, 225; H.D.R., Sp. II, 293. For astrology: Adv., Sp. III, 289; Filum Lab., Sp. III, 503; D.A., Sp. I, 544–60.

63. Agrippa *Opera*, I, p. 3. Of equal interest is G. Naudé, *Apologie pour les grans hommes soupçonnex de Magie*, Amsterdam, 1712, p. 15.

64. *Opus Maius* (Bridges), I, 29, 241, 396; *Opus tertium* (Brewer), 29. For 'beneficial' magic as a means of defence for a Christian society see *Tractatus ad declarandum dicta in libri Secreti secretarum* (Steele), Ch. III, p. 7.

65. Cyprian, *Acta Sanct.*, 1867, VII, 240 seq.; St Augustine, *De Civitate Dei*, X, 9; Hugo of St Victor, *Didasc.*, VI, 15; Migne P.L., 176, 810–12; John of Salisbury, *Polycr*, I, 9; St Thomas, *Quodlibet*, IV, 16; *Contra Gent.*, III, 106; William of Auvergne, *De legibus*, Ch. 24; Albertus Magnus, *Summa*, II, 30, 2.

66. See *MR*, 158–9. Thorndike too finally admits that after humanism 'there was less objection to the word magic and more approving use of it than in the preceding centuries', V, 13) but the

limitations of his views are apparent in the fact that his only comment on this change is that it is 'paradoxical'.

67. D.I.S., Sp. III, 785, and D.O., Sp. I, 144.

68. Cr. C. A. Viano, 'Esperienza e natura nella filosofia di F. Bacone', *RF* 1954, 3, p. 308.

69. C. Agrippa, *De incertitudine et vanitate scientiarum*, Cologne, 1527: Italian trans. Venice, 1659, Ch. XLII, p. 57v; English trans. James Sanford, *Of the Vanitie and Uncertaintie of Artes and Sciences*, London, 1569. Agrippa's works were 'widely read and quoted in England' (M. H. Carré, *Phases of Thought in England*, Oxford, 1949, p. 220). For Agrippa see A. Prost, *Les sciences et les arts occultes au XVIe siècle: Corneille Agrippa, sa vie et ses œuvres*, Paris, 1881, II.

70. Echo, chosen bride of Pan, symbolises for Bacon Philosophy faithfully reproducing the voices of Nature (*Pan sive natura*, is the sixth fable in D.S.V., an augmented version of which is in D.A., see Ch. III, 'Materialistic Naturalism in the Myths of Pan and of Cupid').

71. G. B. Della Porta, *Della chirofisionomia*, Naples, 1677. For Della Porta see C. Gabrieli, 'G. B. della Porta Linceo', *Giornale critico della filosofia italiana*', 1932, pp. 206-77; and F. Fiorentino, *Studi e ritratti della Rinascenza*, Bari, 1911, pp. 233-340.

72. G. B. Della Porta, *Magiae naturalis liber*, Lyons, G. Rovillius, 1569, p. 12.

73. T. Campanella, *Del senso delle cose e della magia*, Bari, 1925, pp. 241-2.

74. Cf. *Parac. Paragranum*, ed. F. Strunz, Leipzig, 1903, p. 26. Paracelsus, *De summis naturae mysteriis commentari tres*, Basel, 1584.

75. *Hieronymi Cardani mediolanensis de propria vita liber*, Paris, 1643; *The Book of my Life*, trans. J. Stoner, 1930, reprinted N.Y. (Dover), 1962. For Cardano see R. Charbonnel, *La pensée italienne au XVIe siècle et le courant libertin*, Paris, 1919.

76. Varchi, *op. cit.*, n. 39 above, pp. 21 seq.

77. *ibid.*, pp. 21-2. For the distinction between the three types of alchemy see pp. 21-6; for the depreciation of alchemy see pp. 2 seq.; for its products see p. 4. Saitta, *Il pensiero italiano pell'Umanesimo e nel Rinascimento*, Bologna, 1948-51, II, 168, stresses Varchi's attitude to the problem of falling weights: 'Questione sull'alchimia', p. 34.

78. C. Luporini, *La mente di Leonardo*, Florence, 1953, p. 23. See E. Garin, 'Nota sull'ermetismo del Rinascimento', *Testi umanistici sull'ermetismo*, Rome, 1955, p. 12.

79. See M. M. Rossi, for Bacon's attitude to nature and his 'juridical attitude'.

80. D.A., Sp. I, 573 (Sp. IV, 366-7).

81. M.N., Sp. III, 167–8. Agrippa, *Italian trans.*, p. 57v., had described the acceleration of the natural processes of maturation and germination, the summoning of thunder and storms, and the production of new animal species. But Della Porta, op. cit., n. 72 above, pp. 76, 79, 98, 126, 145, 147, 195, besides giving recipes for revealing the chastity of maidens and making drinkers abstemious had very similar aims to those of Agrippa and of Bacon.

82. N.O., I, 1, 4, (Sp. IV, 47).

83. D.A., Sp. I, 456–7; cf. N.O., II, 31; D.A., Sp. I, 573 seq. For 'useful discoveries' made by alchemists while searching for gold and the fable of the peasant increasing the produce of his vine by tilling his land in quest of a non-existent hidden treasure see Adv., Sp. III, 289; C.V., Sp. III, 605; R.Ph., Sp. III, 575; N.O., I, 85,

84. For the aims of Bacon's science see T.P.M., Sp. III, 528; Val. Term., Sp. III, 223; I.N.P., Sp. III, 518; C.V., Sp. III, 611.

85 Lemmi attempts to medievalise Bacon's philosophy. Although the conclusions are unconvincing his is one of the more useful studies on Bacon.

86. Bacon's use of the mechanical arts as a 'model' does not imply that he considered them perfect; on the contrary, he repeatedly deplored their status and minimized their achievements. Val. Term., Sp. III, 226; C.V., Sp. III, 591; R.Ph., Sp. III, 580; Praef., Sp. I, 127–8; N.O., I, 75, 88; D.A., Sp. I, 462. But he wanted to extend the progressive, collaborative qualities of technology to all intellectual activities and believed that the cultural progress thus achieved would benefit the mechanical arts as well in the end.

87. J. Dewey, *Reconstruction in Philosophy*, London, 1921, p. 28.

88. Sp. L., I, 109.

89. *Mr Bacon in Praise of Knowledge*, Sp. L. I, 123–6.

90. Sp. L. I, 355–7. As we have seen, Bacon considered that collections of curiosities were an important means of instruction and research. A few contrasting examples of how he intended to make use of them and how they had been used will help to assess the historical significance of his attitude. In the *New Atlantis* the institution attached to Solomon's house aims at 'an understanding of the secret causes and comportment of things so as to extend the limits of human power'; to this end the members dispose of lakes for breeding fishes and birds, orchards, gardens, parks and enclosures for different species of animals. The orchards and gardens are planned not as beauty spots but for the study of soils and grafting; the menageries are not for the amusement and curiosity of the people but for experiments in dissecting and selectivity and development of living organisms. Most Renaissance collections of animals and plants were composed of rare, expensive specimens and were merely a means of

showing off the wealth of the owner (Callot, *op. cit.*, n. 2 above, p. 43). The botanical gardens of Padua, Pisa, Bologna, Heidelberg, Montpelier and later Paris and Altdorf were acknowledged and subsidised by the state. In the sixteenth century, for the first time, the forms and properties of growing plants were observed, and not, as in the Middle Ages, solely for pharmaceutical uses (p. 46). Bacon however saw botanical gardens as a field for new experiments. Collections of rare animals aimed at provoking curiosity or were used for amusement and sport. Throughout the whole of the sixteenth century they produced no other scientific effect than a series of anecdotes and it is only in France under Louis XVI that their use as a means of scientific research and observation was recognised.

91. I.N.P., Sp. III, 519.

92. Adv., Sp. III, 322.

93. Schuhl, *op. cit.*, n. 4 above, pp. 11–12; *i filosofi*, 21 seq.

94. For the attitude to the mechanical arts of scientists before Bacon see for instance R. Boyle, 'Considerations touching the Usefulness of Natural Philosophy' in P. Shaw, *Works of Boyle abridged*, London, 1725, I, 129–30; Hall, 219.

95. T.P.M., Sp. III, 531 (B.F. 65); see also Adv., Sp. III, 358, and D.A., Sp. I, 496; for the definition of art as *homo additus naturae* see D.A., Sp. I, 497; for the incongruity of artificial and natural phenomena see N.O., I, 66, 75, where Bacon asserts that natural and artificial motion, compounds and mixtures are identical; for comparisons between the heat of the sun and that of fire see T.P.M., Sp. III, 531; C.V., Sp. III, 592; between the colours of the spectrum in a drop of water and the rainbow, see D.A., Sp. I, 624; between gold in its natural state and that produced by the flame of a furnace see D.A., Sp. I, 497. For the medieval art-nature opposition and that of modern times see Schuhl, *op. cit.*, n. 4 above, pp. 32–42. Schuhl quotes lines from the *Roman de la Rose* as an example of the gradual modification of this attitude. In Petrarch and Ariosto it reasserts itself in its old form however (*De remediis utriusque fortunae*, Basel, 1554, I, 99; *Orlando furioso*, Ferrara, 1516, IX, 28–9, XI, 22 seq.) Descartes, like Bacon, sees no difference 'between machines made by artisans and the various bodies that nature alone can fashion'. (*Principes*, ed. Adam and Tannery, Paris, 1903, IX, 321). For the relation of art to nature in Shakespeare see Schuhl, 'Perdita, la nature et l'art', *Revue de metaphysique et de morale*, 1946, pp. 335–8.

96. N.O., I, 129 (Sp. IV, 114). See also Val. Term., Sp. III, 223; C.V., Sp. III, 611–12.

97. Cf. Val. Term. Sp. III, 222; Cog. hum., Sp. III, 185; Filum Lab., Sp. III, 498; N.O., I, 81; D.A., Sp. I, 462–3. For the meta-

morphosis of Bacon's ideal of a science at the service of mankind to a science at the service of the state see Hall, 201 seq., where he quotes Leibniz.

98. For the idea of co-operation see *Epistola fratris Rogerii Baconni*, ad Claras Aquas (Quaracchi), 1928, p. 25, and *Op. Tert.* (Brewer), 117. For progress of science see *De viciis contractis in studio Theologiae* (Steele) 5 and *Op. Majus* (Bridges), I, 9. For the diffusion of learning see *Op. Tert.* (Brewer), 11–12.

99. A. C. Crombie, *Robert Grosseteste and the origins of experimental science, 1100–1700*, Oxford, 1953, commits this error; after stressing the points of contact between the two Bacons (p. 300), he limits the discussion of Roger's *Scientia experimentalis* to exposing its modernity and deals in three lines with the question of its third prerogative (p. 142). For the dangers of overestimating the similarity between Roger and Francis see C. Vasoli, 'Il programma riformatore di Ruggero Bacone', *RF*, 1956, 2, pp. 178–96.

100. Cr. R. Carton, *L'expérience physique chez Roger Bacon*, Paris, 1924, pp. 154–61; S. C. Easton, *Roger Bacon and his search for a Universal Science*, Oxford, 1952, pp. 78–83, 114; for the remark by Thorndike see pp. 645 seq. ('Roger Bacon and the experimental Method in the Middle Ages', *Philosophical Review*, 1914, p. 281). The references to Roger Bacon's works are *Op. Majus* (Bridges) II, 15; *Comp. studii philos.* (Brewer) 415–16; *Epistola de secretis op.* (Brewer) 543.

101. *MR*, 171. The notion of occult knowledge had notable ramifications in ancient Greece and later in Christian and medieval civilisations. 'Reveal nothing of all that is, but keep these things to yourself, because silence leads to wisdom', writes Zosima (eighth century). Cf. Berthelot, 181. A basic work on this subject is R. P. Festugière, *La Révélation d'Hermès Trismégiste*, Paris, 1944–54, 4 vols.

102. M. Petri Boni Lombardi Ferrariensis, *Introductio in artem chimiae integra*, Montpelier, 1602, p. 398.

103. *De magia veterum summum sapientiae studium, Arbatel de magia*. We have used the text printed in Prost, *op. cit.*, n. 69 above, I, 576 seq. Cf. Thorndike, VI, 457–8.

104. Cf. *MR*. 293 seq.; F. A. Yates, *Giordano Bruno and the Hermetic Tradition*, London, 1964.

105. Paracelsus, *De summis naturae mysteriis commentarii*, Basel, 1584, p. 27.

106. For Agrippa's interest in mechanical constructions and in engineering see the two letters written in September 1526 and December 1527 (Ep. IV, 44; Ep. V, 20, in Opera, II, 863, 910). For the secret society of which Agrippa was a member during his stay in Paris see E. Garin in *Giornale critico della filosofia italiana*, 1952, p.

270. The first twelve letters of the first book (II, 1–18) concern the relations of a group of intellectuals including Charles de Bovelles, Germain de Ganay and probably Simphorien Champier.

107. To Johannes Trithemius (8. 4. 1510) and to Chrysostom (May 1512). Ep. I, 24, 31 in *Opera*, pp. 704–7. An interesting fact is the mention of secrecy in connection with Fracastoro who would appear to have been in many ways foreign to any sort of occultism (G. Francastoro, *Scritti inediti*, ed. F. Pelligrini, Verona, 1955, p. 297).

108. Ep. I, 31, in Agrippa, *Opera* II, 910; for what precedes see *De occulta philosophia*, III, 45, and *Opera*, I, 250 seq.

109. G. Cardano, *Autobiografia*, in Le Blanc, *op. cit.*, n. 30 above, pp. 117, 207.

110. G. Cardano, *De rerum varietate*, Avignon, 1558, *Epistola nuncupatoria*, p. 5, and *Autobiografia* (see n. 30 above). The list of supernatural powers is in the autobiography but see also *De rerum varietate*, p. 10.

111. For the study of the commonplace, rather than the marvellous, exceptional, phenomena as an important feature of modern science see L. Olschki, *Geschichte der neusprachlichen, wissenschaftlichen Literatur*, Halle, 1927, III, 454 seq.

112. T.P.M., Sp. III, 532–3, 536, 530.

113. G. B. Della Porta, *De i miracoli et maravigliosi effetti della nature prodotti libri IIII*, Venice, 1534, pp. 3, 7. For Della Porta's strange views on culture and the work of the artisan see *Magiae naturalis libri*, Frankfurt, 1607, pp. 3b, 544. See also on the subject of concealing the results of his work the letter of 27.6.1586 to Cardinal d'Este published in Fiorentino, *op. cit.*, n. 71 above, p. 257.

114. N.A., Sp. III, 164. The importance of this passage has been rightly stressed by Corsano whose observations on the relation of technology to philosophy in the Renaissance have been a great help to me: A. Corsano, *Studi sul Rinascimento*, Bari, 1949, pp. 81–117; for Bacon see pp. 94–5. Spedding, with his usual thoroughness, basing his conclusions on ten passages from Bacon, proves that the latter's references to the need for caution in imparting the new methods have nothing to do with a desire to conceal the results of his investigations or to reserve them for an élite. Spedding's objections to Ellis seem to me conclusive. For an appreciation of these passages see Spedding, note B to Ellis' preface to the N.O., in Sp. I, 107–13. For Bacon's views on enigmatic procedures see also D.A., Sp. I, 665, and the essay *On seeming wise*, Sp. VI, 436.

115. Adv., Sp. III, 289 seq.; D.A., Sp. I, 573 seq.

116. Adv., Sp. III, 362; D.A., Sp. I, 574; H.S., Sp. II, 80.

117. T.P.M., Sp. III, 534; R.Ph., Sp. III, 575; N.O., I, 54; for

the trampling of the works of God see Praef., Sp. I, 130; N.O., I, 82; D.A., Sp. I, 460; Adv., Sp. III, 292.

118. Val. Term., Sp. III, 224; C.V., Sp. III, 617; Phaen. Un., Sp. III, 687; N.O., I, 68.

119. N.O., I, 61, 122; see also Val. Term., Sp. III, 250; Filum Lab., Sp. III, 638; R.Ph., Sp. III, 572.

120. R.Ph., Sp. III, 573 (B.F. 119); see also Filum Lab., Sp. III, 638; C.V., Sp. III, 604; N.O., I, 104. See the famous passage where Bacon tells the fable of the old man who left his sons a treasure buried in his vineyard, and says that the alchemists' searching in vain for gold but making useful discoveries in the process are like the old man's sons who increased the produce of the vine while digging for the treasure (Cf. C. V., Sp. III, 605). A similar idea is to be found in John Donne's *Love's alchymie*.

121. Cf. N.O., II, 4; Filum Lab., Sp. III, 496–7; C.V., Sp. III, 592; N.O., I, 85; for the magician's faith see for instance what Agrippa writes to Aurelius of Aquapendente in September 1527 (Ep. I, 24 and V, 14 in *Opera*, 904, 704).

122. See for example Cardano's autobiography, cited in n. 30 above, pp. 135–6. But it would be a serious misrepresentation to see the Renaissance as an epoch where only triumph and joy of living prevailed. See S. A. Nulli, *Erasmo e il Rinascimento*, Torino, 1955, pp. 230, 2.

123. I.N.P., Sp. III, 519–20; see also C.V., Sp. III, 318; Praef., Sp. I, 132.

124. R.Ph., Sp. III, 559 (B.F. 104–5).

125. See J. H. Randall, Jnr., 'The Place of Leonardo da Vinci in the Emergence of Modern Science', *JHI*, 1953, 2, pp. 191–2. For Bacon's ideal of scientific man see also Moody E. Prior, 'Bacon's Man of Science', *JHI*, 1954, 3, pp. 348–70. For the end of the organic and interconnected world of magic and hermetic philosophy and the substitution of mechanistic views to the vitalistic, see M. Nicholson, *The Breaking of the Circle*, Evanstone, 1950 and the article by W. Y. Tindall, 'James Joyce and the Hermetic Tradition', *JHI*, 1954, 1, pp. 23–39, that expounds some interesting views on the disappearance in the age of Locke and Newton of the Renaissance Hermetic tradition and its subsequent reappearance in romantic culture. On the same subject see A. O. Lovejoy, *The Great Chain of Being*, Harvard, 1936.

NOTES TO CHAPTER II

1. W. Rawley, *The Life of the honourable Author*, in Sp. I, 4.
2. Anderson has proved conclusively that this work was written

before 1603 (pp. 44-7). Spedding and most of Bacon's biographers had placed it around 1608. B. Farrington, *The Philosophy of F. Bacon*, Liverpool, 1964, pp. 56-66, has established the date from Bacon's mention of the death of Peter Severinus which took place on the 28 August 1602. Bacon was thus 41 or 42 at the time so that his production can by no means be described as 'juvenile' (though I must confess that I myself have made this mistake).

3. A detailed study of this work can be found in the next chapter.

4. I do not agree with Anderson's appreciation of this work (pp. 44-7, 106). In his exhaustive study of Bacon's history of philosophy he omits to stress the progressive nature of Bacon's *œuvre* so that all his works are presented as being equally important. Levi, pp. 332-81, adopts the same method. Farrington, on the other hand, in his brief study of Bacon's attitude to traditional philosophy (pp. 64-9, 147-9) shows a thorough perception of the development of Bacon's ideas from the *Temporis partus masculus* onwards. To me, his insights have proved invaluable.

5. T.P.M., Sp. III, 535. This notion recurs in C.V., Sp. III, 605, and N.O., I, 122; but here *scientia* has been replaced by *rerum inventio* (invention). Cf. also Adv. Sp. III, 290; Val. Term., Sp. III, 251; N.O., I, 56; D.A., Sp. I, 458. See next chapter for Bacon's views on 'remote antiquity' and myths.

6. T.P.M., Sp. III, 529 (B.F., 63).

7. For Bacon's attitude in 1597 see Med. S., Sp. VII, 239, 250 where Scholastic philosophy is represented as a typical form of religious imposture.

8. E. Cassirer, *The Philosophy of the Enlightenment*, Boston, 1961, p. 9.

9. T.P.M., Sp. III, 528, 538-9 (B.F., 62, 72).

10. Farrington, *op. cit.*, n. 2 above, pp. 21-6.

11. Anthony a'Wood, *The History and Antiquities of the University of Oxford*, ed. J. Cutch, Oxford, 1792-6, II; *c.* Mallet, *History of the University of Oxford*, London, 1924-7, III; J. Bass Mullinger, *The University of Cambridge*, London, 1873-1911, III; for the decadence of the English universities around 1540 see D. Bush, 'Tudor Humanism and Henry VIII', *University of Toronto Quarterly*, VII, 1938, pp. 162-77. Bush objects to the theory of decadence in the universities of that time and sees Henry VIII as the patron of the new humanist culture. A detailed account of the link between university and social life in the early sixteenth century in England can be found in Caspari, pp. 132-56, which is based on A. F. Leach, *English Schools at the Reformation, 1546-1548*, Westminster, 1896. A list of texts considered by the Elizabethan statutes of 1570 will be found in J. E. Sandys, *Education in Shakespeare's England*, Oxford, 1950, I, 241-2.

12. See the excellent study by F. A. Yates, 'Giordano Bruno's Conflict with Oxford', *JWI*, II, 1938–9, pp. 227–42.

13. a'Wood, *op. cit.*, n. 11 above, II, 226.

14. Yates, *art. cit.*, n. 12 above, p. 230.

15. E. Digby, *Theoria analytica*, London, 1579.

16. *idem.*, *De duplici methodo*, London, 1580. Bacon never refers explicitly to Digby, though he must have attended his lectures when at Cambridge where Digby was a prominent figure at the time. Passages from Bacon where Digby's influence is apparent have been collected by J. Freudenthal, 'Beitrage zur Geschichte der englischen Philosophie', *Archiv für Geschichte der Philosophie*, IV, 1891, pp. 601–2.

17. Temple's ripost to Digby's *De duplici methodo* in the *Admonitio de unica P. Rami methodo*, London, 1580. His attack was directed also against Piscator, professor of theology at Herborn and Liebler, professor of physics at Tübingen, who had criticised Ramus' doctrine. For texts referring to this controversy see G. Sortais, *La philosophie moderne depuis Bacon jusqu'à Leibniz*, Paris, 1920, p. 58.

18. Bush, p. 17, shows how Aristotle's influence at Oxford increased after the Laudian statutes (1736). Changes had evidently taken place and the Scholastic tradition in Tudor England was modified by humanism, but Oxford still remained a basically medieval university.

19. C.V., Sp. III, 597 (B.F. 79); Filum Lab., Sp. III, 502; N. O., I, 90.

20. *Bacon to Lord Burghley* (1591), Sp. L, I, 109.

21. T.P.M., Sp. III, 530–1.

22. *ibid.*, 534.

23. Bacon's views on classical scepticism are intimately connected to his method (cf. T.P.M., Sp. III, 537; Adv., Sp. III, 388; R.Ph., Sp. III, 580; Scala Int., Sp. II, 687; N.O., Sp. I, 151; N.O., I, 67; D.A., Sp. I, 621). The affinities he notes between his own philosophy and scepticism (Scala Int., Sp. II, 688) do not imply similar aims, he says; where the sceptics deny the possibility of scientific achievements he denies this possibility only to traditional methods (N.O., I, 37); the sceptics denounced the senses when it is really the mind which is at fault; it is not science one should blame, but the mind, whose distortions can be corrected and whose activities should be assisted.

24. Farrington, *op. cit.*, n. 2 above, p. 40.

25. In D.A.; *leven aliquam mentionem aut narrationes quasdam jejunias* corresponds to the term 'memorials'.

26. C.V., Sp. III, 329–30. In Ch. 4, book II, D.A., Sp. I, 502–4, the history of culture is included among the *desiderata*. See Flugel, 'Bacon's Historia Literarum', *Anglia*, XII, Halle, 1899.

27. C.V., Sp. III, 613–14. In N.O., I, 78, Bacon mentions *six* centuries and says that the three periods of productivity were each of two hundred years. Fowler (p. 272, n. 17) places these as follows: from Thales to Plato; from Cicero to Marcus Aurelius; from the invention of the printing-press to Bacon's own time. In this way, Plato and Aristotle are excluded from the 'productive period' of Greek civilisation.

28. R. Ph., Sp. III, 561 (B.F. 106).

29. *ibid.*, 562.

30. Plato, *Timaeus*, 22b.

31. C.V., Sp. III, 601; R.Ph., Sp. III, 563; N.O., I, 71. We find the same censure in William Gilbert, *De mundo nostro sublunari philosophia nova*, Amsterdam, 1651, book III, p. 240. But it was common to most literary circles; see Charles Gildon, *Miscellaneous Letters and Essays*, London, 1649. Cf. Jones, *art. cit.*, The basic study of Bacon's classical sources is E. Wolff, *Francis Bacon und seine Quellen*, Berlin, 1910–13, 2 vols.

32. R.Ph., Sp. III, 595; but this notion first appears in *Praise of Knowledge*, Sp. L. I, 124.

33. C.V., Sp. III, 564 (B.F. 109). For the revolutionary cultural consequences of geographical discoveries see G. Atkinson, *Les Nouveaux Horizons de la Renaissance française*, Paris, 1935; I. B. Cohen, *La Découverte du nouveau monde et la transformation de l'idée de la nature; la science au XVIe siècle*, Paris, 1960, pp. 189–210; for the social and cultural effects of travel see R. R. Crawley, *Unpathed Waters; Studies in the Influence of the Voyagers on Elizabethan Literature*, Princeton, 1940; G. B. Parks, 'Travel as Education', *The Seventeenth Century* 264–90; B. Penrose, *Travel and Discovery in the Renaissance*, New York, 1962.

34. *Praise of Knowledge*, Sp. L, I, 124.

35. For the ignorance of antiquity see Guicciardini, *Storia d'Italia*, Bari, 1929, II, p. 132. Cf. Romeo, *Le scoperte americane nella coscienza italiana del Cinquecento*, Naples, 1944, pp. 127, 131, who mentions the link between theories such as Guicciardini's and the popular seventeenth-century notion of the superiority of modern to ancient writers. He is less convincing about the Renaissance summons to experience.

36. R.Ph., Sp. III, 564; N.O., I, 72.

37. C.V., Sp. III, 595–7 (B.F. 77); Filum Lab., Sp. III, 499–500; N.O., I, 79–80.

38. R.Ph., Sp. III, 570; De Princ., Sp. III, 84.

39. N.O., I, 71–2. Here Bacon alludes to signs *ex natura temporis et aetatis* and *ex natura loci et nationis*.

40. R.Ph., Sp. III, 557–63 (B.F., 103, 108).

41. *ibid.*, 576 (B.F. 123–4); N.O., I, 73.

42. R.Ph., Sp. III, 578; N.O., I, 74. See also Ch. I of this book.

43. R.Ph., Sp. III, 579; N.O., I, 75. The same notion in C.V., Sp. III, 592.

44. R.Ph., Sp. III, 581. This sign is replaced in the N.O. (I, 76) by the diversity of schools and beliefs, where also three new signs make their appearance: the place (I, 71), the time (I, 72) and great popularity (a symptom of superficiality) (I, 76).

45. Cog. nat., Sp. III, 29; N.O., I, 63.

46. R.Ph., Sp. III, 582 (B.F., 130); N.O., I, 25, 125, but here Bacon does not refer explicitly to Aristotle.

47. Adv., Sp. III, 292; C.V., Sp. III, 593–4; Filum Lab., Sp. III, 498; N.O., I, 86; D.A., Sp. I, 460.

48. Val. Term., Sp. III, 226; C.V., Sp. III, 591; R.Ph., Sp. III, 580; Adv., Sp. III, 293–4; Praef., Sp. I, 127–8; N.O., I, 75.

49. The P.M., C.V., and R.Ph.

50. Aristotle was severely criticised in Renaissance literature for his historical theories and disregard for past philosophers. See Giovanni Francesco Pico, *Examen vanitatis doctrinae gentium et veritatis Christianae disciplinae*, VI, Ch. 14 in *Opera*, Basel, 1573, II, p. 792, for a refutation of Aristotle's beliefs and an unfavourable comparison with Democritus. Also Francesco Patrizzi, *Discussiones peripateticae*, Basel, 1581, IV, 1, pp. 369–74, who opposes the pre-Socratic naturalists to Aristotle; see also III, p. 295.

51. Adv., Sp. III, 352, 365; C.V., Sp. III, 602; R.Ph., Sp. III, 561, 565: N.O., I, 67; D.A., Sp. I, 548, 563.

52. Cog. hum., Sp. III, 187; Adv., Sp. III, 285; D.A., Sp. I, 453.

53. Bacon denounces the theories of 'clinamen' and the causality of the universe in Med. S., Sp. VII, 253; Adv., Sp. III, 357; Essays, Sp. VI, 413. He rejects the anthropomorphic representation of the gods in Val. Term., Sp. III, 241; Adv., Sp. III, 396; D.A., Sp. I, 644.

54. Lewes, *Aristotle: a chapter from the History of Science*, London, 1864 and Grote, *Plato and the other Companions of Socrates*, London, 1865 adopt Bacon's classification of Plato and Aristotle among the sophists.

55. C.V., Sp. III, 602; R.Ph., Sp. III, 570.

56. N.O., I, 63.

57. C.V., Sp. III, 598. Columella (XI, III) and Pliny (*Hist. nat.*, XXIV, 17; XXV, 2) gave Democritus the title of 'magician'. Seneca (*Epist.*, XC) recalls how Democritus was able to colour glass and metals, modify ivory and turn sand into precious stones. At the beginning of the Christian era a number of naturalist theories attributed to Democritus were still current in Egypt; cf. Berthelot,

70, 116-17, 154-9. Pseudo-Democritus was translated into Latin *Democriti Abderitae de arte magna*, Padua, 1573. The German alchemist Johann Conrad Dippel wrote under the pseudonym of Christian Democritus. For the tradition of Democritus as Christian see Edgar Wind, 'The Christian Democritus', *JWI*, I, 1937, 2, pp. 180-2.

58. N.O., I, 51.

59. Cog. nat., Sp. III, 18; N.O., II, 48; these remarks can also be found in the interpretation of the Cupid myth in D.S.V., Sp. VI, 687 seq.

60. Bacon's uncertainty concerning the problem of vacuum is discussed in the next chapter.

61. Adv., Sp. III, 358; D.A., Sp. I, 569.

62. C.V., Sp. III, 603; R.Ph., III, 570; N.O., I, 44.

63. De Princ., Sp. III, 98 seq. For Telesius see also D.A., Sp. I, 564; N.O., II, 37, 41; Bacon is partial to Telesius and A. Donio (see D.A., IV, 3, and the myth of Pan in D.S.V. and D.A.) on account of their theory that the senstive faculties of the mind are due to a physical movement, their anti-Aristotelianism and their attempts to restore pre-Socratic philosophy. Bacon's study of the doctrine of Telesius cannot be dissociated from his own physics. A. Donio, *De natura humanis*, Basel, 1581. For Donio see F. Fiorentino, *B. Telesio*, Florence, 1872-4, I, pp. 321 seq; Saitta, I, *op. cit.*, Ch. I, n. 77, III, pp. 74-7.

64. De Princ., Sp. III, 98 seq.

65. N.O., I, 79.

66. De Princ., Sp. III, 86.

67. Adv., Sp. III, 355; C.V., Sp. III, 601; R.Ph., Sp. III, 569; D.A., Sp. I, 565, In N.O., I, 105, Bacon writes that Plato occasionally uses an inductive method arriving—by a series of rejections—at general conclusions based on negative instances. Fowler (p. 310) rightly observes that this description of Plato's induction should not be too readily contrasted with the 'vague' inductions mentioned in the T.P.M., Sp. III, 530, where Bacon was probably alluding to what is usually understood by the term Platonic or Socratic induction. Plato's method of rejection is sufficiently apparent in the quest for the exact meaning of 'Justice' in the first book of the *Republic*.

68. N.O., I, 51, 106; D.A., Sp. I, 565.

69. Passages cited in n. 67.

70. T.P.M., Sp. III, 530-1 (B.F., 64).

71. N.O., Sp. I, 153 (Sp. IV, 41-2).

72. Adv., Sp. III, 355; R.Ph., Sp. III, 569; C.V., Sp. III, 601; N.O., I, 96, where Bacon refers to Platonism, not to Plato; D.A., Sp. I, 565.

73. Adv., Sp. III, 355; D.A., Sp. I, 569.

74. For the characteristics of superstitious philosophy see C.V., Sp. III, 598. For the dangers of Platonism: N.O., I, 65, For Plato as more poet than philosopher see C.V., Sp. III, 601. The idea of the glorification of errors can be found also—less clearly expressed—in T.P.M., Sp. III, 531.

75. The Cabbala and Hermetic, neo-Platonic themes influenced most of English sixteenth- and seventeenth-century culture; the works of Spenser, Donne, Browne, and Burton all reflect this influence; Sir Walter Raleigh founded a society for the study— among other subjects—of Hermetic doctrines, and Marlowe, Chapman, and Roydon were among its members. See M. C. Bradbrook, *The School of Night*, Cambridge, 1936; also J. F. Budaeus, *Introductio ad historiam philosophiae Hebraeorum*, Halle, 1705.

76. For the controversy Mersenne-Gassendi and Robert Fludd see Sortais, *op. cit.*, n. 16 above, II, 41–51. Fludd's major works were written between 1617 and 1621: they are inspired by Agrippa, Paracelsus, neo-Platonism, the Cabbala, Hermeticism, Rosicrucian theories and allegorical interpretations of the Scriptures: *Tractatus theologo-philosophicus*, Oppenheim, 1617; *Utriusque cosmo, maioris scilicet et minoris metaphysica, physica atque technica historia*, Oppenheim, 1617–18; *Veritatis proscenium*, Frankfurt, 1621. Mersenne attacks Fludd in *Quaestiones celeberrimae in Genesim*, Paris, 1623, to which Fludd replied with two pamphlets: *Sophiae cum Moria Certamen* and *Summum bonum quod est magiae cabalae alchemiae verae, Fratrum Roseae Crucis verorum, verum subjectum*, Frankfurt 1629. Gassendi's *Epistola exercitatio*, Paris, 1630 was answered by in Fludd's *Clavis philosophiae*, Frankfurt, 1633. This controversy was followed by the intelligentsia of most European cities and indicates the proportions such problems acquired. Sortais, (p. 46) says that Fludd's philosophy has a 'psychological interest in that it shows the extent of aberration the human mind can reach', but does no more to elucidate the controversy. The same applies to Cassirer who sees only the contrast between the opponents and ignores their important similarities.

77. Henry More, poet and philosopher, corresponded from Cambridge with Cudworth, Lady Conway's group, Jeremiah Taylor, Descartes, Samuel Hartlib, Joseph Glanville, and other members of the Royal Society. His works include all the principal mid-century cabbalistic and hermetic themes: *An Antidote against Atheism* etc., London, 1679, 3 vols., *Philosophical Poems*, Cambridge, 1647. For More see Cassirer, *The Platonic Renaissance in England*, trans. J. P. Pettegrove, Edinburgh, 1953; F. I. Mackinnon, *Philosophical writings of Henry More*, New York, 1925 (an anthology) and W. K. Jordan, *Development of Religious Toleration in England*, London, 1932–40, IV. For the links with Cartesianism see M. Nicolson,

'Early Stage of Cartesianism in England', *SP*, XXVI, 1929, pp. 356–74. The correspondence with Descartes is in *op. cit.*, Ch. I, n. 95, V. a bibliography in M. W. Landes, *Philosophical writings of H. More*, New York, 1925.

78. For Cardano T.P.M., Sp. III, 530. His works in 10 vols. Lyons, 1663. For Patrizzi, D.A., Sp. I, 564. His book *Nova universis philosophia*, Venice, 1593, is a combination of Ficinian, Platonist, and Stoic theories with hermetic and chaldaic philosophy. For Jean François Fernel (1485?–1558) Royal Physician to Henry II, see T.P.M., Sp. III, 530. For Paracelsus (his *Bücher und Schriften*, Basel, 1589) see T.P.M., Sp. III, 532–3; in R.Ph., Sp. III, 576, with reference to the hue and cry by which Paracelsus urged men to experiment, Bacon says he would have liked to have had him as herald. For Agrippa see T.P.M., Sp. III, 536. For Gilbert see Adv., Sp. III, 292–3; C.V., Sp. III, 609; R.Ph., Sp. III, 571; N.O., I, 54, 70; II, 35–6; D.A., Sp. I, 461; H.G.L., Aditus, Sp. II, 80, here Bacon accuses Gilbert of trying to build a ship from a row-lock, and includes him among the naturalists. To fully appreciate these statements it should be remembered that *De magnete* and *De mundo nostro* were strongly influenced by traditional doctrines. For these traditional elements, the theory of emanations, and the belief in fluids, see Wolf, *op. cit.*, Ch. I, n. 3, pp. 296–7. Also E. Zilsel, 'The Origins of William Gilbert's Scientific Method', *JHI*, 1941, I, pp. 1 seq. According to M. Boas, 'Bacon and Gilbert', *JHI*, 1950, pp. 466–7, Bacon's opinion of Gilbert was based only on *De mundo nostro*, *De magnete* being unknown to him. Further allusions to the thinkers of the Renaissance are restricted to Bruno and Campanella, mentioned only to be included—together with Patrizi, Telesio, Peter Soerensen, and Gilbert—among those whose writings were neither cleverly worded nor successful (*Hist. nat. Auctoris Monitum, Sp.* II, 13); and Fracastoro, cited as having claimed to be the founder of a new philosophy but also as possessing a certain independence of opinion (Adv., Sp. III, 366; C.V., Sp. III, 603; R.Ph., Sp. III, 571). For Fracastoro's empiricism and his anti-magical views see P. Rossi, 'Il metodo induttivo e la polemica antioccultistica in G. Fracastoro', *Rivista critica di storia della filosofia*, 1954, pp. 485–99.

79. Adv., Sp. III, 282. For the humanists' analogy to the reformers in Protestant historiography see W. K. Ferguson, *The Renaissance in Historical Thought*, Boston, 1948, where we find a relevant quotation from Florimond de Remond, *Histoire de l'hérésie de ce siècle*, Paris, 1605, p. 32v.

80. Adv., Sp. III, 283–4. John Sturm (1507–89) founder and leader of the 'Schola Argentiniensis' that became a centre of the

reformation in Strasbourg. Ascham's most influential work was *The Scholemaster*, London, 1570. Cf. *English Works: Toxophilus, Report of Affairs of Germany, The Scholemaster*, ed. W. A. Wright, Cambridge, 1904.

81. Erasmus, *Dialogus ciceronianus*, Basel, 1528, Preface. See also the letters to Francesco Molinio 6 June 1526 and to Giacomo Tussano, 16 May 1526, in *Opus epistolarum D. Erasmi*, ed. Allen, Oxford, 1926, VI, pp. 354–64 and 345–6. The Ciceronians' attacks on Erasmus were violent. Scaligero, *Orationes*, Paris, 1531 and 1537, and E. Dolet, *Dialogus de imitatione ciceroniana*, Lyons, 1540, are documents of this controversy. Also Mario Nizolio, *Observationes in M. Tullium Ciceronem* (Brescia, 1535), that ran to 70 editions between 1535 and 1620.

82. For Bacon's views on Xenophon see R.Ph., Sp. III, 565 (B.F. 110–11).

83. *The complete Works of John Lyly*, Oxford, 1902; *The Works of E. Spenser*, Baltimore, 1932–49; *The Works of George Chapman*, London, 1874–5. The poems *The Shadow of Night* (1594) and *Ovid's Banquet of Sense* (1595) are more particularly influenced by Ficino. see also John Davies, *Mirum in modum* London, 1602 and *Summa totalis* London, 1607; and Sir John Davies, *Nosce te ipsum* London, 1599. See D. L. Clark, *Rhetoric and Poetry in the Renaissance*, New York, 1922; E. Greenlaw, *Studies in Spenser's Historical Allegory*, Baltimore, 1932; C. S. Lewis, *The Allegory of Love*, Oxford, 1936; F. L. Schoell, *Etudes sur l'humanisme continental en Angleterre à la fin de la Renaissance*, Paris, 1926; H. G. Lotspeich, *Classical Mythology in the Poetry of E. Spenser*, Princeton, 1932, and Lemmi.

84. The critical ed. of the Latin text of the *Utopia*, Paris, 1936 (first published Louvain, 1516). *Complete Works of Sir Philip Sidney*, Cambridge, 1922. Elyot, *The Governour*, London, 1531 (London, 1883 ed., 2 vols.).

85. For the humanists' political and social ideals in Tudor England see Caspari, 10 seq.

86. See Morris W. Croll, 'Attic Prose in the Seventeenth Century', *SP*, XVIII, 1921, pp. 79–128; 'Attic Prose: Lipsius, Montaigne, Bacon', *Schelling Anniversary Papers*, New York, 1923; 'The Baroque Style of Prose', *Studies in English Philology, A Miscellany in Honour of F. Klaeber*, Minneapolis, 1929. Most historian shave stressed the *Essays*' anti-Ciceronianism (see Bush, 184 seq.). But all Bacon's writings on the different methods of communicating knowledge and his Preface to the aphoristic method (Adv., Sp. III, 403–8; D.A., Sp. I, 650–69) are equally revealing. Confirmation of this attitude is to be found in his letter to Essex, Sp.L., II, 14.

87. Caspari, 16 seq., distinguishes four phases in the development

of humanism in England. (1) In the last decade of the fifteenth century. (2) Between 1500 and 1530, the beginning of this phase coinciding with the return to England of Grocyn, Colet, and Linacre, and with Erasmus' visit; it is marked by the production of great programmatical works such as More's *Utopia* and Elyot's *The Governour*, and by the humanists' infiltration into Oxford and Cambridge with the works of Fisher, Erasmus, Fox, More, Wolsey, and Colet; and into London when Erasmus and Lyly founded St. Paul's School. (3) Between 1530 and 1558, from the separation from Rome and the reorganisation and secularisation of education: in this phase all the leading Elizabethans grew to maturity. (4) Between 1558 and 1603, coinciding with the reign of Queen Elizabeth; humanism now acquires a social respectability similar to that which it enjoyed in Italy. On the strength of this historical outline Caspari tends, however, to overlook the important contrast between the fourth phase and the other three. Bacon's attitude is, indeed, a remarkable manifestation of this contrast.

88. For an appreciation of *Historia animalium*, see Adv., Sp. III, 288; N.O., I, 98; D.A., Sp. I, 456. For spurious works favourably commented upon by Bacon: *De mirabilibus auscultationibus* in N.O., II, 29; *Problemata*, in Adv., Sp. III, 363; D.A., Sp. I, 563; *Physiognomica* in Adv., Sp. III, 376; D.A., Sp. I, 580; the *Elenchi sofistici* are commended in Adv., Sp. III, 393; D.A., Sp. I, 642.

89. In the *Historia praeter-generationum* Bacon publishes the miracles of nature to show, in the first place, what art might also achieve, and secondly, by exposing the deviations from the norm, to stress the regular course of nature. These 'miracles' have nothing in common with religious miracles, which, when not faked, are outside the sphere of nature. An account of natural miracles should be strictly independent of true natural histories. Cf. Adv., Sp. III, 331; D.G. I., Sp. III, 730; N.O., II, 29; D.A., Sp. I, 498.

90. For Bacon's views on Aristotle's dogmatism see N.O., I, 67; on his verbal dexterity Cog. nat., Sp. III, 29; N.O., I, 63; on his obscurity Cog. hum., Sp. III, 188; R.Ph., III, 566; on his distortions of experiment Cog. hum., Sp. III, 188; R.Ph., Sp. III, 582; N.O., I, 63; on his arbitrary distinctions R.Ph., Sp. III, 566; C.V., Sp. III, 601; N.O., I, 63; on final causes Adv., Sp. III, 293; R.Ph., Sp. III, 569; C.V., Sp. III, 601–2; N.O., I, 54, 63, 96; D.A., Sp. I, 461; on contemplation Adv., Sp. III, 421; D.A., Sp. I 720.

91. Such incitements to escape from Aristotle's intellectual tyranny were a frequent theme of European culture from Roger Bacon to the seventeenth century; Valla, Agricola, Agrippa, Vives, Paracelsus, Nizelius, Ramus, Telesius, Patrizzi, Bruno are notable examples of this attitude. A short, but relevant collection of

quotations from anti-Aristotelian literature can be found in Fowler, pp. 71–86.

92. R.Ph., Sp. III, 568–9 (B.F. 114–15); this passage is remarkable for the humanistic tone of Bacon's evocation of civil, political, and legislative activities. See in the same vein T.P.M., Sp. III, 538, where he compares Aristotle to Tacitus. The works of Tacitus, translated by Sir Henry Savile and Richard Greenwey (1591–8) ran to a great many editions between 1591 and 1640. For the popularity of Tacitus in the last years of Queen Elizabeth's reign see Bush, 209.

93. Anderson, pp. 130–1.

94. These distinctions between Bacon and Aristotle are taken almost literally from Anderson, p. 193.

95. C.V., Sp. III, 596 (B.F. 78).

96. *Ibid.*, 598.

97. Adv., Sp. III, 286. The charge of historical ignorance is linked to that of verbalism and unproductiveness. Compare Bacon's judgement with that of Luis Vives, *Opera*, I, 340, quoted in *La cultura*, 471; but this attitude was common to many writers; see G. Naudé, *op. cit.*, Ch. I, n. 63, pp. 467–8.

98. See Francesco Patrizzi, *Disc. perip.*, Venice, 1571, I, p. 94.

99. C.V., Sp. III, 286.

100. For Bacon's appreciation of Scholasticism see Cog. hum., Sp. III, 187; Adv., Sp. III, 285–7; Filum Lab., Sp. III, 504; N.O., I, 89, 121; D.A., Sp. I, 453–5. For the subtleties see N.O., I, 121, 130.

101. *Dialectique*, (ed. 1555), p. 1.

102. *La cultura*, p. 469. This was the point of intersection of humanist and reformation claims. Cf. D. Cantimori, 'Umanesmo e Luteranesmo di fronte alla Scolastica: Caspar Peucer', *Rivista di studi germanici*, II, 1936, who quotes on page 432 from *Historia Eccl. centuria decimatertia*, Basel, 1624.

103. Cf. Carré, *op. cit.*, Ch. I, n. 69, p. 183.

104. This is a basic theme of the meditations of Valla, Erasmus and many other thinkers of the time; Jacopo Aconcio, *De methodo e opusculi filosofici e religiosi*, ed. G. Radetti, Florence, 1944, where such ideas are intricately interwoven, illustrates the influence of this cultural environment on a minor philosopher. The demands for a 'new' method of technico-scientific research and of religious enquiry are very much in evidence. See P. Rossi, *Giocomo Aconcio*, Milan, 1952, pp. 109 seq.; C. D. O'Malley, *Jacopo Aconcio*, Rome, 1955, pp. 113 seq.

105. Med. S., Sp. VII, 240.

106. Many similar passages were omitted for the same reason

from the translation as it was intended for intellectuals of all nationalities. For the *Index expurgatorius* alluded to by Bacon see Sp. L, VII, 436.

107. Adv., Sp. III, 287.

108. *Ibid.*, 383–4. This passage was also omitted.

109. *La cultura*, 476–7.

110. N.O., I, 56.

111. D.A., VI, 2. See also Agrippa, *Opera*, II, 31–2.

112. Cf. G. Preti, *Il cristianesimo universale di G. G. Leibniz*, Milan–Rome, 1953, p. 70.

113. D.A., Sp. I, 550.

114. Lull's works were reprinted all over Europe in the sixteenth and seventeenth centuries. In 1500 a chair of Lullism was founded at the Sorbonne. For the diffusion of Lullism, cf. the important article by F. A. Yates, 'The Art of Ramon Lull', *JWI*, XVII, 1954, n. 1–2, pp. 115–73, where Lull's doctrine is reviewed from a very different angle to that of Prantl who, seeing it as a 'pure logic', failed to grasp its true importance. The contrast between Bacon and Descartes is evident in Descartes' preoccupation with Lullism and his quest for a universal key to knowledge which becomes, freed from Lull's complex symbolism, a concept of universal mathematics capable of examining the process of thought while ignoring its content; a universal science solving all problems of order and measure without reference to any given substance (*op. cit.*, Ch. I, n. 95, X pp. 156–7, pp. 377–8. In *Clavis Universalis*, I have developed some of the ideas alluded to here.

115. T.P.M., Sp. III, 530; Val. Term., Sp. III, 236; Adv., Sp. III, 407; D.A., Sp. I, 668. The summaries are the pamphlets on liberal arts by P. Ramus, *Scholae in liberales artes*, Basel, 1596.

116. De Maistre, Liebig, Sortais (pp. 289 seq.) and Church, *Bacon*, London, 1908, p. 89, belong to the first group of critics. Fazio Allmayer—who belongs to the second group—explains the contradictions in Bacon's attitude by his ambivalent views, and notes (pp. 154–5) a gradual decrease of Bacon's antagonism to Plato. Levi (p. 355) expresses the same idea but more cautiously. Farrington (pp. 147–8) has a correct view of the problem: Anderson (pp. 127–31) gives the most reliable account of Bacon's debt to Plato; but there is not much point in comparing the texts of Plato and Bacon, as he does, and ignoring the importance of Platonism in the English intellectual world of Bacon's day.

117. I believe that, in fact, Bacon *was* responsible (even if not alone) for a new intellectual outlook. This problem has been misunderstood so often because it is usually incorrectly posed: the question is not whether Bacon's philosophy was new, but what was

the true meaning of his refutation of traditional philosophies, from what did it stem and what did it involve? Besides, what Bacon saw as 'new' in his doctrine is not necessarily new to the historian.

118. Preface, N.O., Sp. I, 153 (Sp. IV, 41); R.Ph., Sp. III, 572; Filum Lab., Sp. III, 638; N.O., I, 61, 122.

119. J. Nordstrom, *Moyen-âge et Renaissance*, Paris, 1933; J. Boulenger, 'Le vrai siècle de la Renaissance', *Humanisme et Renaissance*, 1934, pp. 9–30; these are interesting examples of such interpretations; Jacques Maritain significantly associates the Renaissance with Protestant and Cartesian reforms. Even Thorndike is not exempt from this attitude, nor, more recently Crombie, *op. cit.*, Ch. I, n. 99.

120. From *Opus Majus* (ed. Brewer), III, 54–68.

121. For Artistotle: *Comp. Studii philos.* (ed. Brewer), p. 423; *Secretum secretorum* (ed. Steele), pp. 36–7; for Avicenna: *Comp. Studii philos.*, p. 456; for Plato: *Secretum secretorum*, p. 56.

122. *Op. majus*, III, 14–15; *Comp. Studii philos.*, 429.

123. See R. Carton, *L'expérience mystique de l'illumination intérieure chez Roger Bacon*, Paris, 1924, p. 326. Thorndike, II, 646, though in no way partial to Renaissance philosophy, reaches similar conclusions.

124. Marsilii Ficini, *Opera omnia*, Basel, 1567, p. 866, for his notion of 'sacred philosophy' and its relation to that of Pythagoras, Plato, and Socrates as precursors of Christianity. For Pico's notion of 'philosophical peace', which is related to the same idea, see E. Garin, 'Lo spirito cristiano di Pico della Mirandola', *Pensée humaniste et tradition chrétienne*, Paris, 1950, p. 179. Identical notions are in Patrizi, *Nova universis philosophia*, Venice, 1593, where the *corpus* of theology is said to be present in Plotinus. The theory of a universal revelation is to be found also in Robert Fludd and the whole humanist tradition. See the quotations from Francesco Giorgio Veneto's *De Harmonia mundi* in *Testi umanistici sull'ermetismo*, cit. Ch. I, n. 78, pp. 88, 91, and the notes by Vasoli (*ibid.*, p. 83). J. J. Cross, 'F. Bacon and the History of Philosophy', *Studies in the History of Ideas*, Columbia, 1918, pp. 80–7, is an inadequate study of Bacon's attitude. The first English history of philosophy was T. Stanley, *The History of Philosophy containing the Lives, Opinions, Actions and Discourses of the Philosophers of every Sect*, London, 1659–60; it is a combination of the *Lives* of Diogenes Laertius, the *Platonic doctrine* of Alcinous, the *Platonic Discourses* of Pico della Mirandola, the *Explanation of the doctrine of Pythagoras* by Reuchlin, and *Pirrhonian sketches* by Sextus Empiricus.

125. Ramus, 2.

126. Marius Nizolius, *De veris principiis*, Parma, 1553, p. 1. For

Nizolius see P. Rossi, 'La celebrazione della retorica e la polemica antimetafisica nel De principiis di Mario Nizolio', *La crisi dell'uso dogmatico della ragione*, ed. A. Banfi, Milan, 1953. Some texts in *Testi umanistici su la retorica*, pp. 57–92.

127. C.V., Sp. III, 560–1 (B.F. 106).

128. This was the earlier title of the *Discours sur la methode*, Leiden, 1637.

129. Descartes, *Principia philosophiae*, preface. The earlier quotation is from the same preface: *Lettre de l'auteur à celui qui a traduit le livre*.

130. D.A., Sp. I, 564; Adv., Sp. III, 365–6.

NOTES TO CHAPTER 3

1. Miguel de Cervantes Saavedra, *The Adventures of Don Quixote*, trans. J. M. Cohen, Penguin Books, 1959, pp. 610–11.

2. Cassirer, 74.

3. E. K. Rand, *Ovid and his Influence*, London, 1926; R. Schevill, *Ovid and the Renaissance in Spain*, Berkeley, 1913.

4. The influence of Leone Ebreo's doctrine of love is obvious in the *Galatea*. For the question of myths and allegory from antiquity to the late Renaissance see Seznec. Also E. Panofsky, *Studies in Iconology*, Oxford 1939 (New York, 1962); Yates (especially Ch. VIII, pp. 130–51).

5. For the significance of allegory and symbol in Platonism: P. Monnier, *Le Quattrocento*, Lausanne, 1901, pp. 127 seq.; Lemmi, 14–19 *passim;* Seznec, 88, seq.; Panofsky, *op. cit.*, n. 4 above, pp. 199 seq.

6. Cassirer, 102. Yates, 131–2, correctly stresses the importance for a study of Renaissance culture of such allegorical and emblematic literary and artistic productions. See also Waetzoldt, *Durer and his Time*, trans. R. H. Boothrod, London, 1950, p. 63; R. J. Clements, 'Iconography on the Nature and Inspiration of Poetry in Renaissance Emblem Literature', *Publications of the Modern Language Association of America*, 1955, IV, pp. 781–804.

7. Cassirer, 74.

8. Seznec, 192; Yates, 131.

9. See *M.R.* 90 seq.

10. Bovillus, *Il sapiente*, ed. E. Garin, Torino, 1943, pp. 36–7.

11. Cassirer 102.

12. Seznec, 290.

13. *op. cit.*, Ch. I, n. 1, p. 38.

14. Montaigne, *The Complete Works*, trans. Donald M. Frame, London, pp. 442–3. This attitude was common to a number of

writers. A lucid definition of the different types of allegory can be found in St Thomas, *Summa theologica*, Quest. I, art. 10.

15. J. Plattard, *L'oeuvre de Rabelais*, Paris, 1910.

16. Seznec, 198; P. Villey, *Sources et evolution des Essais de Montaigne*, Paris, 1908.

17. Montaigne, *op. cit.*, n. 14 above, p. 298.

18. G. B. Vico, *La scienza novua*, ed. R. Nicolini, Bari, 1911–16, pp. 212, 220.

19. See Seznec, 191, 198 seq.; Lilio Gregorio Giraldi, *De deis gentium*, Basel, 1548; Natale Conti, *Mythologiae*, Venice, 1551; Vincenzo Cartari, *Le immagini colla sposizione degli dei degli antichi*, Venice, 1556. For other manuals see Seznec. Basic works are: Ravisius Textor, *Officina partim historicis, partim poeticis referta disciplinis*, Basel, 1503; Hermann Torrentinus, *Elucidarius carminum et historiarum, vel vocabularius poeticus continens fabulas*, Strasburg, 1510?; G. Pictor, *Theologia mythologica*, Freiburg, 1532.

20. For Conti and Giraldi see G. Tiraboschi, *Storia della Letteratura Italiana*, (ed. 1792) VII, 854, 1461; 849, 1386. Conti's *Mythologia* ran to 19 eds. between 1551 and 1627, of which 3 are in Venice, 4 in Frankfurt, 3 in Paris and 1 in Geneva, Lyons, Hassau and Padua; the French trans. by J. de Montlyard was published in Paris, Lyons, Rouen and again in Paris. The *Imagini* by Cartari had 24 eds. between 1556 and 1699; 7 in Venice, 4 in Padua, 1 in Lyons in Italian. The Latin ed. was published in Lyons, Rothenburg, Mainz, Frankfurt and again Mainz; the French four times in Lyons and once in Tournon; the English in London and the German in Frankfurt. This will give some idea of the popularity of such works in Europe. At the Braidense Library, Milan, alone there are four eds. of Conti's works and eight of Cartari's. For Conti's statement of the theory of a hidden philosophy in the classical fables see *Mythologia*, I, 1.

21. L. Einstein, *The Italian Renaissance in England*, New York 1902; F. L. Schoell, 'Les Mythologistes italiens de la Renaissance et la poésie élisabethaine', *Revue de litterature comparée*, 1924, pp. 5–25 and *op. cit.*, Ch. II, n. 83; D. Bush, *Mythology and the Renaissance Tradition in English Poetry*, London, 1932; J. Seznec, 'Les Manuels mythologiques italiens et leur diffusion en Angleterre à la fin de la Renaissance', *Mélanges archeol. hist.*, 1933, pp. 276–92 (most of which has been incorporated in his book); F. A. Yates, 'Italian Teachers in Elizabethan England', *JWI*, 1937, pp. 103–6.

22. See F. L. Schoell, *op. cit.*, Ch. II, n. 83, who compares certain passages from Chapman and Natale Conti (pp. 179–97) and W. Schrickx, 'George Chapman's borrowing from Natale Conti', *English Studies*, XXXII, 1951, pp. 107–12. For Marsilio Ficino's

influence: F. L. Schoell, 'Les Emprunts de G. Chapman a Marsile Ficin', *Revue de litterature comparée*, 1923, pp. 2–35. For the medieval inspiration of Chapman's personifications, see M. Praz, *La poesia metafisica inglese del Seicento*, Rome, 1945, pp. 34–5.

23. Seznec, 280. Marston, *Works of John Marston*, London, 1856, III, 218, quotes Cartari and Conti.

24. *Spenser's Faerie Queene*, Everyman ed., London, 1964.

25. T. Wilson, *The Arte of Rhetorique for the Use of All Suche as are Studious of Eloquence*, ed. G. H. Mair, Oxford, 1909, pp. 195 seq. For the use of allegory in English poetry and philosophy see also J. W. H. Atkins, *English Literary Criticism: The Renaissance*, London, 1947, pp. 349 seq.; on pp. 263–72 he discusses Bacon's attitude to poetry.

26. G. Puttenham, *The Arte of English Poesie*, London, 1589; *Elizabethan Critical Essays*, Oxford, 1937, II, 6, 7, 9.

27. Sir J. Harington, *A Preface, or rather a Briefe Apologie of Poetrie, prefixed to the translation of Orlando Furioso*, London, 1591; *Elizabethan Critical Essays*, cit. n. 26 above, II, p. 203.

28. For Lodge see Lemmi, 21. For Reynolds see Willey, 209 seq. For the growth of allegory in seventeenth-century England see Bush, 350 seq., though Bush restricts his study almost exclusively to the Ovidian tradition.

29. Cog. Hum., Sp. III, 183–98; Adv., Sp. III, 259–491; D.S.V., Sp. VI, 687–746; D.A., Sp. I, 423–580; De Princ., Sp. III, 79–118. The date of composition of the De Princ. is conjectural. It was certainly written after 1609 as it includes a more detailed interpretation of one of the fables already interpreted in D.S.V. It also contains notions and expressions used in the *Instauratio* and the *N.O.* which would seem to indicate that it was of a later date (1620). Though Rawley, Bacon's biographer, does not, in fact mention it elsewhere, he mentions 'his revising of his book *D.S.V.*' when referring to Bacon's last years.

30. Anderson, p. 57. Farrington, pp. 76–8. See the studies on Bacon by Sortais and Fischer for the general neglect of the D.S.V.; this was mainly due to its classification by historians of literature among Bacon's literary works. Bush (p. 187) sees the D.S.V. as a companion work to the *Essays*. In fact not more than a dozen of the thirty-one fables interpreted here have similar themes to those dealt with in the *Essays*, all the others being interpreted philosophically. Levi's systematic attitude loses track of the various modifications in Bacon's views. Fazio Allmayer's appreciation of this work is at variance with that of the English editors and of most Bacon scholars; his analysis of Bacon's works is based on his theory of various types of knowledge, expounded in the D.A., rather than

on the plan drawn up by Bacon in the *Instauratio*. This system, though questionable, is substituted for an even more fallacious one, and shows the D.S.V. in an entirely new light; however, even Allmayer tends to insist on the artistic and literary character of the work. M. M. Rossi is also misled in this particular case and writes of Bacon's spiritual misunderstanding and his adhesion to Vico's 'docte arrogance' (p. 60). The limitations of both Levi's and Fazio Allmayer's critiques are probably due to their ignoring the historical and cultural background of the D.S.V. Lemmi is mainly pre-occupied, on the other hand, with this problem and contributes considerably to its solution; but his exact identification of Bacon's sources and of the cultural tradition to which this work belongs is marred by the insubstantiality of his general conclusions; thus he ignores the mutations of Bacon's views on classical fables; and his obsession with sources leads to very debatable conclusions. Bacon's frequent references to Conti's *Mythologia* and the medieval overtones of his work do not justify the hypothesis of Bacon's being acquainted with a number of the classical and medieval texts quoted by Lemmi, nor do they make Bacon into a 'kind of Petrarch' or 'a medieval philosopher haunted by a modern dream'. Many of the theories Bacon expounds in the D.S.V., were already contained in works written before 1609 and there is no reason why they should be derived from Conti as Lemmi suggests. Bacon probably used the *Mythologia* as a dictionary, and this much even Lemmi admits; but it is hard to believe that he was influenced by this dictionary to the point of adopting theories from it and standing by them for nearly ten years, that is, up to the publication of the N.O.

31. Machiavelli was read in the original by English intellec-tuals and the London printer Wolfe published his works, disguising the place of publication. For Machiavelli's influence in England and on Bacon see: Praz *op. cit.*, n. 22 above; E. Mayer, *Machiavelli and the Elizabethan Drama*, Weimar, 1897; C. V. Boyer, *The Villain as Hero in Elizabethan Tragedy*, London, 1914; W. B. Wyndham Lewis, *The Lion and the Fox*, London, 1927.

32. Cog. hum., Sp. III, 86; Sp. VI, 723–5.

33. Fazio Allmayer, pp. 37–57, stresses Bacon's religious attitude and the importance of these early works; the limitations of such an interpretation are, however, set in evidence by M. M. Rossi, pp. 58–60. For the trends of religious thought in Bacon's England see the short but cogent study in Anderson, pp. 49–55; Jordan, *op. cit.*, Ch. II, n. 77, I and II, is most relevant.

34. Machiavelli, *The Prince*, XVIII.

35. Adv., Sp. III, 345.

36. D.S.V., Sp. VI, 625, 695.

37. *ibid.*, 626, 696.
38. *ibid.*, 627, 697.
39. Sp.L. IV, 141.
40. R.Ph., Sp. III, 559 (B.F. 104).
41. T.P.M., Sp. III, 535 (B.F. 59–69); cf. Val. Term., Sp. III, 225.
42. (B.F. 120–1; 86–7); R.Ph., Sp. III, 574; C.V., Sp. III, 604–5.
43. N.O., I, 122.
44. Sp.L. IV, 18–95.
45. Letter to Bishop Andrewes in *Advertisement touching an Holy War*, 1622, Sp. VII, 10.
46. D.S.V., Sp. VI, 628, 698.
47. *ibid.*, 628–99.
48. Two facts should be noted: (*a*) this summary does not include all Bacon's philosophical works written before 1609, nor all those concerning myths, but only those more directly relevant to the subject of our enquiry; (*b*) Bacon's views were much more complex than they can possibly appear in a summary such as this, which can only serve to set in evidence certain relations and developments. To complete the picture we add Bacon's views after 1609: (8) N.O. (published 1620): I, 122, is a variant of a passage written in (5). See notes 42 and 43 above. (9) D.A. (published 1623): Not only does Bacon translate the corresponding passage from the *Advancement* (4), but returns at various points to his treatment of the problem in the preface to D.S.V. (7). He also includes the exposition of three myths from (7) that had been omitted from (4).
49. Thirty-one fables are interpreted in D.S.V.; of these the 30th (*Metis sive consilium*), 9th (*Soror gigantum sive fama*), 12th (*Coelum sive origines*), and 13th (*Proteus sive materia*) had been included in the Cog. Hum. (1605), while the Midas fable of the Cog. Hum. does not appear in the later work. The fables of Pan, Perseus, and Dionysos (the 6th, 7th, and 24th in D.S.V.) were amplified in the D.A. (1623), where Bacon discusses, in passing, certain myths which do not figure in D.S.A., (Aescalupius, Atlas, Scylla, and Ixion). The *De princ.* (1623–4) includes the fable of Cupid (17th) but breaks off just before the interpretation of the fable of the Heavens. Brief allusions to mythological tales are to be found in the T.P.M., Val. Term., and Filum lab. The Adv. contains a summary interpretation of the myths of the Giants, Briareus, and Chiron which appear in D.S.V. In the 1625 ed. of the *Essays* the essay *Of seditions and troubles* appears for the first time and includes the Briareus myth; while the 1612 ed. has one, *Of counsel*, which makes use of the Metis myth. This last is also used in *A fragment of an essay on fame* published by Rawley in 1657. The myth of Prometheus is mentioned in the

essay *Of Adversity* (1625 ed.), and in *Of seditions and troubles* (1625 ed.). In the essay *Of riches* (1612 ed.), the myth of Pluto appears for the first time. In the essay *Of regimen of health* published in 1597, Bacon sets the study of myths beside that of natural history, among the noblest human activities. The myths of the sister of the Giants, Metis, Proteus, and Heaven have been dealt with in the paragraph concerning the Cog. Hum. The remaining twenty-seven fables interpreted in D.S.V. and discussed in this chapter have been grouped according to the four basic themes of this work.

50. Val. Term., Sp. III, 218; see also C.V., Sp. III, 595–7; Med. S., Sp. VII, 231–42 (1597). Natural theology as an insufficient basis for religious life is asserted in Adv., Sp. III, 49–50; D.A., Sp. I, 544.

51. D.S.V., Sp. VI, 645–6, 719–20.

52. Sp. VI, 675, 753. Cf. Val. Term., Sp. III, 218; D.A., Sp. I, 545; D.I.S., Sp. III, 788.

53. Adv., Sp. III, 354; D.A., Sp. I, 551. For the fables of Pan and Cupid cf. D.S.V., Sp. VI, 635 seq., 656 seq.

54. This conception of the part played by the Fall in Divine Creation has little in common with that of St Augustine (*De civ.*, XI, 18) or St Thomas (*Summa*, II, 2, 47) where sin is seen as necessary to the harmony of Divine Creation; Bacon's concept is more probably derived from Plato's *Timaeus*. Cf. Lemmi, 74.

55. In his critique of Eronius of Alexandria's thesis in the Cog. nat. Bacon maintains the different natures of celestial and terrestial bodies; but here as in the D.G.I. and the *Thema coeli* he specifies that this difference is not, as Aristotle stipulates, a difference of *kind;* 'inclinations, passions and notions', he adds, are common to celestial and terrestrial bodies alike.

56. In the *Cog. nat.* Bacon appears to side with Gilbert against Eronius of Alexandria on the question of the existence of a vacuum in space (*Vacuum coacervatum*). In the G.I., he observes that Democritus, with Eronius and Telesius, recognizes the existence of a *vacuum commistum*, and he seems to favour this belief himself. In the De princ. he expresses doubts concerning the doctrine of the *Vacuum coacervatum* which he attributes here to Democritus and to Telesius. In the N.O. (II, 48) his doubts extend to the *vacuum permistum*. Finally in the *canones mobiles* he definitely denies the existence of a vacuum in nature.

57. See above p. 168.

58. N.O., II, 8.

59. D.S.V., Sp. VI, 670–1.

60. For a more detailed analysis of Bacon's interpretation

of the Prometheus myth see P. Rossi, 'Il mito di Prometeo e gli ideali della nuova scienza', *RF*, 1955, 2, pp. 142-57.

61. Niccolo Machiavelli, *The Prince*, trans. George Bull, Penguin Books, 1961, Ch. VII, pp. 57-8.

62. Rossi, *op. cit.*, Ch. II, n. 104, p. 112.

63. D.S.V., Sp. VI, 643.

64. *Advertisement touching an Holy War. The epistle dedicatory*, Sp. VII, 13-14.

65. Sp.L., VII, 436. *Letter to the King accompanying the gift of De augmentis.*

66. D.A., Sp. I, 520 seq. For Bacon's views on poetry see A. Faggi, 'F. Bacone e il suo concetto di poesia', *Atti dell'Istituto Veneto*, 1913-14; M. W. Bundy, 'Bacon's true opinion of Poetry', *SP*, XXVII, 1930, pp. 244-64.

67. For the myths of Scylla, Atlas, Ixion, Aesculpius, see D.A., Sp. I, 454, 640-1, 573, 588.

68. *Advertisement touching an Holy War*, Sp. VII, 13-14. This passage is omitted from the English translation.

69. De Princ., Sp. III, 80-1. (Sp. V, 462-3).

70. *ibid.*, 81 (463-4).

71. N.O., II, 16. For the method of exclusion cf. N.O., II, 15.

72. De princ., Sp. III, 82 (Sp. V, 464).

73. *ibid.*, 86 seq. (468 seq.).

74. *ibid.*, 111 (492).

75. N.O., II, 8.

76. Levi, p. 216. N.O., II, 48; H.R.D., Sp. II, 303 (Sp. V, 398).

77. N.O., I, 66.

78. D.A., Sp. I, 551; N.O., I, 51; De princ., Sp. III, 80; N.O., I, 66. For a detailed discussion of Bacon's attitude to the doctrine of principles see Levi, pp. 214-seq.

79. Cf. D.O., Sp. I, 142; D.G.I., Sp. III, 733; N.O., II, 48; D.A., Sp. I, 560: (for identifying simple natures and virtues and the connection between motion and appetites and inclinations of matter). D.A., Sp. I, 611; Sylva, Sp. II, 602-3 (for universal perceptions).

80. *Thema Coeli*, Sp. III, 780 (Sp. V, 559).

81. N.O., I, 48.

82. Hist. nat., Sp. II, 14 (Sp. V, 132).

83. R. Descartes, *The Philosophical Works of Descartes*, trans. Elizabeth S. Haldane and G. R. T. Ross, London, 1955, I, 12.

84. G. De Ruggiero, *Storia della filosofia. La filosofia moderna, I: L'età cartesiana*, Bari, 1930, p. 17.

85. B. Croce, *La filosofia di Giambattista Vico*, Bari, 1911, pp. 63-4.

86 G. B. Vico, *La scienza nuova*, ed. F. Nicolini, Bari, 1913, pp.

383. A Corsano, *G. B. Vico*, Bari, 1956, pp. 197–8, reaches very different conclusions.

87. Adv., Sp. III, 345.

88. D.A., Sp. I, 520 (Sp. IV, 317)

89. *ibid.*, 652 (Sp. IV, 439–40). For the theory of *real characters* in relation to the *universal language* in seventeenth-century England, cf. *Clavis Universalis*, pp. 203 seq.

NOTES TO CHAPTER 4

1. D.A., Sp. I, 671; Adv., Sp. III, 409–10. We know that for Bacon the terms 'dialectic' and 'logic' are synonymous; the Latin text reads *dialectica* where the English has 'logic'. For the use of these words see Vives, 100.

2. Adv., Sp. III, 409; D.A., Sp. I, 671. For Bacon's treatment of rhetoric cf. further on pp. 289–301.

3. Adv., Sp. III, 383–4; D.A., Sp. I, 615–16.

4. Adv., Sp. III, 389.

5. D.O., Sp. I, 139–40 (Sp. IV, 27).

6. A typical example of such a view is that of Cassirer, who argues that Bacon's philosophy is the theory of knowledge; it is valid only where it is critical or negative. Thus Bacon's originality and significance are due only to his psychological essays or his 'pathology of human actions and judgements'.

7. J. Spedding, *Preface* to the third part of the philosophic works in Sp. III, 171.

8. B. Farrington, 'On misunderstanding the Philosophy of F. Bacon', *Science, Medicine and History*, Oxford, 1953, I, 439.

9. Cf. G. Preti, *Newton*, Milan, 1950, pp. 111–12, discussing Newton's attitude to the 'hypothesis'. See also Crombie, *op. cit.*, Ch. I, n. 3, pp. 397–8.

10. Bacon's attitude to mathematics is defined by Rossi, *op. cit.*, Ch. I, n. 79, pp. 131–45.

11. G. Aubrey, *Letters and Lives of Eminent Men*, London, 1813, II, 2, p. 391.

12. *Praise of Knowledge*, Sp. L., 124–5.

13. Spedding, *Preface*, in Sp. III, 173.

14. Spedding believes that the three titles were added later, but see Anderson, p. 283. Their divergencies of opinion arise from a difference in their dating of the T.P.M.

15. T.P.M., Sp. III, 529, (B.F., 62).

16. *ibid.*, 536–9.

17. D.O., Sp. I, 139; N.O., I, 69.

18. Adv., Sp. III, 405; D.A., Sp. I, 665–6.

19. Adv., Sp. III, 383-4, 392. The connection between the passages in D.A., Sp. III, 392 developing the theory of Adv. Sp. III, 392, and paragraphs 30, 31 of Spinoza's *De intellectus emendatione* has been stressed by Levi, p. 384.

20. See L. G. Salingar, *The Elizabethan Literary Renaissance*, and R. G. Cox, *A survey of Literature from Donne to Marvell.*, *A Guide to English Literature*, ed. Boris Ford, Penguin Books, 1956, II and III respectively; Saintsbury, *A History of Criticism and Literery Taste in Europe*, London, 1900-4, 3 vols. D. L. Clark, *Rhetoric and Poetry in the Renaissance*, New York, 1922; J. W. H. Atkins, *English Literary Criticism: 17th and 18th centuries*, London, 1947; H. Craig, *The Enchanted Glass: the Elizabethan Mind in Literature*, Oxford, 1952 (first ed. New York 1936) with a chapter on 'persuasion and eloquence'; R. F. Jones, art. cit.; *Science and English Prose Style in the Third Quarter of the Seventeenth Century; Science and Language in England in the Mid-Seventeenth Century*, all three reprinted in *The Seventeenth Century*. For the popularity of Ramism and the cultural situation in England, cf. L. S. Hultzen, *Aristotle's Rhetoric in England to 1660*, New York, 1932; C. Waddington, *Ramus, sa vie, ses écrits et ses opinions*, Paris, 1856; F. P. Graves, *Ramus and the Educational Reformation of the Sixteenth Century*, London, 1912; P. A. Duhamel, 'The Logic and Rhetoric of Peter Ramus', *Modern Philology*, 1948-9, pp. 163-71; K. D. McRae, 'Ramist Tendencies in the thought of Jean Bodin', *JHI*, 1955, 3, pp. 306-23; N. E. Nelson, *P. Ramus and the Confusion of Logic, Rhetoric, and Poetry*, Michigan, 1947. For the popularity of Ramism in Calvinistic circles see Friedrich, *Politica methodice digesta of J. Althusius*, Cambridge, 1932. For the link between Ramism and jurisprudence see V. Piano Mortari, *Dialettica e giurisprudenza, Studio sui trattati di Dialettica legale del sec. XVI*, Milan, 1955. For Bacon, cf. R. K. Wallace, *Francis Bacon on Communication and Rhetoric*, Chapel Hill, 1943, where the situation of rhetoric in sixteenth-century England is also described. See the review of this work by R. F. Jones in *Modern Languages Quarterly*, VI, 1945, pp. 235-6. For further details see Ch. V, n. 51.

21. R. Hooker. *Of the Laws of Ecclesiastical Polity*, London, 1900, I, 148. The first four books were published in 1593. For Hooker cf. W. K. Jordan, *The Development of Religious Toleration in England*, Cambridge, 1932, I, 222-32.

22. Hooker, *op. cit.*, n. 21 above, pp. 166-7.

23. *ibid.*, p. 168.

24. Adv., Sp. III, 383-4; D.A., Sp. I, 616.

25. T. Wilson, *The Arte of Rhetorique for the Use of All Suche as are Studious of Eloquence*, ed. G. H. Mair, Oxford, 1909, first ed. 1553. Wallace, in the work quoted in n. 20, indicates a more recent and

accurate ed. by R. H. Wagner, Cornell University Doctoral Disserta-
tion, 1929, and suggests—for reference for the various eds.—an
article also by Wagner: 'The Text and Editions of Wilson's Arte of
Rhetorique', *Modern Language Notes*, Nov. 1929, pp. 421–8. For a
different subdivision of rhetoric see *La Retorica di M. Bartolomeo
Cavalcanti, gentil'huomo fiorentino*, Venice, 1559, pp. 24–5, first ed.
1549.

26. Ramus, *op. cit.*, Ch. II, n. 125, II, preface to books IX–XX,
pp. 2, 3, 77,

27. Cicero, like the Stoics, uses the term 'axiom' in the sense of
'proposition' (*Acad.*, II, 29, *Tusc.*, I, 7). J. Milton, 'Artis logicae
plenior institutio ad Petri Rami methodum concinnata', *The Prose
Works of J. Milton*, ed. R. Fletcher, London, 1835, p. 861, defines the
two fundamental uses of the word 'axiom' in Aristotle, confirms the
justice of the second (identifying axiom and proposition) and quotes
Cicero, Plutarch, Diogenes Laertius, Aulus Gellius, Galen. Cf. P. F.
Fisher, 'Milton's Logic', *JHI*, 1962, 1, pp. 37–60.

28. The *Dissertatio* is included in Leibniz' ed. of the *De principiis* of
Nizolio (Marii Nizolii, *De veris principiis et vera ratione philosophandi . . .
ab editore G.G.L.L. qui dissertationem praeliminarem de instituto operis
atque optima philosophi dictione . . . adeicit*, Frankfurt, 1670). For the
controversy see A. Corsano, *G. W. Leibniz*, Naples, 1952, pp. 35–45
and P. Rossi, 'Il *De principiis* di M. Nizolio', in *Testi umanistici su la
retorica*, ed. E. Garin, P. Rossi, C. Vasoli, Rome-Milan, 1953, where
Leibniz' text is extensively quoted.

29. *MR*, pp. 124–49.

30. Rossi, art. cit., Ch. II, n. 78.

31. P. Ramus, *Institutionum Dialecticarum libri tres*, Paris, 1547,
pp. 186–7. A refutation of Aristotelian logic stemming from the
need for a form of logic capable of providing arguments for use in
discussions can be found in Vives, p. 104.

32. P. de la Ramée, *La dialectique*, Paris, 1555, p. 69, for a comparison between *inventio-dispositio* and grammar-synthesis.

33. Adv., Sp. III, 394–5. Cf. D.A., Sp. I, 643; Val. Term., Sp.
III, 241; P.I.D., Sp. III, 548; C.V., Sp. III, 607.

34. For the 'cosmology' of the Elizabethan age see Craig, *op.
cit.*, n. 20 above, pp. 1–32. Also Carré, *op. cit.*, Ch I. n. 69, pp. 196–
216; E. M. Tillyard, *The Elizabethan World Picture*, London, 1943,
1963.

35. See E. Forset, *A Comparative Discourse of the Bodies Natural and
Politique*, London, 1606. For the problem of the 'place' of man in
Shakespeare's work see T. Spencer, *Shakespeare and the Nature of Man*,
Cambridge, 1943.

36. A history of this vision of the world is outlined in Lovejoy,

and Nicolson, *op. cit.*, Ch. I, n. 125, shows how the birth of scientific knowledge at the beginning of the modern age helped to destroy this chain.

37. Cf. A. P. d'Entrèves, *Riccardo Hooker, contribute alla teoria e alla storia del diritto naturale*, Torino, 1932, p. 41; for Hooker's medieval sources, pp. 71–80.

38. Hooker, *op. cit.*, n. 21 above, pp. 150, 157, 160.

39. E. Digby, *Theoria analytica, viam ad monarchiam scientiarum demonstrans. . . .* London, 1559, p. 130.

40. *Tamburlaine*, II, 7, 21–6. M. Praz, *Storia della letteratura inglese*, Florence, 1954, p. 67; on pp. 119–20 Praz rightly discredits the oversimplification of Elizabethan drama (Greene, Kyd, Marlowe) with its unlimited faith in human powers, and affirms the drama of 1598–1611 when the new science and political upheavals combined to destroy the ancient conception of the world. It is not easy to agree with Praz when he suggests (p. 138) that Bacon's inductive and experimental method was the same as that which Galileo was advocating independently in Italy.

41. Praef. Gen., Sp. 129 (Sp. IV, 18). For the passage quoted see Preface to the N.O., Sp. I, 152 (Sp. IV, 40); D.O., Sp. I, 137–8 (Sp. IV, 26).

42. Preface N.O., Sp. I, 151–2 (Sp. IV, 40); cf. Praef. Gen., Sp. I, 129. For the link between the humanistic appreciation of rhetoric and the refutation of final constructions and strict conceptual frames see *MR*, 127.

NOTES TO CHAPTER 5

1. Adv., Sp. III, 384, 389–90; D.A., Sp. I, 633–4.

2. In Adv., Sp. III, 384, only science and axioms are mentioned; in D.A., Sp. I, 617, the mechanical and liberal arts are added.

3. Adv., Sp. III, 387–8; D.A., Sp. I, 621.

4. *ibid.*, 623–33.

5. Adv., Sp. III, 389; D.A., Sp. I, 633.

6. Adv., Sp. III, 347; D.A., Sp. I, 543.

7. *ibid.*, 636–9 the *Topica particularia sive articuli inquisitionis de gravi et levi;* for other passages on the *topics* see Ch. VI.

8. Ramus, *op. cit.*, Ch. IV, n. 31, p. 77.

9. B. Riposati, 'Problemi di retorica, antica', *Introduzione alla filosofia classica*, Milan, 1951, p. 749.

10. Adv., Sp. III, 384.

11. D.A., Sp. I, 640 (Sp. IV, 428); cf. Adv., Sp. III, 392, where the same ideas are expressed more concisely.

12. D.A., Sp. I, 641 (Sp. IV, 429); in Adv., Sp. III, 393, the definition is totally different.

13. Ramus, II, 1.

14. Arnauld, *Logica sive ars cogitandi*, Amsterdam, 1718, p. 209. See Vico, *Autobiografia*, Bari, 1911, p. 14, for an opposition to the 'logique of Arnauld' in favour of the Ramistic interpretation.

15. *De partitione oratoria*, X, 33. For polemics against conclusions drawn from 'true' premises (in the Aristotelian sense) see Vives, 108.

16. Adv., Sp. III, 394, is not translated in the D.A.

17. Cf. Adv., Sp. III, 393–4; D.A., Sp. I, 641–2.

18. Bacon also calls the idols fictions, superstitions, errors, kinds of fallacies in the mind of man (Val. Ter., Sp. III, 241–2; Adv., Sp. III, 396); *spectra* (C.V., Sp. III, 607; D.A., Sp. I, 643); *volantes phantasiae* (Praef., Sp. I, 130); *imagines* (D.A., Sp. I, 643).

19. N.O., I, 40.

20. Val. Term., Sp. III, 241–2.

21. N.O., I, 38–68; D.A., Sp. I, 643–6; Val. Term., Sp. III, 241–2, 245.

22. Cf. Anderson, 98.

23. Adv., Sp. III, 394–7.

24. P.I.D., Sp. III, 528.

25. D.O., Sp. I, 139 (Sp. IV, 27).

26. Cf. Levi, 321–2. I am entirely with Levi in refuting Spedding's theory (*On some changes in Bacon's treatment of his doctrine of Idols*, Sp. I, 113–17) that Bacon omitted the distinction between innate and adventitious idols from the N.O. because he saw the logical inconsistency of classifying the idols of the market-place among the former, and the practical inconvenience of classifying them among the latter.

27. *Praise of Knowledge*, Sp. L. I, 123–6; Conf., Sp. VII, 219 seq.; Val. Term., Sp. III, 224, 239, 241–5; Adv., Sp. III, 264–5, 395; P.I.D., Sp. III, 548; C.V., Sp. III, 607, 617; R.Ph., Sp. III, 385, 585; D.O., Sp. I, 140; Praef., Sp. I, 130; N.O., I, 26–8, 54, 68; II, 52; D.A., Sp. I, 434, 614; Hist. nat., Sp. II, 14.

28. N.O., Sp. I, 145 (Sp. IV, 32–3).

29. There is an undeniable link between Bacon's religious attitude and some of his basic philosophical theories; Farrington (pp. 146 seq.) has noted an ever-present Christian symbolism in Bacon's work; but attempts at detecting Calvinist influences in his philosophy should be made with caution. It is too easy to refer current notions of the time, deriving from quite different sources, to Calvinism; thus a so-called Calvinist theme of Bacon's is to be found in Telesio, *De rerum natura*, ed. V. Spampanato, Modena, 1910, I, pp. 5–6. For the idols of the tribe cf. N.O., I, 41, 45, 52; D.A., Sp. I, 643–5.

30. For the idols of the cave cf. N.O., I, 42, 53-8; D.A., Sp. I, 645.

31. For the art of communication cf. Adv., Sp. III, 399-403; D.A., Sp. I, 650-62.

32. D.A., Sp. I, 653 (Sp. IV, 440); cf. Adv., Sp. III, 400.

33. D.A., Sp. I, 651 (Sp. IV, 439); cf. Adv., Sp. III, 399.

34. D.A., Sp. I, 649; cf. Adv., Sp. III, 399.

35. G. B. Vico, *La scienza nuova*, Bari, 1911, I, pp. 142, 272.

36. A. Corsano, 'G. B. Vico e la semantica', *RF*, 1954, 4, p. 402, n. 5, points out a passage where Vico expressed his views on ideograms stressing their value for uniting men of different tongues in a single understanding. Vico believed in the non-arbitrary, non-conventional, natural and spontaneous character of such modes of communication which would overstep the barriers of language (*De Universi iuris uno principio et fine uno*, Bari, 1936, V, III, p. 625). Bacon expresses similar views in D.A., Sp. I, 651.

37. *ibid.*, 655 (Sp. IV, 442); this passage has been omitted from the Adv., as also the distinction between philosophical grammar and logic.

38. R. F. Jones, 'Science and Language in England of the Mid-Seventeenth Century, *loc. cit.*, Ch. IV, n. 20, p. 143 for a brief enquiry into Bacon's attitude to language, and a study of the part played by the new status of scientific knowledge in the radical reform of 'style' that typifies late seventeenth-century English prose.

39. R.Ph., Sp. III, 581 (B.F., 129).

40. Passages referred to in the following paragraph are: Adv., Sp. III, 396-400; C.V., Sp. III, 599 (B.F., 81); N.O., I, 15, 16, 43, 59, 60; D.A., Sp. I, 645-6 (Sp. IV, 433).

41. Adv., Sp. III, 400.

42. D.A., Sp. I, 645; the passage has been omitted from the corresponding pages of N.O., I, 59.

43. Preti, *op. cit.*, Ch. IV, n. 9, p. 79. See also pp. 78-9.

44. Cf. Sp. III, 403, n. 3 (by R. L. Ellis). For the method of communication cf. Adv., Sp. III, 403-8; D.A., Sp. I, 650-69.

45. Ramus, *op. cit.*, Ch. IV, n. 31, p. 171. For the distinction between *methodus doctrinae* and *methodus prudentiae*, cf. p. 129.

46. Ramus, *op. cit.*, Ch. II, n. 115. p. 11.

47. *idem.*, *La Dialectique*, Paris, 1555, p. 1.

48. Cf. C. A. Viano, *La logica di Aristotele*, Turin, 1955, p. 140. For a limpid exposition of the Ramistic dichotomic method see the revision and amplification of Ramus' logic by A. Wotton, London, 1626, p. 94. The text is reproduced in K. R. Wallace, *F. Bacon on Communication and Rhetoric*, Chapel Hill, 1943, p. 139.

49. D.A., Sp. I, 663 (Sp. IV, 448–9). Omitted from the Adv. Cf. also D.A., Sp. I, 668.

50. Temple, *op. cit.*, Ch. II, n. 17, pp. 31–2, 39, 74–5.

51. Freudenthal, art. cit., Ch. II, n. 16, pp. 601–2. Digby's popularity is recognized in W. Temple, *Pro Mildapetti de unica methodo defensione contra Diplophilum,* Frankfurt, 1584, pp. 19–20.

52. Adv., Sp. III, 403–4; D.A., Sp. I, 663.

53. W. S. Howell, 'N. Carpenter's Place in the Controversy between Rhetoric and Dialectic', *Speech Monographs,* 1934, I, 20–41; Wallace, *op. cit.,* n. 46 above, pp. 187–94. For the place of rhetoric in sixteenth- and seventeenth-century English culture, besides the works mentioned in Ch. IV, n. 20, see M. W. Bundy, 'Invention and Imagination in the Renaissance', *Journal of English and Germanic Philology,* 1930, pp. 535–45, who studies the evolution of the rhetorical concept of 'invention', and its slow metamorphosis to that of imagination and fancy; a typical instance quoted is Ronsard, *Abregé de l'art poétique Françoys.* M. T. Herrick, 'The Early History of Aristotle's Rhetoric in England', *Philological Quarterly,* 1926, pp. 242–57, stresses Bacon's extensive knowledge of Aristotle's *Rhetoric* and notes the relation between the essay *Of Youth and Old Age* and the famous chapter of the *Rhetoric,* book II. See also E. E. Hale, Jr., 'Ideas of Rhetoric in the Sixteenth Century', *Publ. of Modern Language Assoc.,* 1903, pp. 242–4. The most exhaustive study of these problems is now that of W. S. Howell, *Logic and Rhetoric in England, 1500–1700,* Princeton, 1956, to which may be added N. W. Gilbert, *Renaissance Concepts of Method,* New York, 1960.

54. Adv. Sp. III, 409; D.A. Sp. I, 670. For rhetoric cf. in the works quoted pp. 408–16, and 670–708 respectively.

55. Val. Term., Sp. III, 248.

56. Adv., Sp. III, 409; D.A., Sp. I, 671–2.

57. D.G.I., Sp. III, 727; D.A., Sp. I, 495.

58. Adv., Sp. III, 382; D.A., Sp. I, 614.

59. For the definition of the 'colours' cf. also Adv., Sp. III, 464.

60. D.A., Sp. I, 674–5 (Sp. IV, 459). In a different form in Adv., Sp. III, 412.

61. Wallace, *op. cit.,* n. 46 above, pp. 170–8, makes an excellent analysis of the relation between Bacon's attitude and that of Aristotle and of Plato.

62. E. A. Abbott's ed. of the *Essays,* 2 vols., was published in London, 1879.

63. Essays, Sp. VI, 393, 396.

64. The fragment 'A table of colours or appearances of good and evil, and their degrees, as places of persuasion and discussion, and

their several fallaxes and the elenches of them' was published in the 1597 ed. of the *Essays* (cf. Sp. VII, 73–92).

65. *Promus* was published for the first time from a MS. of the British Museum, by H. Pott, London, 1883; now in Sp. VII, 197–211. For the relation of *Promus* to Bacon's later works cf. E. A. Abbott, *F. Bacon, An Account of his Life and Works*, London, 1885, pp. 436 seq.

66. Adv., Sp. III, 413; D.A., Sp. I, 707.

67. Craig, *op. cit.*, Ch. IV, n. 20.

68. Ben Jonson, 'Timber or discoveries made upon men and matter', *Works*, ed. Gifford-Cunningham, London, 1875, IX, pp. 183–4. For Nicholas Bacon's oratory see George Puttenham, *The Arte of English Poesie*, London, 1589, in *Elizabethan Critical Essays*, cit. Ch. III, n. 26, II, pp. 144–5.

69. Adv., Sp. III, 410; D.A., Sp. I, 672. The polemic against Plato's estimation of rhetoric occupies a prominent place in seventeenth-century rhetorical texts. Cf. for instance, Bellot, 1; Vives, pp. 146 seq.

70. T. Sprat, *History of the Royal Society*, London, 1702, p. 62 (first ed., 1667).

71. For the *georgica animi* cf. Adv., Sp. III, 432–45; D.A., Sp. I, 731–44.

72. Bush, 185. For the connection between the *Essays* and the *Instauratio magna*, cf. R. S. Crane, 'The Relation of Bacon's Essays to his Program for the Advancement of Learning', *Schelling Anniversary Papers*, cit. Ch. II, n. 86.

NOTES TO CHAPTER 6

1. C.V., Sp. III, 611–12; N.O., I, 129.

2. C.V., Sp. III, 613 (B.F. 94).

3. D.A., Sp. I, 827–8 (Sp. V, 109–10); also cf. D.A., Sp. I, 514.

4. C.V., Sp. III, 612.

5. Preface, Sp. I, 132–3; D.O., Sp. I, 154; I.N.P., Sp. III, 520.

6. See Ch. II, n. 32.

7. N.O., I, 29.

8. Preface, Sp. I, 129 (Sp. IV, 17); D.O., Sp. I, 135 (Sp. IV, 23). Cf. N.O., I, 26 for the distinction between 'intellectual anticipations' and 'natural anticipations'.

9. Cf. P.I.D., Sp. III, 547 seq.; D.O., Sp. I, 135–7 (Sp. IV, 23–6) for the distinction between ordinary logic and the new logic.

10. The plan for a general restoration of knowledge is systematically presented for the first time in the *Delineatio*, linked here to the 'reform of the method' already mentioned in the Val. Term. and the

Adv. See Sp. I, 107 for the discrepancy in time between the first mention of the idea of *Instauration* (posterior to 1609) and that of a reform of induction.

11. Adv., Sp. III, 392.

12. *ibid.*, 389.

13. I.N.P., Sp. III, 518. In Anderson, 16, we find a lucid explanation of the title (*Valerius Terminus, Of the interpretation of Nature with the annotations of Hermes Stella*) which had seemed ambiguous to many scholars. See also Sp. III, 201.

14. Val. Term., Sp. III, 242.

15. *ibid.*, 232–3, 235, 242–3.

16. Cf. Viano, art. cit., Ch. I, n. 68, p. 309.

17. Val. Term., Sp. III, 246.

18. *ibid.*, 235–6.

19. T.P.M., Sp. III, 530 (B.F., 63–4).

20. Ramus, Book IX, II, 77.

21. *An Post.*, 73a–74a. Cf. W. D. Ross, *Aristotele*, Bari, 1946, pp. 66–7.

22. Ramus, p. 55.

23. *idem.*, Scholarum physicarum libri octo, in totidem acromaticos libros Aristotelis, Paris, 1565, preface.

24. The expression is from Ellis in Sp. I, 42.

25. Val. Term., Sp. III, 242.

26. See besides the Val. Term., Adv., Sp. III, 356; D.A., Sp. I, 566; and especially N.O., II, 23 where the process is included in the *migratory instances.*

27. See Val. Term., Sp. III, 236–9.

28. *ibid.*, 243.

29. *ibid.*, 239.

30. Levi, 401.

31. *ibid.*, 398, 403.

32. N.O., II, 3. For Bacon's opposition to the Platonic notion of form cf. Adv., Sp. III, 355; N.O., I, 51, 106; II, 17; D.A., Sp. I, 564–6.

33. Viano, art. cit., Ch. I, n. 68, p. 10.

34. See Anderson, 213 seq. Levi, 248, has pertinent views on this subject.

35. Levi, 398, has missed the juridical implications of the term.

36. Cf. N.O., II, 11, 12, 13.

37. For the process of exclusion see *ibid.*, 15. For the relation of form and nature see *ibid.*, 12–13.

38. *ibid.*, 20.

39. *ibid.*, 4.

40. C.V., Sp. III, 619 (B.F., 100–1).

41. C.S., Sp. III, 626-8.

42. Respectively in Sp. III, 623-40; 644-52; 657-80.

43. Inq. Leg., Sp. III, 638-40.

44. *ibid.*, 633, 637-8.

45. Praef., Sp. I, 129 (Sp. IV, 18).

46. P.I.D., Sp. III, 553; cf. also N.O., II, 20.

47. B. Riposati, 'Problemi di retorica antica', *Introduzione alla filologia classica*, Milano, 1951, p. 773.

48. For an historical relation of this literature see: H. Hajdu, *Das mnemotechnische Schriftum des Mittelalters*, Vienna, 1936. Still worth consulting are: F. Aretin, *Theorie und Praxis der Mnemonik*, Sulzbach, 1810; E. Pick, *Memory and its Doctors*, London, 1888; L. Volkmann, 'Ars memorativa', *Jahrbuch der kunsthistorischen Sammlungen in Wien*, neue Folge, 1929, III, 111-200. An important work is that by F. A. Yates, 'The Ciceronian Art of Memory', *Medioevo e Rinascimento, studi in onore di B. Nardi*, Florence, 1956, pp. 873-903 which, unfortunately, I was only able to consult when the Italian ed. of my book was going to press. Iacopo Publicio, *Ars memoriae*, Venice, 1482 and 1485, Augusta, 1490. Pietro da Ravenna, *Foenis domini Petri Ravennatis memoriae magistri*, Venice, 1491 is mentioned by Giordano Bruno in *Triginta sigillorum explicatio* (F. Tocco, *Le opere latine di Bruno*, Florence, 1889, pp. 37, 93). Conrad Celtis, *Epitoma in utramque Ciceronis rhetoricam cum arte memorativa nova*, Ingolstadt, 1492. Cosimo Rosselli, *Thesaurus artificiosae memoriae*, Venice, 1579. A list of mnemonic texts can be found in *Plutosofia del rev. mo. padre F. Filippo Gesualdo generale dei Minori conventuali, nella quale si spiega l'arte della memoria*, Vicenza, 1600, p. 11. Rosselli and Ravenna were quoted by R. Burton in *The Anatomy of Melancholy*, Everyman's Library ed., II, 95. See also *Clavis Universalis*.

49. *Dialogo di M. Ludovico Dolce nel quale si ragion del modo di accrescere et conservar la memoria*, Venice, 1586, p. 90. Dolce's work is only a vulgarisation of one of the best known mnemonic texts, Johannes Romberch, *Congestorium artificiosae memoriae*, Venice, 1533.

50. Bellot, 329. On Bellot see Thorndike, V, 507-10; apart from the ed. of Bellot's works mentioned by Thorndike (Lyons, 1654) there exists a later ed. by Pierre Amiot (Rouen, 1688). For the meaning of 'paulines and armadelles' cf. Thorndike, II, 282, and, by the same author, 'Alfodhol and Almadel. Hitherto unnoted Medieval Books of Magic in Florentine Manuscripts', *Speculum*, 1927, pp. 326-31.

51. Bellot, 33.

52. For Bellot's quotations of Bruno see 37-8, 93-4. On p. 334 he says that, besides Pietro da Ravenna, Petrarca and Bruno 'ont

fait merveilles' for the furtherance of the art of memory. For references to Agrippa cf. pp. 37-8. Bellot's definitions of dialectics and syllogisms (pp. 63, 98) are similar to Ramus'. Bellot's references to Bruno were entirely justified, for although Bruno attempted to divert the problem from the rhetorical to the metaphysical field, the *De umbris idearum* follows the mnemonic tradition very closely. Indeed, Bruno's next work, the *Ars memoriae*, stresses the need for memory to refer to the sensory world—to facts of 'form and figure', to 'signs', and to 'notes'—and gives examples for the execution of this art. Cf. G. Bruno, *De umbris idearum implicantibus artem querendi . . .,* Paris, 1532. For a study of Bruno's mnemonic works see Tocco, *op. cit.,* n. 48 above, p. 37; A. Corsano, *Il pensiero di G. Bruno nel suo svolgimento storico,* Florence, 1940, pp. 40 seq.; *Clavis Universalis* 108-34. As to Agrippa, though he judged Lull without indulgence (which may account for Bacon's estimation of the latter), his exposition of the *ars brevis* includes a discussion of the problem of memory. Cf. Agrippa, *Opera,* II, 31-2.

53. P. Ramus, *Dialecticae institutiones,* Paris, 1543, p. 19v; *op. cit.,* Ch. II, n. 115. p. 14.

54. Melanchthon, 'Erotemata dialectices', *Corpus reformatorum,* XIII, c. 573, cited in V. Piano Mortari, *Dialettica e giurisprudenza, studio sui trattati di dialettica legale del sec. XVI,* Milan, 1955, p. 89.

55. Adv., Sp. III, 398, seq. D.A., Sp. I, 635 seq.

56. *ibid.,* 657-9 (Sp. IV, 435-7); Adv., Sp. III, 398-9.

57. D.A., Sp. I, 648 (Sp. IV, 436); Adv., Sp. III, 398.

58. For a study of humanist eloquence and what Bacon called 'delicate learning' cf. Adv., Sp. III, 289 seq.

59. D.A., Sp. I, 647 (Sp. IV, 435); this passage has been omitted from the corresponding section of the Adv., Sp. III, 397-8.

60. In D.A., Sp. I, 649, Bacon refers explicitly to artificial memory, recalling the most typical aspects of mnemonic texts and the elaboration of topological systems where parts of the city, the house, or the human body serve as a basis for linking images together. In case some doubt should remain as to the relation between Bacon's works and this form of literature, it must be remembered that in the N.O., II, 26, Bacon recommends the use of just such 'topological' methods. Sixteenth- and seventeenth-century texts on the art of memory included lists, diagrams, and illustrations. Girolamo Marafioto, *Nova inventione et arte del ricordarsi per luoghi et imagini et per segni et figure poste nelle mani,* Venice, 1605, is mainly an emblematic and diagrammatic organisation of 'places'. The parallel between physical and dialectical 'places' predominates in these works (see J. Paepp, *Artificiosae memoriae fundamenta ex Aristotele, Cicerone, Thoma Aquinate . . . ,* Lyons, 1619, pp. 12, 49), and we also find the Baconian

notion of similitude between place and image (see Guglielmus Leporeus Avallonensis, *Ars memorativa*, Paris, 1520, f. XIIv; in the fourth book there is a kind of medical treatise on the conservation of memory). According to Bacon emblems make intellectual notions perceptible to the senses, and, as memory is more easily impressed by what is perceived by the senses, these are more readily retained: for instance, it is easier to remember an image of a hunter pursuing a hare than the notion of 'invention'. Leporeus, apparently a very uninhibited man, uses rather more daring images than Bacon's, but to exactly the same purpose (see f. XIv).

61. P.I.D., Sp. III, 552.

62. P. Melancthon, *Rhetorices Elementa*, Venice, 1534, p. 8.

63. N.O., I, 117.

64. N.O., II, 14.

65. *ibid.*, 18.

66. *ibid.*, 21.

67. N.O., I, 92.

68. Hist. nat., Sp. II, 16 (Sp. V, 133–4); N.O., I, 130.

69. *I filosofi* 118–22.

70. Parasceve, Sp. I, 394.

71. D.A., Sp. I, 636 seq.

72. E. Cassirer, *Das Erkenntnisproblem*, Italian trans., Torino, 1955, I, 426, II, 28.

73. *Catalogus historiarum particularium secundum capita*, Sp. I, 405–10.

74. Parasceve, Sp. I, 398–9 (Sp. V, 257).

75. Galileo, *Opere*, VI, p. 232; trans. *The Achievement of Galileo*, ed. J. Brophy and H. Paolucci, New York, 1962, p. 31.

76. See E. May, *Kleiner Grundriss der Naturphilosophie*, Meisenheim-am-Glan, 1949, II, c.

77. Galileo to Pietro Carcavy (5 June 1637), in *Opere*, VII, 156.

78. R.Ph.Sp. III, 582 (B.F., 130); N.O., I, 125.

79. G. Vailati, *Scritti*, Florence, 1911, p. 138.

80. D.A., Sp. I, 640–1 (Sp. IV, 428–9); and with a slight variation in Adv., Sp. III, 392.

81. Cf. J. Dewey, *Ricostruzione filosofica*, Bari, 1931, p. 60.

82. Vailati, *op. cit.*, 79 above, p. 132, has clearly noted the significance of Bacon's attitude, and makes some highly relevant observations on the historical importance of the 'vindication of induction'.

Index of names and topics

Abbott, E. A., 182, 268
Achelous, 114
Aconcio, G., 115
Acosta, C., 219
Acteon, 112
Adam, 69, 128-9
Aesculapius, 69, 120
Agricola, G., 2-8, 63
Agricola, R., 65
Agrippa, C., 17, 19, 21, 29-30, 31, 35, 41, 57, 146, 220, 235, 236, 237, 239, 240, 241, 247, 248, 271
Alberic, 75
Albertus Magnus, 10, 65
Albutt, Sir C., 8, 232
Alchemy, 13-22, 104-5
Alciati, 74, 93
Alexander the Great, 52
Allegory, 73-81, 86-7, 116-19
Anaxagoras, 52, 123, 124
Anaximander, 123
Anaximenes, 123
Anderson, F., xiv, 37, 60, 67, 81, 233, 241, 242, 251, 252, 256, 270
Andrews, L., 89
Anglicus, B., 4
Apollo, 69

Aretin, F., 270
Ariosto, L., 238
Aristotle, xiii, 5, 12, 14, 15, 24, 25, 26, 36, 38, 40, 41, 42, 43, 45, 47, 49, 51, 52, 53, 54, 59-67, 68, 70, 71, 72, 109, 112, 123, 128, 132, 143, 147, 156, 159-160, 165, 166, 167, 175, 181, 186, 187, 195-7, 202, 210
Arnaldo of Villanova, 43
Arnauld, A., 265
Ascham, R., 57, 249
Atalanta, 101
Atlas, 69, 119-20
Attic style, 59
Attila, 47
Atkins, J. W. H., 256, 262
Atkinson, G., 244
Aubrey, G., 261
Audiat, L., 232
Augustine, St, 17, 41, 76
Averroes, 27
Avicenna, 70

Bachelard, G., 234
Bacon, R., 11, 17, 27-8, 39, 43, 65, 69-70, 239
Banfi, A., xv, 231
Barebone, J., 40

Bayle, P., 233
Bellot, J., 208–9, 270–1
Berthelot, M., 235, 239, 245
Besson, J., 231
Biringuccio, V., 2, 230
Boas, A., xvi, 248
Boas, G., xvii
Boccaccio, G., 75, 78, 93
Bodley, Sir T., 89
Boëthius, 65
Bonardo, G. M., 4, 231
Bonaventure, St, 65
Bona of Ferrera, 29
Boulanger, J., 253
Bovillus, C., 18, 76, 240
Boyer, C. V., 257
Boyle, R., xiii, 218, 238
Bradbrook, M. C., 246
Brinkmann, D., 234
Brown, H., 230
Browne, Sir T., xii, 12, 233, 247
Bruno, G., 39, 66, 75–6
Budaeus, J., 253
Budé, G., 63
Bundy, M. W., 260, 266
Burghley, Lord, 23, 42
Burton, R., 78, 247
Burtt, E. A., 230
Bush, D., 185, 229, 243, 251, 255, 256
Butterfield, H., 230

Cabbala, 56, 247
Callot, E., 229
Calvin, J., 167
Campanella, T., 19
Cantimori, D., 251
Capella, M., 76, 207
Cardano, G., 8, 12, 19, 20, 30–31, 34, 35, 38, 57, 219, 240, 241, 248
Carneades, 78
Carré, M. H., 236, 251, 263
Cartari, V., 78, 93

Carton, R., 239, 253
Casaubon, I., 185
Case, J., xii, 41, 42
Caspari, F., 231, 249
Cassandra, 106
Cassirer, E., 38, 75–6, 217, 242, 247, 254, 272
Castelli, B., 2, 231
Celtis, C., 207
Cervantes, M. de, 73–75, 76, 254
Champié, S., 240
Chapman, G., 58, 78
Charbonnel, R., 236
Charles, V., 3
Charpentier, J., 173
Chrysippus, 86
Church, R. W., 252
Cicero, 38, 53, 57, 58, 143, 145, 158, 160, 165, 180, 207
Clark, D. L., 249, 262
Clark, G. M., 230
Clements, R. J., 254
Cohen, I. B., 244
Colet, J., x, 64
Columbus, C., 40
Conti, N., 78, 80, 93
Conway, Lady, 247
Copernican, xii, xiii, 40
Copernicus, 67, 220, 223
Cornutus, 93
Corsano, A., 240, 263, 266, 271
Cox, L., 134, 178
Cox, R. G., 262
Craig, H., 262, 263
Crane, R., 268
Crawley, R. R., 244
Croce, B., 133, 260
Croll, M. W., 249
Crombie, A. C., 229, 239, 253, 261
Cromwell, O., xi
Cross, J. J., 248
Crowther, J., xvi

Cudworth, R., 247
Cupid, 98–100, 121, 126
Cusanus, N., 66
Cyclopes, 110
Cyprian, 17

D'Alembert, J., 25
Davies, Sir J., 58
Davy, N., 230
Dedalus, 103
Dee, J., 39, 219
De Ganay, G., 238
Della Porta, G. B., 12, 19, 31, 219, 236, 237, 240
De Maistre J., ix, xiv, 67, 252
Democritus, 14, 43, 47, 52, 53, 70, 90, 99, 122, 123, 124, 189
D'Entrèves, A. P., 264
Descartes, R., 11, 18, 66, 69, 71–72, 131, 186, 200, 218, 238, 247, 252, 260
Deucalion, 105
Dewey, J., 237, 272
Digby, E., xii, 41, 148–9, 150, 173, 175, 176, 243
Digges, T., 39
Diogenes Laertius, 53
Diomede, 115
Dionysos, 107, 110, 113
Dolce, L., 208
Dollet, E., 249
Donio, A., 246
Donne, J., xii, 241, 247
Drake, F., xi
Dryden, J., ix
Ducasse, C. J., 229
Dugas, R., 231
Duhamel, P. A., 262
Duhem, P., 232
Dunn, W. P., 234
Duns Scotus, 8, 38, 39, 65
Dupin, E., 232

Easton, S. C., 239

Ebreus, L., 75
Einstein, L., 255
Elizabeth I, ix, xi
Ellis, R. L., 80, 233
Empedocles, 123
Encyclopedists, 22, 25, 138
Endymion, 111
Enlightenment, 38, 218
Epicurus, 43, 52, 99
Erasmus, R., 3, 57
Erichthonius, 101, 105
Euclid, 45
Euripedes, 52

Faggi, A., 260
Farnaby, T., 143
Farrington, B., xiv, xv, xvi, 8, 10, 103, 138, 215, 232, 233, 242, 252, 256, 261, 265
Fazio Almayer, V., 252, 256, 257
Fenner, D., 178
Ferdinand, I, 3
Ferguson, W. K., 248
Fernel, J. F., 248
Festugière, R. P., 239
Ficino, M., 18, 27, 29, 58, 65, 75, 219, 253
Fiorentino, F., 236, 246
Fischer, 256
Fisher, P. F., 263
Fludd, R., 56, 151, 219, 247, 253
Flugel, 243
Forbes, R. J., 231, 234
Forset, E., 263
Fowler, T., 234, 244, 246, 251
Fracastoro, G., 147, 192, 240
France, A., 232
Freudenthal, J., 176, 243, 267
Friedrich, 262
Fulgentius, 93

Gabrielli, C., 236

Galen, 26–7, 38, 45, 71
Galileo, G., xiii, 2, 34, 67, 69, 138, 220, 221, 223
Garin, E., xiv, 17, 233, 236, 239, 251, 253
Gassendi, P., 11, 18, 56
Gilbert, Sir H., 6, 7
Gilbert, N. W., xvi, 267
Gilbert, W., 57, 67, 166, 223, 244, 248, 251
Gildon, C., 244
Giraldi, L. G., 78, 93
Glanville, J., xiii, 247
Gorgias, 52
Gratarolo, G., 214
Graves, F. P., 262
Greenlaw, E., 249
Grosseteste, R., 223
Grote, R., 245
Guicciardini, F., 111, 113, 244

Hajdu, H., 270
Hale, E. E., 267
Hall, A. R., xvi, 229, 230, 231
Hanschmann, A. B., 232
Harington, Sir J., 79
Hartlib, S., 247
Harvey, W., 2, 67
Haskins, C. H., 231
Heath, D. D., 80
Helvetius, ix
Henry VIII, x
Heraclitus, 43, 52, 123
Hermes, 56, 69
Hermeticism, 56
Hermetic tradition, 241
Herrick, M. T., 267
Hippias, 52
Hippocrates, 45
Holmyard, E. J., 234
Holtzen, L. S., 262
Hooker, R., xii, 143–4, 148–9, 150
Howell, A. C., 233, 234

Howell, W. S., xvi, 178, 266
Hoykaas, R., 229
Hugh of St Victor, 17
Humanism, x, 3, 25, 56, 58
Hume, 69
Huntley, F. L., 234

Icarus, 103
Idols, 141, 160–6, 170
Isidore of Seville, 4
Ixion, 120

James I, xii, 24, 116
Jannet, P., 230
John of Salisbury, 11, 17
Jones, R. F., 170, 230, 244, 262, 266
Jonson, B., 183, 268
Jordan, W· K., 247, 257, 262
Jove, 112
Juvenal, 47

Kant, E., xv
Kepler, J., 11, 56, 67
Kocher, P. H., 229

Lactantius, 17, 76
Landes, M. W., 245
Landino, C., 75
Larsen, R. E., 229
Leach, A. F., 242
Leibniz, G., xii, 66, 146, 218
Lemmi, C., 93, 234, 237, 249, 254, 256, 257
Lever, R., 142
Levi, A., 125, 162, 242, 252, 256, 257, 260, 265
Lewes, 245
Lewis, C. S., 249
Liebig, J., xiv, 10, 232, 233 252
Lipsus, J., 59
Locke, J., ix, xiv, 172, 241
Lodge, T., 80

Logic, 135–42, 144–7, 151, 152–177, 212, 214
Lotspeich, H. G., 249
Louis XI, 42
Lovejoy, A. O., 241
Lucian, 93
Lucretius, 53
Lull, R., 65–6, 208–9, 252
Luporini, C., 21, 236
Luther, M., 57
Lyly, J., 58

Macaulay, T., x
Machiavelli, N., 18, 41, 59, 81–82, 84, 96, 109, 110–11, 113, 115
Mackinnon, F. I., 247
Macrobius, 76, 77, 93
Magellan, F., ix
Magic, 10–35, 56, 104–5
Mallet, C., 242
Malpet, J., 4
Marion, H., 234
Maritain, J., 253
Marlowe, C., ix, xii, 150, 247
Marston, J., 78
May, E., 272
McRae, K. D., 262
McRae, R. F., 229
Mechanical arts, 1–11, 23–5, 26, 31, 103
Melanchthon, F., 3, 209–10, 214, 220
Memnon, 106
Memory, 207, 214
Mercury, 69
Mersenne, M., 11, 56
Merton, R. K., 230
Method, 32–4, 49–50, 138–9, 150–1, 198–206
Metis, 81–2
Meyer, E., 257
Milton, J., 146, 263

Monnier, P., 254
Montaigne, M. de, 59, 77
More, H., 247
More, T., x, 58, 64
Moses, 28, 56
Moya, J. P., 75
Mullinger, J., 242
Munsterberg, M., 233
Myth, 73–81, 84–7, 88, 129

Narcissus, 112
Naudé, G., 235, 251
Nef, J. U., 230
NeoPlatonists, 40–1, 58, 75, 78, 80, 93
Nelson, N. E., 200
Nemesis, 106
Newton, I., x, 34, 69, 172, 220, 223, 241
Nicholson, M., 241, 247
Nicolini, F., 133
Nizolius, M., 63, 65, 71, 146, 147, 249, 253
Nordstrom, J., 253
Nulli, S. A., 241

Occam, W., x, 39, 65
Odysseus, 107–8
Olschki, L., 240
O'Malley, C. D., 251
Onions, C. T., 231
Ornstein, M., 230
Orpheus, 102, 107, 108
Ovid, 58

Palissy, B., 8–9
Pan, 97–8, 119, 155
Pandora, 108
Panofsky, E., 254
Paracelsus, 8, 13, 19, 20, 29, 31, 34, 35, 38, 43, 57, 236, 239, 247, 248
Parks, G. B., 244
Parmenides, 124

Patrizzi, F., 57, 63, 65, 245, 248, 251
Penrose, B., 244
Perseus, 113, 119
Petrarch, F., 238
Pettegrove, J. P., 247
Physics, 97–101, 120–6
Piano Mortari, W., 262
Picke, E., 270
Pico, G. F., 245
Pico della Mirandola, 18, 66, 70, 75, 253
Plato, 5, 25–6, 38, 42, 43, 45, 46, 47, 51–9, 67, 68, 70, 71, 123, 128, 132, 143, 147, 160, 165, 184, 189, 259
Plattard, J., 255
Pliny, 12, 40, 219
Plotinus, 56
Plutarch, 38, 53, 58, 93
Poliziano, 75, 80
Pomponazzi, P., 234
Porphyry, 71
Pouchet, F. A., 231
Praz, M., 256, 257, 264
Preti, G., 252, 261, 266
Prior, M. E., 241
Proclus, 56
Prometheus, 10, 69, 96–7, 102–103, 108
Prost, A., 236
Protagoras, 52
Proteus, 82–3
Pseudo-Aristotle, 12
Pseudo-Dionysus, 41, 56
Ptolemy, 40, 45
Publicio, J., 207
Puttenham, G., 79, 178, 183, 268
Pyrrho, 43
Pythagoras, 15, 27, 43, 47, 56, 99

Quintillian, 143, 145, 207

Rabelais, F., 1, 77
Raleigh, W., ix, xi
Ramelli, 2
Ramists, 40–1, 195, 197–8
Ramus, P., xii, xv, 8, 38, 64, 66–7, 69, 70, 142, 144, 145, 146, 147–8, 153, 158–9, 173–175, 192, 195–8, 209, 214, 220, 253, 263, 264
Rand, E. K., 254
Randall, J. H. jr., 241
Ravenna, P. da, 207
Rawley, W., 11, 36, 121, 241, 256
Recorde, R., 39
Redgrove, H. S., 234
Remond, F., 248
Reuchlin, J., 41
Reynolds, H., 80
Rhetoric, 143–4, 145–8, 178–85, 192, 207, 212, 214
Ripa, C., 74
Riposati, B., 264, 270
Romberch, J., 214
Romeo, R., 244
Rosselli, C., 207, 214
Rossi, M. M., xiv, 236, 257
Rossi, P., 242, 251, 254, 260, 263
Royal Society, xiii, 25, 138, 184, 218, 247
Roydon, M., 247
Ruggiero, G. de, 260

Sackville, T., xii
Saintsbury, G., 262
Saitta, G., 236, 246
Salingar, L. G., 262
Sandys, G., 12, 233
Sandys, J. E., 242
Saturn, 83
Scagliero, G., 12
Scherill, R., 254
Schoell, F. L., 249, 255, 256

Scholasticism, 39, 40, 41, 59–67, 69, 72, 147
Scholastics, 119, 197
Schrickx, W., 255
Schuhl, P. M., 230, 238
Scylla, 119
Seneca, 38, 58, 108, 143
Servius, 76, 93
Severinus, P., 43
Seznec, J., 76, 78, 254, 255, 256
Shakespeare, W., x, xii
Sherry, R., 178
Sidney, Sir P., x, 69, 148–9
Siegel, P. N., 231
Singer, C., 233
Sirens, 107
Smith, S., 42
Socini, L. &. F., 115
Socrates, 47, 54, 160
Sophists, 52, 54, 210
Sortais, G., 67, 243, 247, 252, 256
Spedding, J., 80, 92, 121, 130, 138, 140, 234, 240, 242, 261
Spencer, T., 263
Spenser, E., xii, 58, 59, 78, 148–149, 247
Sphinx, 101–2
Sprat, T., 184, 268
Stanley, T., 253
Starkey, T., 7, 232
Steele, R., 234
Strabo, 40
Strada, G. of Rosberg, 2, 231
Sturm, J., 57, 248
Styx, 115–16

Tables, 201–7, 213–14, 215
Tacitus, 43, 143, 251
Talaeus, A. (Talon, O.), 178
Taylor, F. S., 234, 235
Taylor, J., 247
Telesius, B., 37, 38, 53–4, 66, 124

Temple, W., 41, 173, 175, 267
Tertullian, 17, 76
Textor, 77
Thales, 123
Theophrastus, 52
Thomas, St, 17, 38, 41, 65, 259
Thornedike, L., 21, 28, 231, 234, 235, 239, 253, 270
Tiberius, 111
Tillyard, E. M., 263
Tindal, W. Y., 241
Tiraboschi, G., 255
Tithonus, 106
Tocco, F., 270–1
Topics, 156–7, 214–19
Torricelli, E., 221
Trithemius, J., 240
Tyndale, W., 64
Typhon, 114

Usher, A. P., 231

Valla, L., 69, 75, 76, 78
Varchi, B., 20, 21, 232
Vasco de Gama, 40
Vasoli, C., 239
Veranzio, F., 2, 231
Viano, C. A., 236, 266
Vicars, T., 143, 178
Vico, J., xiv, xv, 74, 77–9, 127, 133–4, 168, 260, 265
Villey, P., 255
Vitruvius, 8
Vives, J. L., 1, 63

Waddington, C., 262
Waetzoldt, W., 254
Wagner, R. H., 263
Waley, T., 74
Wallace, K. R., xiv, 178, 262, 267
Wallis, xiii
Webbe, W., 79

White, L. jr., 231
Willey, B., 229, 234, 256
William of Auvergne, 40
Wilson, T., 79, 142–3, 144–5,
   153, 178, 262
Wind, E., 246
Wolf, A., 230
Wolff, E., 244, 248
Wood, A., 232, 242, 243
Woodward, W. H., 231

Wyndham Lewis, D. B., 257

Xenophon, 57

Yates, F., xvi, 40, 230, 239, 243,
   252, 254, 255, 270

Zilsel, E., 248
Zonca, V., 2, 231
Zoroaster, 56, 69